INTERSCIENCE TRACTS ON PHYSICS AND ASTRONOMY

Edited by R. E. Marshak
University of Rochester

1. **D. J. Hughes**
   NEUTRON OPTICS
2. **M. S. Livingston**
   HIGH-ENERGY ACCELERATORS
3. **L. Spitzer, Jr.**
   PHYSICS OF FULLY IONIZED GASES
   second edition
4. **T. G. Cowling**
   MAGNETOHYDRODYNAMICS
5. **D. ter Haar**
   INTRODUCTION TO THE PHYSICS OF MANY-BODY SYSTEMS
6. **E. J. Öpik**
   PHYSICS OF METEOR FLIGHT IN THE ATMOSPHERE
7. **K. Mendelssohn**
   CRYOPHYSICS
8. **J. L. Delcroix**
   INTRODUCTION TO THE THEORY OF IONIZED GASES
9. **T. E. Sterne**
   AN INTRODUCTION TO CELESTIAL MECHANICS
10. **J. Weber**
    GENERAL RELATIVITY AND GRAVITATIONAL WAVES
11. **R. E. Marshak and E. C. G. Sudarshan**
    INTRODUCTION TO ELEMENTARY PARTICLE PHYSICS
12. **J. L. Olsen**
    ELECTRON TRANSPORT IN METALS
13. **M. Françon**
    MODERN APPLICATIONS OF PHYSICAL OPTICS

14. **P. B. Jones**
THE OPTICAL MODEL IN NUCLEAR AND PARTICLE PHYSICS

15. **R. K. Adair and E. C. Fowler**
STRANGE PARTICLES

16. **R. Wilson**
THE NUCLEON-NUCLEON INTERACTION: EXPERIMENTAL AND PHENOMENOLOGICAL ASPECTS

17. **J. F. Denisse and J. L. Decroix**
PLASMA WAVES

18. **W. F. Brown, Jr.**
MICROMAGNETICS

19. **A. Rose**
CONCEPTS IN PHOTOCONDUCTIVITY AND ALLIED PROBLEMS

20. **A Guinier and D. L. Dexter**
X-RAY STUDIES OF MATERIALS

21. **T. G. Northrup**
THE ADIABATIC MOTION OF CHARGED PARTICLES

22. **G. Barton**
INTRODUCTION TO ADVANCED FIELD THEORY

23. **C. D. Jeffries**
DYNAMIC NUCLEAR ORIENTATION

24. **G. B. Benedek**
MAGNETIC RESONANCE AT HIGH PRESSURE

25. **D. L. Dexter and R. S. Knox**
EXCITONS

26. **D. H. Sampson**
RADIATIVE CONTRIBUTIONS TO ENERGY AND MOMENTUM TRANSPORT IN A GAS

27. **P. A. Carruthers**
INTRODUCTION TO UNITARY SYMMETRY

Additional volumes in preparation

INTRODUCTION TO UNITARY SYMMETRY

PETER A. CARRUTHERS

Cornell University, Ithaca, New York

1966

INTERSCIENCE PUBLISHERS

a division of John Wiley & Sons,
New York · London · Sydney

Library of Congress Catalog Card Number 66-20390
Printed in the United States of America

Preface

In recent years the "eightfold way" symmetry scheme has greatly clarified the systematics of the strong interactions of elementary particles. In this theory the previously known conservation laws for isospin and strangeness have been unified in an especially elegant manner. It has been known for a long time that the strongly-interacting particles can be grouped into multiplets whose members have nearly the same mass. The associated law of conservation of isospin is enforced mathematically by requiring the theory to be invariant under certain transformations of the group $SU(2)$. The latter group is generated by unitary transformations (with determinant unity) in a two-dimensional complex vector space. In the new theory it becomes useful to group together various isospin multiplets (composed of particles with identical spin, parity and baryon number). The isospin and strangeness quantum numbers can then be associated directly with the eigenvalues of diagonal operators in a certain class of representations of the group $SU(3)$, the latter being the group of linear unitary transformations (having unit determinant) in a three-dimensional complex vector space.

The aim of this book is to provide physicists with a practical, elementary introduction to the use of unitary symmetry in strong interactions. It is assumed that the reader has a thorough understanding of the rotation group based on the algebra of the "angular momentum" operators. Whenever possible an $SU(3)$ problem is solved in analogy to a familiar problem in $SU(2)$. A knowledge of group theory, especially representation theory, is recommended but is not essential.

No attempt has been made to give proper credit for priority. References have been cited in proportion to their familiarity to the author and probable usefulness to the reader. We only wish to recall the important role played by Sakata, Ikeda, Ogawa, and Ohnuki in introducing $SU(3)$ (and in assigning the pseudoscalar mesons to the regular representation) and the development of the "final" version of the theory (the "eightfold way") by Gell-Mann, Ne'eman and Okubo.

Many interesting and important subjects have been omitted from this volume. Nothing has been said about the weak interactions, mainly because the author does not feel competent to write on this subject. Although the author is especially interested in the connection between symmetry and dynamics, only one section (7.3) is given to this aspect of $SU(3)$ on account of the perishable nature of "knowledge" in the field of strong interaction dynamics. Similarly, the brave and possibly profound speculations on the existence of symmetries higher than $SU(3)$ have been completely ignored.

The following general references should be called to the reader's attention.

1. R. Behrends, J. Dreitlein, C. Fronsdal, and B. W. Lee, *Rev. Mod. Phys.*, **34**, 1 (1962).
2. R. E. Cutkosky, *Ann. Rev. Nucl. Sci.*, **14**, 175 (1964).
3. M. Gell-Mann and Y. Ne'eman, *The Eightfold Way*, W. A. Benjamin, Inc., New York, 1965.
4. H. J. Lipkin, *Lie Groups for Pedestrians*, Interscience, New York, 1965.
5. S. Okubo, *Lectures on Unitary Symmetry* (University of Rochester preprint), unpublished.
6. J. J. de Swart, *Rev. Mod. Phys.*, **35**, 916 (1963).

About equal parts of the book were written at Cornell University, the California Institute of Technology and the Aspen Institute for Theoretical Physics. The support of the Alfred P. Sloan Foundation throughout this period is gratefully acknowledged. The author is indebted to Professor J. J. de Swart for permission to reproduce his tables of isoscalar factors.

Contents

Chapter 1

$SU(2)$: Angular Momentum and Isospin

1.1 Rotations and Angular Momentum

Consider a fixed vector $\mathbf{r} = (x,y,z)$. If we rotate the coordinate system by an angle θ about an axis given by the unit vector $\mathbf{n}$ the fixed vector $\mathbf{r}$ appears to be $\mathbf{r}' = (x',y',z')$ in the rotated frame, where

$$\mathbf{r}' = \mathbf{r}\cos\theta + \mathbf{r}\times\mathbf{n}\sin\theta + \mathbf{n}(\mathbf{n}\cdot\mathbf{r})(1-\cos\theta) \qquad (1.1)$$

This expression clearly exhibits the fact that three independent parameters are required for the unique specification of a rigid rotation, and also that $\mathbf{r}'^2 = \mathbf{r}^2$. The usual way of writing (1.1) is in terms of an orthogonal matrix with components O_{ij}:

$$r_i' = O_{ij}r_j \qquad (1.2)$$

The redundancy of this description (O has only three independent parameters among its nine components) is not very convenient for practical calculations. Other well-known descriptions were invented long ago (Euler angles, quaternions, Cayley-Klein parameters).

A simple description of rotations is provided by the close connection of transformations in spin space to rotations in ordinary three-dimensional space. The usual spinor has two complex components v_1 and v_2. Under a rotation of the coordinate system by an angle θ about $\mathbf{n}$, the spinor $v = (v_1,v_2)$ transforms to v':

$$v' = Uv; \qquad U = \exp\left(i\frac{\theta}{2}\mathbf{n}\cdot\boldsymbol{\sigma}\right) = 1\cos\frac{\theta}{2} + i\mathbf{n}\cdot\boldsymbol{\sigma}\sin\frac{\theta}{2}; \qquad (1.3)$$

$$\sigma_x = \begin{pmatrix}0 & 1\\ 1 & 0\end{pmatrix} \qquad \sigma_y = \begin{pmatrix}0 & -i\\ i & 0\end{pmatrix} \qquad \sigma_z = \begin{pmatrix}1 & 0\\ 0 & -1\end{pmatrix} \qquad (1.4)$$

$\boldsymbol{\sigma}$ is the Pauli spin matrix vector. It will be observed that U is unitary, $U^\dagger U = 1$, and has det $U = 1$. The transformations U clearly form a group and are specified by the parameters $\mathbf{n}$, θ associated with a rotation. The correspondence is not unique since the physically equivalent angles θ and $\theta + 2\pi$ correspond to $\pm U$; one says that the spinors form the basis of a double-valued (irreducible) representation of the rotation group.

We can now explicitly exhibit the correspondence of the spin transformation and the rotation, Eq. (1.1). Define the traceless Hermitian matrix R by

$$R \equiv \mathbf{r}\cdot\boldsymbol{\sigma} = \begin{pmatrix} z & x - iy \\ x + iy & -z \end{pmatrix} \tag{1.5}$$

Then we have the following theorem

$$R' = \mathbf{r}'\cdot\boldsymbol{\sigma} = URU^{-1} \equiv U(\mathbf{r}\cdot\boldsymbol{\sigma})U^{-1} \tag{1.6}$$

where U is given by Eq. (1.4) and $\mathbf{r}'$ by Eq. (1.1). (This elegant result is due to W. R. Hamilton; U and R are essentially quaternions.) The proof is as follows:

$$\begin{aligned} URU^{-1} &= R + [U,R]U^{-1} \\ &= \mathbf{r}\cdot\boldsymbol{\sigma} + (\mathbf{r}\times\mathbf{n})\cdot\boldsymbol{\sigma}\sin\theta + 2\sin^2\tfrac{1}{2}\theta[(\mathbf{r}\times\mathbf{n})\times\mathbf{n}]\cdot\boldsymbol{\sigma} \\ \mathbf{r}'\cdot\boldsymbol{\sigma} &= \mathbf{r}\cdot\boldsymbol{\sigma} + (\mathbf{r}\times\mathbf{n})\cdot\boldsymbol{\sigma}\sin\theta + (1-\cos\theta)[(\mathbf{n}\cdot\boldsymbol{\sigma})(\mathbf{n}\cdot\mathbf{r}) - \mathbf{r}\cdot\boldsymbol{\sigma}] \\ \mathbf{r}'\cdot\boldsymbol{\sigma} &= [\mathbf{r}\cos\theta + \mathbf{r}\times\mathbf{n}\sin\theta + \mathbf{n}(\mathbf{n}\cdot\mathbf{r})(1-\cos\theta)]\cdot\boldsymbol{\sigma} \end{aligned} \tag{1.7}$$

in agreement with (1.1). Liberal use has been made of the identity

$$(\boldsymbol{\sigma}\cdot\mathbf{A})(\boldsymbol{\sigma}\cdot\mathbf{B}) = \mathbf{A}\cdot\mathbf{B} + i\boldsymbol{\sigma}\cdot(\mathbf{A}\times\mathbf{B}) \tag{1.8}$$

In words, (1.6) tells us the following: If we associate with the vector $\mathbf{r}$ the matrix R in the two-dimensional spin space, the unitary transformation U in this space is in direct correspondence with the rotation in three dimensions. Further, (1.6) suggests that $\boldsymbol{\sigma}$ transforms as a vector with $\boldsymbol{\sigma}' = U^{-1}\boldsymbol{\sigma}U$ given by Eq. (1.1) with $\mathbf{r}$ replaced by $\boldsymbol{\sigma}$. (Check this as an exercise.) Thus $\mathbf{r}\cdot\boldsymbol{\sigma} = \mathbf{r}'\cdot\boldsymbol{\sigma}'$.

We shall also define the above transformations in a way that is not so directly tied to physics. Consider the set of linear unitary transformations in a complex two-dimensional space

$$\begin{aligned} v_1' &= \alpha v_1 + \beta v_2 \\ v_2' &= \gamma v_1 + \delta v_2 \end{aligned} \tag{1.9}$$

subject to the unimodularity condition

$$\det U = 1; \qquad U = \begin{pmatrix} \alpha & \beta \\ \gamma & \delta \end{pmatrix} \tag{1.10}$$

The unitarity-unimodular condition implies

$$\begin{pmatrix} \alpha^* & \gamma^* \\ \beta^* & \delta^* \end{pmatrix} = \begin{pmatrix} \delta & -\beta \\ -\gamma & \alpha \end{pmatrix} \Rightarrow \begin{aligned} \delta &= \alpha^* \\ \gamma &= -\beta^* \end{aligned} \tag{1.11}$$

so that the transformation matrix U is

$$U = \begin{pmatrix} \alpha & \beta \\ -\beta^* & \alpha^* \end{pmatrix}; \qquad |\alpha|^2 + |\beta|^2 = 1 \tag{1.12}$$

The matrices U clearly form a group, known as $SU(2)$, the group of unitary 2×2 matrices with unit determinant. The correspondence between (1.4) and (1.8) is

$$\begin{aligned} \alpha &= \cos\frac{\theta}{2} + in_z \sin\frac{\theta}{2} \\ \beta &= i(n_x - in_y)\sin\frac{\theta}{2} \end{aligned} \tag{1.13}$$

We have discovered two irreducible representations of the rotation group, irreducible because it is impossible to form subsets of linear combinations of the basis functions [(x,y,z) and (v_1,v_2) for the two cases discussed] that transform only among themselves under arbitrary rotations. (For rotations about the z axis, x and y span an invariant subspace, as does z alone. In this case the representation is reducible and the matrix O is in block diagonal form.) There is no question about which representation is more fundamental, since we can build the three-dimensional representation out of direct products of the spinors, but can never obtain the double-valued representations by reducing tensors formed from x_j.

We mention here the basic weapon one has for generating representations of some group once a representation has been found. This is most easily expressed in terms of basis functions. Suppose we have a set of functions ψ_j, $j = 1, 2, \ldots, N$, which are transformed into each other under the operations (designated R) of the group. Then the transformed functions are

$$R\psi_j \equiv \psi_j' = \sum_i D_{ij}(R)\psi_i \tag{1.14}$$

and the matrices D form an N-dimensional representation of the group. Then automatically the products $\psi_i\psi_j\ldots\psi_z$ generate a direct product representation, e.g.,

$$(\psi_i\psi_j)' = \sum_{k,l} D_{ki}(R)D_{lj}(R)\psi_k\psi_l \tag{1.15}$$

but these representations will in general be reducible. [For example, from the tensor x_iy_j where x_i and y_j obey (1.1) and $i = 1, 2, 3$ one can form the symmetric traceless tensor $T_{ij} = x_iy_j + x_jy_i - \frac{2}{3}\delta_{ij}\mathbf{x}\cdot\mathbf{y}$, the skew tensor $S_{ij} = x_iy_j - x_jy_i$ and the scalar $\mathbf{x}\cdot\mathbf{y}$. T_{ij}, S_{ij}, $\mathbf{x}\cdot\mathbf{y}$ form bases for the irreducible representations contained in the direct product $O \times O$.]

In the usual treatments of angular momentum the problem is generally stated and solved in a slightly different way. One seeks all possible representations of the (Hermitian) angular momentum operators J_i obeying the following algebra:

$$[J_i,J_j] = i\varepsilon_{ijk}J_k \tag{1.16}$$

ε_{ijk} being the completely antisymmetric Cartesian tensor ($\varepsilon_{123} = 1$). In the usual way one seeks eigenfunctions of $\mathbf{J}^2 = J_iJ_i$ and J_3, and finds that the eigenvalue of $\mathbf{J}^2$ is $j(j+1)$, where $2j$ is any nonnegative integer and j_3 runs from $-j$ to $+j$. Addition of angular momentum proceeds by taking direct products as in

(1.15); since the standard procedure is generalizable, we sketch it again. Consider the $(2j_1 + 1)(2j_2 + 1)$ states $\psi_{j_1 m_1}\psi_{j_2 m_2}$. To reduce the resulting representation into irreducible representations, one begins with the "stretched" configuration $\psi_{j_1 j_1}(a)\psi_{j_2 j_2}(b)$, which is the only state with $J_3 = j_1 + j_2$ and has $j = j_1 + j_2$. Remembering that $\mathbf{J} = \mathbf{J}_a + \mathbf{J}_b$ and introducing the standard raising and lowering operators $J_\pm = J_1 \pm iJ_2$, the remaining states with $j = j_1 + j_2$ are found by applying J_-. The multiplet with $j = j_1 + j_2 - 1$ is then begun by constructing the state orthogonal to that with $j = j_1 + j_2, j_3 = j_1 + j_2 - 1$ and again applying J_- repeatedly. Finally, one gets one multiplet each for j running from $j_1 + j_2$ to $|j_2 - j_1|$. The coefficients relating the direct product basis functions to the eigenfunctions of $\mathbf{J}^2$ and $J_3, j_1{}^2, j_2{}^2$ are the Clebsch-Gordan coefficients.

It will be observed that every representation of the commutation relations, and hence of the rotation group, can be obtained by adding up spin 1/2 enough times, since (1.16) is equivalent to the following definition of the rotation operator ($\hbar = 1$)

$$R(\mathbf{n},\theta) = \exp(i\theta\mathbf{n}\cdot\mathbf{J}) \tag{1.17}$$

The lowest dimensional (nontrivial) representation of (1.16) is $\mathbf{J} = \frac{1}{2}\boldsymbol{\sigma}$.

1.2 Isospin

As in the case of the electron spin, the discovery of isospin arose from the detection of previously unsuspected energy degeneracies. There is every reason to believe that the strong interactions possess, to a high degree of accuracy, the symmetry known as "isospin conservation." This symmetry is commonly taken to have the following meaning. The observed members of a multiplet (dimension $2T + 1$) of strongly interacting particles transform into each other under transformations of $SU(2)$ (equivalently: "rotations in isospin space") according to an irreducible representation of dimension $2T + 1$. (The multiplets are believed to be "pure" to an accuracy of order 1/137 due to electromagnetic effects.) The interactions between the strongly interacting particles are invariant under these same transformations. Everybody is familiar with the dramatic conceptual simplification brought about by this symmetry. Extensive treatments are given in the books by Roman (1) and by Marshak and Sudarshan (2).

Although isospin is an extremely familiar concept, we shall review certain aspects of the formalism that help elucidate similar procedures in unitary symmetry. We shall label the components of the most fundamental mathematical entity in the theory (the two-component spinor) with the names p (proton) and n (neutron) ($T_3 + \pm 1/2$) in honor of their historical priority. The basic spinor,

$$N = \begin{pmatrix} p \\ n \end{pmatrix} \tag{1.18}$$

is subject to infinitesimal transformations of $SU(2)$

$$N \rightarrow N' = (1 + i\delta\boldsymbol{\alpha}\cdot\tfrac{1}{2}\boldsymbol{\tau})N \tag{1.19}$$

where $\boldsymbol{\tau}$ is formally the same as $\boldsymbol{\sigma}$ in Eq. (1.4) and $\delta\boldsymbol{\alpha}$ is a real, infinitesimal vector. (Recall that only infinitesimal transformations are needed.) To conduct an interesting experiment we have to bring two nucleons together. The product wave functions break up additively into parts of distinct isospin (according to the law of vector addition of angular momenta) which may behave quite differently. Mathematically, this resolution of a direct product into terms of definite isospin (by means of the Clebsch-Gordan coefficients) corresponds to a decomposition into irreducible representations. If we consider two nucleons (labeled 1 and 2) with spinors $N_i(1)$ and $N_j(2)$, where i and j are $+$ or $-$ corresponding to p or n, the product function $N_i(1)N_j(2)$ transforms under infinitesimal transformations according to the operator

$$[1 + i\delta\boldsymbol{\alpha}\cdot\tfrac{1}{2}(\boldsymbol{\tau}_1 + \boldsymbol{\tau}_2)] \tag{1.20}$$

so that the infinitesimal generator is $\mathbf{T} = \frac{1}{2}(\boldsymbol{\tau}_1 + \boldsymbol{\tau}_2)$. The transformed state is clearly a linear combination of the original states and so is manifestly a representation. This representation is, however, reducible. The resulting irreducible representations are the isospin 1 and 0 states:

T_3	$T = 1$	$T = T_3 = 0$	
1	$p(1)p(2)$		
0	$\frac{1}{\sqrt{2}}[p(1)n(2) + n(1)p(2)]$	$\frac{1}{\sqrt{2}}[p(1)n(2) - n(1)p(2)]$	(1.21)
−1	$n(1)n(2)$		

The same transformation that arranges the states $N_i(1)N_j(2)$ into the isospin states (1.21) transforms the product matrices in Eq. (1.15) to block diagonal form. Labeling these matrices with the relevant isospin, this result is usually written symbolically as

$$D^{(1/2)} \times D^{(1/2)} = D^{(0)} + D^{(1)} \tag{1.22}$$

Next consider the somewhat less familiar idea of the complex conjugate representation. Since N transforms as

$$N \to N' = UN \tag{1.23}$$

the complex conjugate of this shows that the complex conjugate spinor $N^* = \begin{pmatrix} p^* \\ n^* \end{pmatrix}$, which transforms as

$$N^* \to N^{*\prime} = U^*N^* \tag{1.24}$$

also generates a representation of $SU(2)$ in terms of the matrices U^*. [Note: In field theory p will designate the Dirac field that destroys a proton and creates an antiproton; p^* will be the adjoint field, creating a proton and destroying an antiproton; etc.] In the case of $SU(2)$ [but not $SU(3)$] the complex conjugate representation is equivalent (but not identical) to the representation having the spinor N as the basis. The criterion for equivalence is the existence of a similarity transformation by a matrix S such that

$$U = SU^*S^{-1} \tag{1.25}$$

Using the infinitesimal transformation we see that

$$N \to \left(1 + \frac{i}{2}\,\delta\boldsymbol{\alpha}\cdot\boldsymbol{\tau}\right)N$$
$$N^* \to \left(1 - \frac{i}{2}\,\delta\boldsymbol{\alpha}\cdot\boldsymbol{\tau}^*\right)N \tag{1.26}$$

so that equivalence obtains for S such that

$$\boldsymbol{\tau} = -S\boldsymbol{\tau}^*S^{-1} \tag{1.27}$$

Since $\tau_1 = \tau_1^*$, $\tau_3 = \tau_3^*$ and $\tau_2 = -\tau_2^*$ we need S to obey

$$\tau_1 S + S\tau_1 = 0$$
$$\tau_2 S - S\tau_2 = 0 \tag{1.28}$$
$$\tau_3 S + S\tau_3 = 0$$

Eqs. (1.28) are clearly solved by $S \propto \tau_2$. A convenient (unitary) S is $S = i\tau_2$. Multiplying the second member of (1.26) by S we see that the spinor N_c

$$N_c \equiv SN^* = i\tau_2 N^* = \begin{pmatrix} 0 & 1 \\ -1 & 0 \end{pmatrix}\begin{pmatrix} \bar{p} \\ \bar{n} \end{pmatrix} = \begin{pmatrix} \bar{n} \\ -\bar{p} \end{pmatrix} \tag{1.29}$$

transforms identically to N

$$N_c \to N_c' = \left(1 + \frac{i}{2}\,\delta\boldsymbol{\alpha}\cdot\boldsymbol{\tau}\right)N_c \tag{1.30}$$

In using the usual Clebsch-Gordan coefficients it is essential to have all states transforming in the same way. Equation (1.29) shows how the extra minus sign arises in the antinucleon wave functions. For instance, the $T = 0$ and $T = 1$ wave functions for a nucleon–antinucleon system are (an overall minus sign has been inserted)

$T = 1$	$T = 0$
$-p\bar{n}$	
$\frac{1}{\sqrt{2}}(p\bar{p} - n\bar{n})$	$\frac{1}{\sqrt{2}}(p\bar{p} + n\bar{n})$ (1.31)
$n\bar{p}$	

The isotopic triplet has (for S wave, $J = 0$ configuration) zero baryon number and odd intrinsic parity, just as the pions $(\pi^\pm,\pi^0)$ do. Such a correspondence does not, of course, imply that pions are bound states of $N\bar{N}$.

The spinor N^* is said to transform contragradiently to N. The inner product $N^\dagger N = \sum_i N_i^* N_i$ is a scalar under rotations, as follows from (1.26) or equivalently

$$N^\dagger N \rightarrow N^\dagger U^\dagger U N = N^\dagger N \tag{1.32}$$

Note that $N^{*\dagger}N$ is not a scalar but $N_c^\dagger N$ or $N_c^\dagger N_c$ or $N^\dagger N_c$ are scalars.

We illustrate these considerations by constructing the isospin-conserving Yukawa couplings between baryons and pseudo-scalar mesons. First consider the nucleon–eta coupling (η has $T = 0$). Omitting space–time quantities to account for spin and parity the obvious invariant is

$$g_{\eta NN}\bar{N}N\eta \tag{1.33}$$

writing the more suggestive $\bar{N}$ in place of $N^\dagger$. [We are now using the symbol N to stand for the Dirac field operator. The unitary operators required to generate transformations like (1.19) are discussed in Appendix II.] The other invariants involving N_c either do not conserve baryon number ($\bar{N}_c N$ or $\bar{N}N_c$) or are equivalent to (1.33) ($\bar{N}_c N_c$). A more interesting example is the vertex $\Xi\Lambda\bar{K}$. The Λ has to absorb a $\bar{K}$ to become a Ξ. Since the conjugate of $\bar{K} = \text{col}\,(K^+,K^0)$ does not transform like $\Xi = \text{col}\,(\Xi^0,\Xi^-)$ the quantity $\bar{\Xi}\bar{K}^T\Lambda$ is not an isoscalar. However $K_c = \text{col}\,(\bar{K}_0, -K^-)$ does transform properly so that

$$g_{K\Lambda\Xi}\bar{\Xi}\Lambda K_c + \text{H.c.} \tag{1.34}$$

is the appropriate form.

Next we consider the *regular representation* of $SU(2)$. Notice that the three pions form an isotopic triplet and give rise to a three-dimensional matrix representation of $SU(2)$. Also notice that the number of independent generators of infinitesimal transformations is just three. Because of the fundamental structure of the commutation rules we can construct a special set of representation matrices t_k from the *structure constants* $i\varepsilon_{ijk}$ defined by the commutation rules

$$[J_i,J_j] = i\varepsilon_{ijk}J_k \tag{1.35}$$

as follows:

$$(t_k)_{ij} = -i\varepsilon_{ijk} \tag{1.36}$$

This can be checked by using the identity $\varepsilon_{ijk}\varepsilon_{lmk} = \delta_{il}\delta_{jm} - \delta_{im}\delta_{jl}$. (Later we shall see that these results can be greatly generalized.) This set of matrices is explicitly

$$t_1 = \begin{pmatrix} 0 & 0 & 0 \\ 0 & 0 & -i \\ 0 & i & 0 \end{pmatrix} \quad t_2 = \begin{pmatrix} 0 & 0 & -i \\ 0 & 0 & 0 \\ i & 0 & 0 \end{pmatrix} \quad t_3 = \begin{pmatrix} 0 & -i & 0 \\ i & 0 & 0 \\ 0 & 0 & 0 \end{pmatrix} \tag{1.37}$$

and clearly all representations with $T = 1$ are equivalent to (1.37). As an exercise we suggest that the reader show $(\mathbf{n}\cdot\mathbf{t})^3 = \mathbf{n}\cdot\mathbf{t}$, and hence, that the rotation operator is

$$\begin{aligned} R(\mathbf{n},\theta) &= \exp\,(i\theta\mathbf{n}\cdot\mathbf{t}) \\ &= 1 + i\mathbf{n}\cdot\mathbf{t}\sin\theta + (\mathbf{n}\cdot\mathbf{t})^2(\cos\theta - 1) \end{aligned} \tag{1.38}$$

Apply this to ordinary spatial rotations and show that (1.38) applied to $\mathbf{r} = (x,y,z)$ gives $\mathbf{r}'$ as given in Eq. (1.1). Thus (x,y,z) "transforms according to the regular representation" of the rotation group. This exercise shows that the pion isovector $\boldsymbol{\phi} = (\phi_1\phi_2\phi_3)$ transforms according to the regular representation. The connection to the usual complex field ϕ that creates π^- and destroys π^+ is $\phi = (\phi_1 + i\phi_2)/\sqrt{2}$.

Suppose we discover somehow that we have the triplet $(\phi_1\phi_2\phi_3)$ transforming according to (1.37) and (1.38)

$$\phi_i \to (1 + i\delta\boldsymbol{\alpha}\cdot\mathbf{t})_{ij}\phi_j \tag{1.39}$$

(for instance, by finding a bound-state pole in the $T = 1$, $N\bar{N}$ amplitude). Then how are we to construct the isospin-conserving pion–nucleon Yukawa interaction? Clearly, we must form a linear combination of the $N\bar{N}$ amplitude

$$\bar{N}^i C_{ij}{}^k N^j \tag{1.40}$$

such that (using matrix rotation)

$$\bar{N} C^k N \phi_k \tag{1.41}$$

is invariant under $SU(2)$ transformations. Alternatively, since the direct product in (1.40) has the reduction of Eq. (1.22), only the $T = 1$ combination makes (1.41) invariant $[D^{(1)} \times D^{(1)} = \mathrm{D}^{(0)} + D^{(1)} + \mathrm{D}^{(2)}$ but $D^{(1)} \times D^{(0)} = D^{(1)}]$. Invariance requires

$$\bar{N}' C^k N' \phi_k' = N \bar{C}^k N \phi_k \qquad (N' = UN, \quad \phi' = V\phi) \tag{1.42}$$

where $U = 1 + (i/2)\delta\boldsymbol{\alpha}\cdot\boldsymbol{\tau}$ and $V = 1 + i\delta\boldsymbol{\alpha}\cdot\mathbf{t}$. Thus we obtain the condition

$$UC^iU^{-1} = C^j V_{ji} \tag{1.43}$$

or, using the infinitesimal generators:

$$[\tfrac{1}{2}\tau_i, C^j] = i\varepsilon_{ijk} C^k \tag{1.44}$$

using (1.36). The unique solution of (1.44) is (to a constant factor)

$$C^j = \tau_j \tag{1.45}$$

so one obtains the standard answer

$$g_{\pi NN} \bar{N} \boldsymbol{\tau} N \cdot \boldsymbol{\phi} \tag{1.46}$$

Note that by sandwiching the three Pauli matrices $\boldsymbol{\tau}$ between the basic spinors we obtain an isovector $\mathbf{V} = \bar{N}\frac{1}{2}\boldsymbol{\tau}N$ transforming according to the regular representation:

$$\bar{N}\tfrac{1}{2}\boldsymbol{\tau}N \rightarrow (1 + i\delta\boldsymbol{\alpha}\cdot\mathbf{t})\bar{N}\tfrac{1}{2}\boldsymbol{\tau}N \tag{1.47}$$

as is easily shown. We have emphasized these somewhat esoteric points in order that the analogous results in $SU(3)$ will not seem astonishingly new.

As a final example, consider the $\pi\Sigma\Sigma$ coupling. Now all three particles have isospin 1; in analogy to the pion field $\boldsymbol{\phi}$ we write

$\boldsymbol{\Sigma} = (\Sigma_1,\Sigma_2,\Sigma_3)$. Following the same argument as in the πN case we seek a 3×3 matrix C such that

$$\bar{\Sigma}^i C_{ij}{}^k \Sigma^j \phi_k \tag{1.48}$$

is invariant. The matrix C satisfies

$$[t_i,C^j] = i\varepsilon_{ijk}C^k \tag{1.49}$$

so that $C^k \equiv t_k$. Hence the $\pi\Sigma\Sigma$ Yukawa coupling is

$$g_{\pi\Sigma\Sigma}\bar{\Sigma}\mathbf{t}\Sigma\cdot\boldsymbol{\pi} = -ig_{\pi\Sigma\Sigma}\bar{\boldsymbol{\Sigma}} \times \boldsymbol{\Sigma}\cdot\boldsymbol{\pi} \tag{1.50}$$

the second form being more common.

We have done most of the work towards deriving the general isospin-invariant Yukawa coupling of the eight baryons (N,Λ,Σ,Ξ) with the eight pseudoscalar mesons $(\pi,K,\bar{K},\eta)$. For later reference we write this down, omitting as usual the required Dirac matrix γ_5:

$$\begin{aligned} g_{\pi NN}\bar{N}\boldsymbol{\tau}N\cdot\boldsymbol{\pi} &+ g_{\pi\Lambda\Sigma}(\bar{\Lambda}\boldsymbol{\Sigma}\cdot\boldsymbol{\pi} + \text{H.c.}) \\ &+ g_{\pi\Sigma\Sigma}(-i\bar{\boldsymbol{\Sigma}} \times \boldsymbol{\Sigma}\cdot\boldsymbol{\pi}) + g_{\pi\Xi\Xi}\bar{\Xi}\boldsymbol{\tau}\Xi\cdot\boldsymbol{\pi} \\ &+ g_{KN\Lambda}(\bar{N}\Lambda K + \text{H.c.}) + g_{KN\Sigma}(\bar{N}\boldsymbol{\tau}K\cdot\boldsymbol{\Sigma} + \text{H.c.}) \\ &+ g_{K\Xi\Lambda}(\bar{\Xi}\Lambda\bar{K}_c + \text{H.c.}) + g_{K\Xi\Sigma}(\bar{\Xi}\boldsymbol{\tau}\bar{K}_c\cdot\boldsymbol{\Sigma} + \text{H.c.}) \\ &+ g_{\eta NN}\bar{N}N\eta + g_{\eta\Lambda\Lambda}\bar{\Lambda}\Lambda\eta + g_{\eta\Sigma\Sigma}\bar{\boldsymbol{\Sigma}}\cdot\boldsymbol{\Sigma}\eta + g_{\eta\Xi\Xi}\bar{\Xi}\Xi\eta \end{aligned} \tag{1.51}$$

where the particle symbols have the usual significance

$$N = \begin{pmatrix} p \\ n \end{pmatrix}, \quad \Xi = \begin{pmatrix} \Xi^0 \\ \Xi^- \end{pmatrix}, \quad \boldsymbol{\Sigma} = \begin{pmatrix} \Sigma_1 \\ \Sigma_2 \\ \Sigma_3 \end{pmatrix}, \quad \Lambda = \Lambda^0$$

$$K = \begin{pmatrix} K^+ \\ K^0 \end{pmatrix}, \quad \bar{K} = \begin{pmatrix} K^- \\ \bar{K}^0 \end{pmatrix}^T, \quad \bar{K}_c = i\tau_2\bar{K}^T = \begin{pmatrix} \bar{K}^0 \\ -K^- \end{pmatrix} \tag{1.52}$$

$$\boldsymbol{\pi} = \begin{pmatrix} \pi_1 \\ \pi_2 \\ \pi_3 \end{pmatrix}, \quad \eta = \eta^0$$

1.3 Field Operators for Arbitrary Isospin Multiplets

In order to make use of the extensive results (3,4) available for the group $SU(2)$ it is often essential to pay close attention to phase conventions among states and operators. For example, when constructing the $SU(2)$ invariant πNN coupling it was convenient to use the vector form of the pion field $\boldsymbol{\pi} = (\pi_1,\pi_2,\pi_3)$. However, physical states require the use of the spherical basis, in which T_3 is diagonal. The commonly used complex fields ϕ, ϕ_0, ϕ^* ($\phi = (\pi_1 - i\pi_2)/\sqrt{2}$ creates π^- and destroys π^+, ϕ_0 creates and destroys π^0, $\phi^* = (\pi_1 + i\pi_2)/\sqrt{2}$ creates π^+ and destroys π^-) do not create states related by the standard (Condon-Shortley) phase convention unless a judicious minus sign is supplied to the π^+ state. This can be seen by explicitly constructing the isospin operator for the pion field. Rather than work out this special case, we turn to the general problem (5). As the space–time properties are of no special concern here, we consider boson fields. We shall consider two types of fields: (*1*) self-conjugate fields for which a particle and its antiparticle belong to the same isospin multiplet and (*2*) pair-conjugate fields, for which the antiparticles of a given isospin multiplet constitute a distinct isospin multiplet. The two fields shall be called $\phi^{(\mu)}$ and $\psi^{(\mu)}$, respectively, where μ denotes the decrease in T_3 which results from application of the field to a state. Clearly, the pion triplet (π^+,π^0,π^-) is a familiar example of a self-conjugate isomultiplet. The conjugate doublets of K mesons (K^+,K^0); $(\bar{K}^0,K^-)$ are typical pair-conjugates.

For the self-conjugate field we introduce the operator $a_\mu(k)$ which destroys particles of momentum **k**, isospin T (label suppressed), and T_3 component μ. The Hermitian conjugate operator $a_\mu^*(k)$ is required to create an isomultiplet of ϕ-particles of momentum **k**

$$a_\mu^*(k)|0\rangle = |T\mu,k\rangle \tag{1.53}$$

in which the different states are related by the standard phase convention

$$\begin{aligned} T_\pm|T\mu\rangle &= \Gamma_\pm(\mu)|T,\mu \pm 1\rangle \\ \Gamma_\pm(\mu) &= [(T \mp \mu)(T \pm \mu + 1)]^{1/2} \end{aligned} \tag{1.54}$$

Introducing a phase factor $\eta_\mu{}^T$ of unit magnitude, we may write

$$\phi^{(\mu)}(x) = \sum_{\mathbf{k}} [a_\mu(k) f_k(x) + \eta_\mu{}^T a_{-\mu}{}^*(k) f_k{}^*(x)] \tag{1.55}$$

$$f_k(x) = e^{-ik\cdot x}/(2\omega V)^{1/2} \tag{1.56}$$

where $k\cdot x = \omega t - \mathbf{k}\cdot\mathbf{x}$, $\omega = (\mathbf{k}^2 + m^2)^{1/2}$, and V is the quantization volume. The functions $f_k(x)$ are normalized by

$$(f_{k'}, f_k) \equiv i \int f_{k'}{}^*(x) \overleftrightarrow{\partial_0} f_k(x) d^3x = \delta_{kk'} \tag{1.57}$$

The symbol $A\overleftrightarrow{\partial_0}B$ signifies $A(\partial B/\partial t) - (\partial A/\partial t)B$.

The condition (1.53) suggests that $\phi^{(\mu)*}$ be required to transform as a spherical tensor (3,4), i.e.,

$$\mathcal{O}_\alpha \phi^{(\mu)*} \mathcal{O}_\alpha{}^{-1} = \sum_\nu \phi^{(\nu)*} D_{\nu\mu}(\alpha) \tag{1.58}$$

$$\mathcal{O}_\alpha \equiv \exp(i\boldsymbol{\alpha}\cdot\mathbf{T}) \tag{1.59}$$

Here $\boldsymbol{\alpha}$ is the set of three real parameters describing $SU(2)$ transformations and $\mathbf{T}$ is the isospin operator. [The reader may enjoy demonstrating that $\mathcal{O}_\alpha \boldsymbol{\pi} \mathcal{O}_\alpha{}^{-1} = \exp(-i\boldsymbol{\alpha}\cdot\mathbf{t})\boldsymbol{\pi}$ where the regular representation matrices $\mathbf{t}$ were defined in Eq. (1.36).] The $D_{\nu\mu}$ are the standard representation matrices (in the convention of Edmonds (4)) usually labeled by three Euler angles α, β, γ. If we choose $\mathcal{O}_\alpha$ to be a rotation by π about the 2 axis, we find, using $D_{\nu\mu}(0,\pi,0) = (-1)^{T+\mu}\delta_{\mu,-\nu}$:

$$e^{i\pi T_2} \phi^{(\mu)*} e^{-i\pi T_2} = (-1)^{T+\mu} \phi^{(-\mu)*} \tag{1.60}$$

The phase $\eta_\mu{}^T$ is therefore required to obey

$$\eta_{-\mu}{}^T = (-1)^{2\mu} \eta_\mu{}^T \tag{1.61}$$

We may construct the isospin operator in terms of the fields $\phi^{(\mu)}$ and the $(2T + 1)$-dimensional matrices t_1, t_2, t_3 by means of the standard isospin matrices $t_\pm \equiv t_1 \pm it_2, t_3$:

$$\begin{aligned} (t_3)_{\mu\nu} &\equiv (\mu \mid t_3 \mid \nu) = \mu\delta_{\mu\nu} \\ (t_\pm)_{\mu\nu} &\equiv (\mu \mid t_\pm \mid \nu) = [(t \pm \mu)(t \mp \mu + 1)]^{1/2}\delta_{\mu,\nu\pm 1} \end{aligned} \tag{1.62}$$

Taking (2.5) into account, one may write the isospin operator in the form

$$\mathbf{T} = \sum_{\mu,\nu} \tfrac{1}{2}i \int d^3x \phi^{(\mu)*} \mathbf{t}_{\mu\nu} \overleftrightarrow{\partial_0} \phi^{(\nu)} \equiv \tfrac{1}{2}(\phi,\mathbf{t}\phi) \tag{1.63}$$

By substituting the explicit expressions (1.55) and (1.62), one finds

$$T_3 = \sum_{\mu,\mathbf{k}} \mu a_\mu^*(k) a_\mu(k)$$

$$T_\pm = \sum_{\mu,\mathbf{k}} \tfrac{1}{2}[(t \mp \mu + 1)(t \pm \mu)]^{1/2} \times \{a_\mu^*(k)a_{\mu\mp1}(k) - \eta_\mu{}^{T*}\eta_{\mu\mp1}{}^T a_{-\mu\pm1}(k)a_{-\mu}(k)\} \tag{1.64}$$

If the operators $T_\pm$ are to conform to Eq. (1.53), the coefficients $\eta_\mu{}^T$ must satisfy

$$\eta_{-\mu}{}^{T*}\eta_{-\mu\mp1}{}^T = -1 \tag{1.65}$$

One member of the multiplet can be chosen to have $\eta = 1$, whereupon Eq. (1.65) indicates that $\eta_\mu{}^T$ alternates in sign as we go from one member of the multiplet to its neighbor. If the multiplet has a neutral member with $T_3 = 0$ (as occurs for integral T, the only observed types of self-conjugate isospin multiplets) the corresponding field component is real if we make the choice $\eta_0{}^T = 1$. Then we find $\eta_\mu{}^T = (-1)^\mu$. Although this is the conventional choice for this special case, it is more convenient to adopt a universal convention. To discover the most useful choice, consider the case in which $2T$ is an odd integer. Then a real $\eta_\mu{}^T$ is $(-1)^{T\pm\mu+1}$. The choice of sign is arbitrary but should be adhered to. We choose the plus sign in accordance with the definition (1.59) of $\mathcal{O}_\alpha$. The extra factor of unity has been introduced so that this $\eta_\mu{}^T$ reduces to $(-1)^\mu$ for the only existing nontrivial self-conjugate boson fields, which have integral isospin. We therefore have

$$\eta_\mu{}^T = (-1)^{T+\mu+1} \tag{1.66}$$

The presence of the factor $(-1)^{T+\mu}$ can be understood easily in terms of the analysis of the complex conjugate representation of $SU(2)$ (6). The matrix $C_{\mu\nu}$ with elements $(-1)^{T+\mu}\delta_{\mu,-\nu}$ applied to the complex conjugate basis gives a basis transforming in the standard way. The requirement that both components of $\phi^{(\mu)}$ transform in the same way under $SU(2)$ transformations has already been imposed in Eq. (1.58).

A similar analysis for the "pair field," for which we introduce the operators a_μ and b_μ referring to the distinct multiplets,

$$\psi^{(\mu)}(x) = \sum_{\mu,\mathbf{k}} [a_\mu(k)f_k(x) + \zeta_\mu{}^T b_{-\mu}{}^*(k)f_k{}^*(x)] \tag{1.67}$$

shows that $\zeta_\mu{}^T = \eta_\mu{}^T$. [The $a_\mu{}^*$ and $b_\mu{}^*$ are required to create the two isospin multiplets, within which the convention (1.54) is maintained.] The isospin operators are

$$\mathbf{T} = \sum_{\mu\nu} i \int d^3x \psi^{(\mu)*} \mathbf{t}_{\mu\nu} \overleftrightarrow{\partial_0} \psi^{(\nu)} \equiv (\psi, \mathbf{t}\psi)$$

$$T_\pm = \sum_{\mu,\mathbf{k}} [(t \mp \mu + 1)(t \pm \mu)]^{1/2} \{a_\mu{}^*(k) a_{\mu\pm 1}(k) + b_{-\mu\pm 1}{}^*(k) b_{-\mu}(k)\} \tag{1.68}$$

It is frequently useful to discuss the behavior of states and operators under the transformations of charge conjugation and G conjugation. We define charge conjugation by the following transformation, which connects a state $|\mu\rangle$ with its antiparticle state $|-\mu\rangle'$:

$$C|\mu\rangle \equiv \eta_\mu{}^T |-\mu\rangle' \tag{1.69}$$

omitting an arbitrary phase factor.

For a ϕ-type field, $|-\mu\rangle'$ is $a_{-\mu}{}^*|0\rangle$, while for the ψ-field it is $b_{-\mu}{}^*|0\rangle$. Corresponding to (1.69), one has the operator transformations

$$\begin{aligned} C a_\mu{}^* C^{-1} &= \eta_\mu{}^T a_{-\mu}{}^* \\ C a_\mu{}^* C^{-1} &= \eta_\mu{}^T b_{-\mu}{}^* \end{aligned} \tag{1.70}$$

for the ϕ and ψ fields, respectively. Comparison with the definitions (1.55) and (1.67) shows that

$$\begin{aligned} C\phi^{(\mu)} C^{-1} &= \phi^{(\mu)*} \\ C\psi^{(\mu)} C^{-1} &= \psi^{(\mu)*} \end{aligned} \tag{1.71}$$

Applying (1.71) to the isospin operators (1.63) or (1.68) shows that (explicitly for (1.68))

$$CT_kC^{-1} = (\psi^*, t_k\psi^*) = -(\psi, \tilde{t}_k\psi) \tag{1.72}$$

The transpose $\tilde{t}_k$ of the matrix t_k is given by

$$\begin{aligned} \tilde{t}_1 &= t_1 \\ \tilde{t}_2 &= -t_2 \\ \tilde{t}_3 &= t_3 \end{aligned} \tag{1.73}$$

so that (1.72) reduces to

$$\begin{aligned} CT_1C^{-1} &= -T_1 \\ CT_2C^{-1} &= +T_2 \\ CT_3C^{-1} &= -T_3 \end{aligned} \tag{1.74}$$

(The same result clearly holds for the ϕ field.)

Another operator useful for the description of strong interactions is G conjugation, defined as (7,8)

$$G = CR \tag{1.75}$$

where R is rotation by π about the 2-axis in isospin space:

$$R = \exp(i\pi T_2) \tag{1.76}$$

We have previously noted the relation

$$R\phi^{(\mu)}R^{-1} = (-1)^{T+\mu}\phi^{(-\mu)} \tag{1.77}$$

This relation clearly holds for $\psi^{(\mu)}$.

From the explicit forms of the isospin matrices, Eqs. (1.62), one notes the relations

$$\begin{aligned} (t_1)_{\mu\nu} &= (t_1)_{-\mu,-\nu} \\ (t_2)_{\mu\nu} &= -(t_2)_{-\mu,-\nu} \\ (t_3)_{\mu\nu} &= -(t_3)_{-\mu,-\nu} \end{aligned} \tag{1.78}$$

Therefore under transformation by R, as indicated in Eq. (1.77), the isospin operators (1.63) or (1.68) transform as follows:

$$\begin{aligned} RT_1R^{-1} &= -T_1 \\ RT_2R^{-1} &= T_2 \\ RT_3R^{-1} &= -T_3 \end{aligned} \tag{1.79}$$

Combining Eqs. (1.74) and (1.79) now reveals the most important property of the G operator:

$$GTG^{-1} = \mathbf{T} \tag{1.80}$$

Finally, the fields ϕ and ψ transform under G conjugation as follows:

$$\begin{aligned} G\phi^{(\mu)}G^{-1} &= (-1)^{T+\mu}\phi^{(-\mu)*} \\ G\psi^{(\mu)}G^{-1} &= (-1)^{T+\mu}\psi^{(-\mu)*} \end{aligned} \tag{1.81}$$

Note the familiar result that the pion field $\boldsymbol{\pi} = (\pi_1,\pi_2,\pi_3)$ is odd under G conjugation. This follows from (1.81) on using $\pi^{(\pm 1)} = \mp(\pi_1 \pm i\pi_2)/\sqrt{2}$, $\pi^{(0)} = \pi_3$.

The use of isospin conservation to simplify the description of strong interactions is too well known to require review here. A thorough discussion may be found in references 1, 2, and 9.

1.4. Violation of Isospin Conservation by Electromagnetism

Experience shows that isospin is conserved to within a few per cent so long as the relative kinetic energy of the colliding particles is substantially greater than the mass differences within isospin multiplets. As remarked earlier, the fractional deviations $\Delta M/M$ from the average mass M of a multiplet are of the same order of magnitude (a few per cent) as the fine-structure constant $e^2/4\pi \cong 1/137$ which enters into simple theoretical estimates of $\Delta M/M$. It is commonly believed that departures from perfect $SU(2)$ isospin symmetry can be completely ascribed to electromagnetism (apart from tiny effects due to weak interactions). This belief persists despite the absence of any widely accepted, numerically successful calculations of these effects. We shall adopt this position here, not only because the hypothesis is simple and plausible, but also because no good competitive ideas seem to exist.

Since charge varies from state to state within an isospin multiplet in accordance with the Gell-Mann-Nishijima relation

$$Q = T_3 + \tfrac{1}{2}Y \qquad Y = S + B \tag{1.82}$$

where the hypercharge Y is composed of the strangeness S and baryon number B, the electromagnetic current cannot commute with the isospin operator $\mathbf{T}$. The presence of electromagnetic couplings therefore "violates" the conservation of T that follows from the supposedly $SU(2)$ invariant strong interactions. (It is popular to pretend that the electromagnetic couplings can be turned off, and that in such a limit perfect $SU(2)$ isospin symmetry obtains.) This "violation" of the symmetry is not random, however, but is exactly prescribed by (1.82), which states that the electromagnetic current is composed of an isoscalar part (Y) and the third component of an isovector.

This transformation property, though not so powerful in its implications as complete isospin symmetry, leads to definite and meaningful predictions by means of the Wigner-Eckart theorem, which essentially states that the matrix elements of operators having the same $SU(2)$ transformation properties are proportional to one another. More precisely, consider the *spherical tensor* $T_\mu{}^J$ of rank J having $2J+1$ components ($\mu = -J, \ldots, +J$). By definition, a spherical tensor operator of rank J transforms according to the irreducible representation D^J of $SU(2)$:

$$\mathcal{O}_\alpha T_\mu{}^J \mathcal{O}_\alpha{}^{-1} = \sum_{\mu'} T_{\mu'}{}^J D_{\mu'\mu}{}^J \tag{1.83}$$

(A particular instance of this definition has been used in Eq. (1.58).)

Consider the matrix elements of $T_\mu{}^J$ between states $|\alpha jm\rangle$ and $|\beta' j'm'\rangle$ where $j(j+1)$ and $j'(j'+1)$ are the eigenvalues of $\mathbf{J}^2$ and m, m' the azimuthal projection J_3; α, β denote other quantum numbers necessary to specify the state. Then the *Wigner-Eckart theorem* states that

$$\langle \beta' j'm' |\, T_\mu{}^J \,| \alpha jm \rangle = \delta_{m',m+\mu} C(jJj';m\mu) \langle \beta' j' \|\, T^J \,\| \alpha j \rangle \tag{1.84}$$

where $C(jJj';m\mu)$ is the Clebsch-Gordan coefficient in the notation of ref. 3 and the "reduced matrix element" $\langle\beta'j'\|\, T^J \,\|\alpha j\rangle$ is *independent* of the azimuthal quantum numbers.

As an application of (1.84) let us consider two examples involving electromagnetism. First, consider the magnetic moment operator μ, which is linear in the current and therefore is of the form $\mathcal{S} + V_3$, according to (1.82), where $\mathcal{S}$ is an isoscalar operator and V_3 transforms as the third component of an isovector. According to (1.84), within an isospin multiplet the matrix elements of V_3 are proportional to those of T_3 (with a *common* factor). Hence for the Σ triplet (10)

$$\begin{aligned}\mu(\Sigma^+) &= \mathcal{S} + \mathcal{V}\\ \mu(\Sigma^0) &= \mathcal{S}\\ \mu(\Sigma^-) &= \mathcal{S} - \mathcal{V}\end{aligned} \tag{1.85}$$

from which we obtain the relation

$$\mu(\Sigma^0) = \tfrac{1}{2}[\mu(\Sigma^+) + \mu(\Sigma^-)] \tag{1.86}$$

No restrictions are obtained for the other baryon multiplets.

Next consider the photoproduction of pions from nucleons, $\gamma + N \rightarrow \pi + N$. Treating the electromagnetic interaction to lowest order gives a matrix element of the form

$$\langle\pi N|\,(\mathcal{S} + V_3)\,|N\rangle \tag{1.87}$$

where the interaction Hamiltonian $\mathcal{S} + V_3$ is $-\int d^3x\mathbf{j}\cdot\mathbf{A}$, $\mathbf{j}$ being the current and $\mathbf{A}$ the vector potential. The scalar part cannot change the isospin of the initial state as shown by

$$\langle T'\mu'|\,\mathcal{S}\,|T\mu\rangle = \delta_{TT'}\delta_{\mu\mu'}\langle T'\|\,\mathcal{S}\,\|T\rangle \tag{1.88}$$

while the isovector part V_3 can change the isospin:

$$\langle T'\mu'|\,V_3\,|T\mu\rangle = C(T\,1\,T';\mu 0)\delta_{\mu'\mu}\langle T'\|\,V_3\,\|T\rangle \tag{1.89}$$

Thus three reduced matrix elements

$$\langle 1/2\|\,\mathcal{S}\,\|1/2\rangle, \quad \langle 3/2\|\,V_3\,\|1/2\rangle, \quad \text{and} \quad \langle 1/2\|\,V_3\,\|1/2\rangle$$

are required to describe the four charge state reactions $\gamma + p \to p + \pi^0$, $\gamma + p \to n + \pi^+$, $\gamma + n \to p + \pi^-$, and $\gamma + n \to n + \pi^0$. It happens that the low energy region is dominated by the 3–3 resonance ($T = J = 3/2^+$), so that in this special case one amplitude is adequate. Then the Clebsch-Gordan coefficients give simple ratios for the charge state ratios.

References

1. P. Roman, *Theory of Elementary Particles*, North-Holland, Amsterdam, 1960.
2. R. E. Marshak and E. C. G. Sudarshan, *Introduction to Elementary Particle Physics*, Interscience, New York, 1960.
3. M. E. Rose, *Elementary Theory of Angular Momentum*, Wiley, New York, 1957.
4. A. R. Edmonds, *Angular Momentum in Quantum Mechanics*, Princeton University Press, Princeton, N.J., 1960.
5. P. Carruthers and J. P. Krisch, *Ann. Phys. (N.Y.)*, **33**, 1 (1965).
6. E. P. Wigner, *Group Theory*, Academic Press, New York, 1959, p. 288.
7. L. Michel, *Nuovo Cimento*, **10**, 319 (1953).
8. T. D. Lee and C. N. Yang, *Nuovo Cimento*, **13**, 749 (1956).
9. G. Källen, *Elementary Particle Physics*, Addison Wesley, Reading, Mass., 1964.
10. R. E. Marshak, S. Okubo, and E. C. G. Sudarshan, *Phys. Rev.*, **106**, 599 (1957).

Chapter 2

$SU(3)$: Symmetry in Strong Interactions

2.1 Introduction

In Chapter 1 we discussed the fact that the strongly interacting particles all seem to belong to isospin multiplets. [For experimental evidence one may consult the review of Dalitz (1) or that of Rosenfeld et al. (2).] If we now compare particles which have different isospin, but are otherwise identical (having the same spin, parity, strangeness, and baryon number), further interesting patterns emerge (Fig. 2.1). These isospin multiplets, when grouped in this way, suggest a degree of organization more pervasive than that made possible by isospin conservation. It is further apparent that any "higher symmetry" introduced to account for these similarities is much less accurate than the approximation of isospin conservation. Indeed, the masses of the isospin multiplets comprising the "super-multiplets" are so disparate, especially for the pseudoscalar mesons, that one may doubt whether considerations based on symmetry arguments have any relevance to the real world. In some cases, however, the masses are close enough to suggest a vestigial degeneracy, masked by some moderately strong symmetry-breaking interaction, in the absence of which the members of the super-multiplets really would be degenerate. This idea has a counterpart in the way in which electromagnetism "breaks" isospin conservation. The electromagnetic interaction contains a part proportional to the third component of an isovector and so is not invariant under the appropriate $SU(2)$ transformations. In Chapter 1 we discarded the (weak) electromagnetic interaction and studied the hypothet-

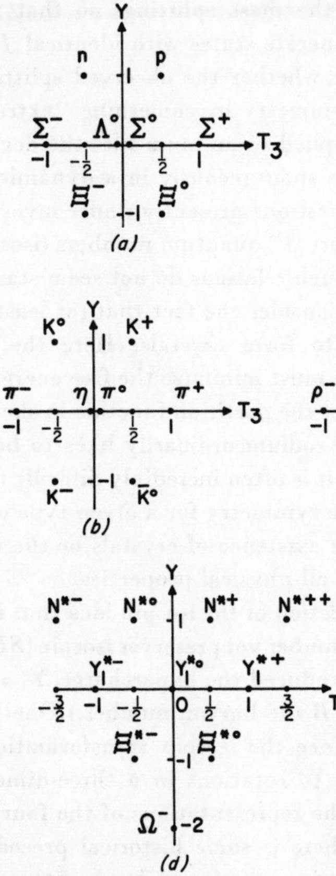

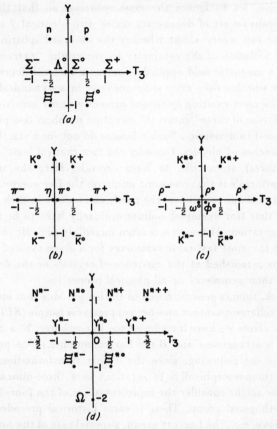

Fig. 2.1. Supermultiplets of particles of the same spin, parity, and baryon number fall into simple geometrical patterns when placed on a hypercharge–3rd component of isospin plot.

ical limit of perfect *SU*(2) symmetry. We follow a similar (less plausible) procedure here. At present, it has to be admitted that the unusual success of predictions based on perfect *SU*(3) symmetry (in apparent defiance of the large symmetry-breaking terms) is not understood in any deep way.

To begin, let us ignore the mass splittings so that there is (theoretically) a set of degenerate states with identical J and P. Later, we can worry about whether the observed splittings are due to a violation of the symmetry by something "extraneous" (e.g., as a magnetic field applied to an atom lifts the degeneracy in J_z), or whether they arise spontaneously in a dynamical way. One of the most exciting questions presently under investigation is the relation of these "internal" quantum numbers (isospin and strangeness) to dynamics. Such relations do not seem startling in older branches of physics. Consider the fact that (at least at low temperatures) atoms like to form crystals. Here the mathematical principle is that one must minimize the free energy. With sufficient skill one can dissect the partition function in such a way to show that (for example) sodium ordinarily likes to be in the fcc configuration. Although it is often incredibly difficult to really calculate the most favorable symmetry for a given type of atom, nobody is astonished at the existence of crystals or the decisive effect of their symmetry on all physical properties.

We seek, then, a generalization of the isospin idea that includes the hypercharge quantum number yet preserves isospin [$SU(2)$] invariance. (Here we have introduced the hypercharge $Y = S + B$ where S is strangeness and B the baryon number.) One possible scheme is the following: since the isospin transformations correspond (homomorphically) to rotations in a three-dimensional space, one might consider the representations of the four-dimensional orthogonal group. There is some historical precedent for such a move, e.g., the Lorentz group, a special case of the complex orthogonal group O_4, contains the rotation group as a subgroup. This approach is discussed in reference 3. It should be clear, however, that the isospin group is really $SU(2)$ and not O_3. Hence no enormous surprise should be felt at the greater success obtained by generalizing $SU(2)$ to $SU(3)$.

2.2 Infinitesimal Generators of $SU(3)$

To discover $SU(3)$ let us recall our discussion of isospin. There the fundamental entity was the nucleon spinor. Not only could we build up all representations of $SU(2)$ with this spinor, we could even pretend that all nonstrange strongly interacting particles could be built up from bound states of nucleons and antinucleons. Unfortunately the idea of strangeness seems quite remote from that theory. One can, however, introduce strangeness by adding one more "fundamental" baryon to the nucleon doublet. The best candidate for this is the Λ, since it is an isotopic singlet. Thus we have the basic triplet

$$\psi = \begin{pmatrix} p \\ n \\ \Lambda \end{pmatrix} \tag{2.1}$$

where we pretend as usual that p, n, and Λ are degenerate. Now all particles are to be built up out of ψ and anti-ψ. This is the Sakata model (4) which was developed in the context of the group $U(3)$ by Ikeda, Ogawa, and Ohnuki (5). It turns out that the specific assignments in (2.1) are incorrect, and the Sakata model has to be abandoned in its details. We shall use the historical approach because of its intuitive appeal and because it leads naturally to the more successful "eightfold way" of Gell-Mann (6) and Ne'eman (7). The quadratic structure of Lagrangian theories dictates that the symmetry transformations be unitary:

$$\psi' = U\psi \qquad U^\dagger U = 1 \tag{2.2}$$

Since the determinant of a unitary matrix is $e^{i\eta}$, η real, we can separate this phase transformation (it corresponds to baryon conservation) and deal entirely with unimodular transformations:

$$\det U = 1 \tag{2.3}$$

The group associated with continuous unitary unimodular transformations U in n dimensions is called $SU(n)$.

We write the basic $SU(3)$ transformation as

$$U = \exp\,(i\boldsymbol{\alpha}\cdot\boldsymbol{\lambda}/2) \tag{2.4}$$

where $\boldsymbol{\alpha}$ is an eight-component real vector and the λ_j are a set of eight traceless 3×3 Hermitian matrices, in exact analogy to the

Pauli spin matrices $\boldsymbol{\sigma}$ of $SU(2)$. For most purposes we only need to work with the infinitesimal transformation

$$U = 1 + \tfrac{1}{2}i\delta\boldsymbol{\alpha}\cdot\boldsymbol{\lambda} \tag{2.5}$$

The λ_j are required to be traceless by the condition

$$\det U = 1 + \frac{i}{2}\,\delta\boldsymbol{\alpha}\cdot \mathrm{Tr}\,\boldsymbol{\lambda} + 0(\delta\boldsymbol{\alpha})^2 = 1 \tag{2.6}$$

neglecting as always terms of second order in $\delta\boldsymbol{\alpha}$. There are $3^2 - 1 = 8$ independent 3×3 traceless Hermitian matrices (cf. $2^2 - 1 = 3$ independent 2×2 traceless Hermitian matrices σ_j) which we shall write down shortly.

The "self-representation" (2.4) generated by transformations on the basic triplet (2.1) is referred to by the symbol **3**, or by $D(1, 0)$ [or simply (1,0)], in a notation to be explained in Chapter 3.

As in the case of angular momentum it is sometimes convenient to use the Hermitian generators and sometimes the raising and lowering operators. The latter are especially useful in constructing representations. For $SU(3)$ we can define six operators that permute the various particles p, n, and Λ. The normalization is chosen to give maximum symmetry to the diagram displaying the eigenvalues of the diagonal generators defined below.

$$E_1 = \frac{1}{\sqrt{6}}\begin{pmatrix} 0 & 1 & 0 \\ 0 & 0 & 0 \\ 0 & 0 & 0 \end{pmatrix} \qquad E_{-1} \equiv E_1{}^\dagger$$

$$E_2 = \frac{1}{\sqrt{6}}\begin{pmatrix} 0 & 0 & 0 \\ 0 & 0 & 0 \\ 1 & 0 & 0 \end{pmatrix} \qquad E_{-2} \equiv E_2{}^\dagger \tag{2.7}$$

$$E_3 = \frac{1}{\sqrt{6}}\begin{pmatrix} 0 & 0 & 0 \\ 0 & 0 & 1 \\ 0 & 0 & 0 \end{pmatrix} \qquad E_{-3} \equiv E_3{}^\dagger$$

It will be noticed that most standard works (e.g., ref. 8) use E_{-2} for our E_2. The present choice increases the symmetry between E_1, E_2, and E_3 and permits one to write the commutation rules in a more succinct form than is otherwise possible. E_{-2} changes a Λ into a p. In addition to these six matrices we need two traceless matrices, independent of (2.7). These can be chosen to be diagonal. We choose one (H_1) to correspond to T_3 [(1/2,−1/2,0) for p, n, and Λ, respectively] and the other (H_2) to be the same for p and n and different for Λ, so that H_2 will be simply related to strangeness or hypercharge.

$$H_1 = \frac{1}{2\sqrt{3}}\begin{pmatrix} 1 & 0 & 0 \\ 0 & -1 & 0 \\ 0 & 0 & 0 \end{pmatrix} \qquad H_2 = \frac{1}{6}\begin{pmatrix} 1 & 0 & 0 \\ 0 & 1 & 0 \\ 0 & 0 & -2 \end{pmatrix} \tag{2.8}$$

Clearly we can express the λ_j and also the matrix U of Eq. (2.5) in terms of (2.7) and (2.8). The physical interpretation of Y and T_3 require us to choose H_1 and H_2 diagonal. Next we write down the commutation relations between these generators. As we know from Chapter 1, the algebra defined by these commutators poses a much more general problem than the specific three-dimensional one. In particular we can seek all possible representations of the algebra (i.e., matrices satisfying the commutation rules); in so doing we also find all representations of the group (9).

Before writing down the commutation relations it is helpful to discuss the eigenvalues of H_1 and H_2 in the defining three-dimensional representation. For purposes of discussion we treat the basic triplet ψ in (2.1) as a wave function so that the three entries are the probability coefficients for p, n, and Λ. We now drop the p, n, and Λ notation in favor of numbering these respective positions 1, 2, and 3. Now a "1" state has wave function $\psi^1 = \text{col}\,(\phi,0,0)$, where ϕ is the spatial wave function, etc. Dropping the common factor ϕ, the wave functions ψ^k with lth component δ_{kl} ($k,l = 1,2,3$) are eigenfunctions of the vector $\mathbf{H}$:

$$\mathbf{H} = (H_1,H_2) \tag{2.9}$$

$$\mathbf{H}\psi^k = \mathbf{m}_k\psi^k \tag{2.10}$$

$$\mathbf{m}_1 = \left(\frac{1}{2\sqrt{3}}, \frac{1}{6}\right)$$

$$\mathbf{m}_2 = \left(-\frac{1}{2\sqrt{3}}, \frac{1}{6}\right) \qquad |\mathbf{m}_k| = \frac{1}{3} \tag{2.11}$$

$$\mathbf{m}_3 = \left(0, -\frac{1}{3}\right)$$

These two-component vectors $\mathbf{m}_k$ are the *weight vectors* of the defining representation **3**. The corresponding *weight diagram* is displayed in Fig. 2.2, along with the *root vectors* $\mathbf{r}(\alpha)$; $\alpha = 1, 2, 3$,

$$\mathbf{r}(1) = \mathbf{m}_1 - \mathbf{m}_2 = \left(\frac{1}{\sqrt{3}}, 0\right)$$

$$\mathbf{r}(2) = \mathbf{m}_3 - \mathbf{m}_1 = -\left(\frac{1}{2\sqrt{3}}, \frac{1}{2}\right) \qquad |\mathbf{r}(\alpha)| = \frac{1}{\sqrt{3}} \tag{2.12}$$

$$\mathbf{r}(3) = \mathbf{m}_2 - \mathbf{m}_3 = \left(-\frac{1}{2\sqrt{3}}, \frac{1}{2}\right)$$

As shown below, the weights [eigenvalues of $\mathbf{H}$, Eq. (2.9)] of any representation lie on a two-dimensional lattice whose translation vectors are any two of the root vectors. We also make the definition

$$\mathbf{r}(-\alpha) \equiv -\mathbf{r}(\alpha) \tag{2.13}$$

which is demanded by the structure of the commutation rules set down below. The effect of the matrices E_α on the ψ^k is given in the following

$$\sqrt{6}\,E_1\psi^2 = \psi^1 \qquad \sqrt{6}\,E_2\psi^1 = \psi^3 \qquad \sqrt{6}\,E_3\psi^3 = \psi^2 \tag{2.14}$$

while $E_1\psi^1$ vanishes, etc.

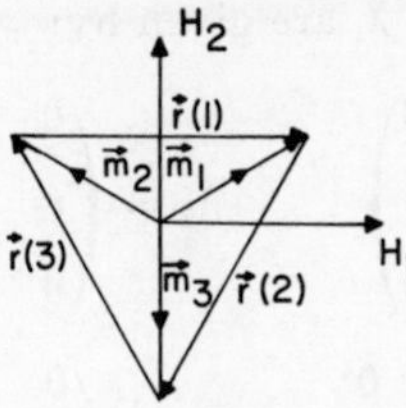

Fig. 2.2. Weight diagram for the defining representation **3** of $SU(3)$. The vectors $\mathbf{m}_i$ are the weight vectors, eigenvalues of the operator $\mathbf{H}$. The $\mathbf{r}(\alpha)$ are the root vectors.

The result of computing the commutators of the eight matrices $E_{\pm\alpha}$ ($\alpha = 1,2,3$), H_1, and H_2 can now be summarized:

$$[E_\alpha, E_\beta] = -\frac{1}{\sqrt{6}}\varepsilon_{\alpha\beta\gamma}E_{-\gamma} \tag{2.15}$$

$$[E_\alpha, E_{-\beta}] = \delta_{\alpha\beta}\mathbf{r}(\alpha)\cdot\mathbf{H} \qquad \text{(no sum)} \tag{2.16}$$

$$[\mathbf{H}, E_\alpha] = \mathbf{r}(\alpha)E_\alpha \qquad \text{(no sum)} \tag{2.17}$$

Here α, β, and γ run over 1, 2, and 3. In Eq. (2.15) the index γ is summed over. Equation (2.13) follows by requiring (2.16) to be consistent for $\beta = \alpha$. Further relations involving the $E_{-\alpha}$ follow from (2.15) to (2.17) by Hermitian conjugation, recalling $E_\alpha{}^\dagger = E_{-\alpha}$.

We may now construct a set of Hermitian generators from the set $E_{\pm\alpha}$, H_i. These are defined by the relations:

$$\begin{aligned}
\lambda_1 &= \sqrt{6}(E_1 + E_{-1}) & \lambda_2 &= \sqrt{6}i(E_{-1} - E_{+1}) \\
\lambda_3 &= 2\sqrt{3}H_1 & \lambda_4 &= \sqrt{6}(E_2 + E_{-2}) \\
\lambda_5 &= \sqrt{6}i(E_2 - E_{-2}) & \lambda_6 &= \sqrt{6}(E_3 + E_{-3}) \\
\lambda_7 &= \sqrt{6}i(E_{-3} - E_3) & \lambda_8 &= 2\sqrt{3}H_2
\end{aligned} \tag{2.18}$$

Explicitly the matrices λ_i are given by:

$$\lambda_1 = \begin{pmatrix} 0 & 1 & 0 \\ 1 & 0 & 0 \\ 0 & 0 & 0 \end{pmatrix} \qquad \lambda_2 = \begin{pmatrix} 0 & -i & 0 \\ i & 0 & 0 \\ 0 & 0 & 0 \end{pmatrix}$$

$$\lambda_3 = \begin{pmatrix} 1 & 0 & 0 \\ 0 & -1 & 0 \\ 0 & 0 & 0 \end{pmatrix} \qquad \lambda_4 = \begin{pmatrix} 0 & 0 & 1 \\ 0 & 0 & 0 \\ 1 & 0 & 0 \end{pmatrix} \tag{2.19}$$

$$\lambda_5 = \begin{pmatrix} 0 & 0 & -i \\ 0 & 0 & 0 \\ i & 0 & 0 \end{pmatrix} \qquad \lambda_6 = \begin{pmatrix} 0 & 0 & 0 \\ 0 & 0 & 1 \\ 0 & 1 & 0 \end{pmatrix}$$

$$\lambda_7 = \begin{pmatrix} 0 & 0 & 0 \\ 0 & 0 & -i \\ 0 & i & 0 \end{pmatrix} \qquad \lambda_8 = \begin{pmatrix} \frac{1}{\sqrt{3}} & 0 & 0 \\ 0 & \frac{1}{\sqrt{3}} & 0 \\ 0 & 0 & -\frac{2}{\sqrt{3}} \end{pmatrix}$$

The first seven λ_i have been chosen to resemble the ordinary Pauli matrices. Note that λ_1, λ_2, and λ_3 generate the algebra of $SU(2)$. In analogy to the Pauli spin matrix relations,

$$[\tau_i,\tau_j] = 2i\varepsilon_{ijk}\tau_k \tag{2.20}$$

$$\{\tau_i,\tau_j\} \equiv \tau_i\tau_j + \tau_j\tau_i = 2\delta_{ij}I \tag{2.21}$$

the λ's have the following relations:

$$[\lambda_i,\lambda_j] = 2if_{ijk}\lambda_k \tag{2.22}$$

$$\{\lambda_i,\lambda_j\} = \tfrac{4}{3}\delta_{ij}I + 2d_{ijk}\lambda_k \tag{2.23}$$

In (2.22) f_{ijk} is clearly antisymmetric in i and j, and also real by virtue of the Hermiticity of the λ_i and the antisymmetry. Using the trace property

$$\mathrm{Tr}\ \lambda_i\lambda_j = 2\delta_{ij} \tag{2.24}$$

we can see that f_{ijk} is totally antisymmetric. Multiply (2.22) by λ_l and apply (2.24):

$$\begin{aligned} 4if_{ijl} &= \mathrm{Tr}\,(\lambda_l\lambda_i\lambda_j - \lambda_l\lambda_j\lambda_i) \\ &= \mathrm{Tr}\,(\lambda_j\lambda_l\lambda_i - \lambda_j\lambda_i\lambda_l) \\ &= \mathrm{Tr}\,\lambda_j[\lambda_l,\lambda_i] = 4if_{lij} \\ &= -4if_{ilj} \end{aligned} \tag{2.25}$$

using the cyclic invariance of the trace and the basic definition (2.23). Antisymmetry in the first and third indices is a consequence of the relations already noted. Similarly, the real coefficients d_{ijk} are totally symmetric in i, j, and k. Note that the 4/3 in (2.23) is necessary for the compatibility of (2.23) and (2.24).

The actual values of f_{ijk} and d_{ijk} are found by patiently working out the commutation properties of the matrices listed in Eq. (2.19). The nonzero coefficients are given in Table 2.1.

TABLE 2.1

The Nonvanishing Structure Constants f_{ijk} of the Hermitian Generators Are Given. The d_{ijk}, Which Are Useful as Clebsch-Gordan Coefficients, Are Defined by the Anticommutation Rules of Eq. (2.23) for the 3 × 3 Generators (1/2)$\boldsymbol{\lambda}$.

ijk	f_{ijk}	ijk	d_{ijk}
123	1	118	$1/\sqrt{3}$
147	1/2	146	1/2
156	−1/2	157	1/2
246	1/2	228	$1/\sqrt{3}$
257	1/2	247	−1/2
345	1/2	256	1/2
367	−1/2	338	$1/\sqrt{3}$
458	$\sqrt{3}/2$	344	1/2
678	$\sqrt{3}/2$	355	1/2
		366	−1/2
		377	−1/2
		448	$-1/(2\sqrt{3})$
		558	$-1/(2\sqrt{3})$
		668	$-1/(2\sqrt{3})$
		778	$-1/(2\sqrt{3})$
		888	$-1/\sqrt{3}$

It will be noted that the Hermitian generators $G = \frac{1}{2}\boldsymbol{\lambda}$ lead to a more succinct expression for the commutation rules

$$[G_a,G_b] = if_{abc}G_c \tag{2.26}$$

$(a,b,c = 1,2,\ldots,8)$ than do the non-Hermitian generators $E_{+\alpha},H_i$. The structure constants if_{abc} are extremely important in the study of the group and shall be the subject of much discussion in subsequent sections. An $n \times n$ Hermitian representation of the algebra (2.26) of $SU(3)$ by eight matrices G_a leads to unitary representations of the form exp $(i\boldsymbol{\alpha}\cdot\mathbf{G})$, where $\boldsymbol{\alpha}$ is a real eight-component vector with continuously varying components describing $SU(3)$ transformations. The manifold of the parameters α_k always includes the origin, which corresponds to the identity transformation of the group. Although the $n \times n$ matrices $2G_a$ do not satisfy a relation like (2.23), the coefficients d_{abc} are also useful and will reappear later as Clebsch-Gordan coefficients for the "regular representation" basis functions.

Finally, we include for completeness, one other useful sct of generators used extensively by Okubo (10). One defines a set of nine real traceless matrices A_j^i with matrix elements $(A_j^i)_{\mu\nu}$ $(i,j,\mu,\nu = 1,2,3)$ by

$$(A_j^i)_{\mu\nu} = \delta_{i\nu}\delta_{j\mu} - \tfrac{1}{3}\delta_{ij}\delta_{\mu\nu} \tag{2.27}$$

Only eight of these matrices are independent since

$$A_1^1 + A_2^2 + A_3^3 = 0 \tag{2.28}$$

The commutation rules are easily computed

$$[A_j^i,A_l^k] = \delta_l^i A_j^k - \delta_j^k A_l^i \tag{2.29}$$

and the connection of A_j^i to E_α, H_j is as follows:

$$\begin{aligned} A_2^1 &= \sqrt{6}E_{-1} \quad A_3^1 = \sqrt{6}E_2 \quad A_3^2 = \sqrt{6}E_{-3} \\ A_1^2 &= \sqrt{6}E_1 \quad A_1^3 = \sqrt{6}E_{-2} \quad A_2^3 = \sqrt{6}E_3 \\ A_1^1 - A_2^2 &= 2\sqrt{3}H_1; \qquad A_1^1 + A_2^2 = 2H_2 \end{aligned} \tag{2.30}$$

We now show that the allowed weights must lie on the two-dimensional lattice having any two of $\mathbf{r}(1)$, $\mathbf{r}(2)$, $\mathbf{r}(3)$ as primitive

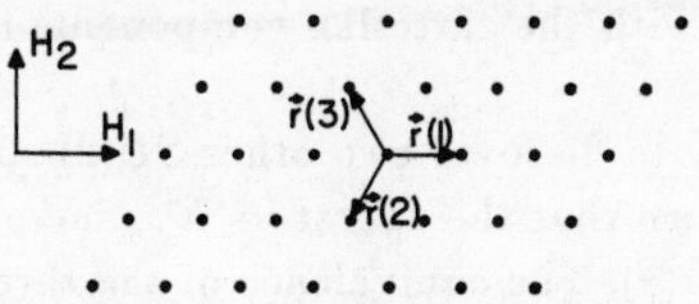

Fig. 2.3. The allowed eigenvalues (weights) of **H** lie on a two-dimensional hexagonal lattice whose translation vectors are any two of the roots $\mathbf{r}(\alpha)$.

translation vectors (Fig. 2.3). Suppose $\psi(\mathbf{m})$ is an eigenfunction of **H** with eigenvalue **m**. Then Eq. (2.17) shows that the state $E_\alpha\psi(\mathbf{m})$ has eigenvalue $\mathbf{m} + \mathbf{r}(\alpha)$, unless it is identically zero:

$$\begin{aligned} \mathbf{H}E_\alpha\psi(\mathbf{m}) &= [\mathbf{H},E_\alpha]\psi(\mathbf{m}) + E_\alpha\mathbf{H}\psi(\mathbf{m}) \\ &= (\mathbf{r}(\alpha) + \mathbf{m})E_\alpha\psi(\mathbf{m}) \end{aligned} \tag{2.31}$$

Similarly, $E_{-\alpha}\psi(\mathbf{m})$ either vanishes or has weight $\mathbf{m} - \mathbf{r}(\alpha)$.

2.3 $SU(2)$ Subgroups of $SU(3)$

In the Sakata model the first two components of the triplet ψ are an isospin doublet (p,n). From Eq. (2.11) we see that this identification can be made more generally for the basic triplet, the correspondence being $T_3 = \sqrt{3}\,H_1$. The third component of ψ is accordingly an isosinglet. (Incidentally the hypercharge operator in the Sakata model is $Y = 2H_2 + 2/3$.) Moreover, the operators $\sqrt{6}\,E_{\pm 1}$ correspond to the raising and lowering operators $\tau_\pm$ (see Eq. 2.7 or 2.14). The isosinglet is simply annihilated by $E_{\pm 1}$.

From the commutation rules (2.16) and (2.17) it follows immediately that an isospin subalgebra composed of the operators

$$T_\pm = \sqrt{6}\,E_{\pm 1} \quad \text{and} \quad T_3 = \sqrt{3}\,H_1 \tag{2.32}$$

exists, independent of the special features of the **3** representation. Setting $\alpha = \beta = 1$ in Eq. (2.16) and (2.17) yields

$$[T_+,T_-] = 2T_3 \qquad [T_3,T_\pm] = \pm\, T_\pm \tag{2.33}$$

The connection with the cartesian components is as usual $T_{\pm} = T_1 \pm iT_2$.

It is now easy to discover two other $SU(2)$ subalgebras. From Eq. (2.31) we learn that the operators $E_{\pm\alpha}$ increase the weight in the direction of $\mathbf{r}(\alpha)$. The equivalence of the three directions suggests that $\sqrt{6}E_{\pm 2}$, $\sqrt{6}E_{\pm 3}$ are just as good raising and lowering operators as $\sqrt{6}E_{\pm 1}$. Equating α and β in Eq. (2.16) leads to the suspicion that the projection of $\mathbf{H}$ on the root vector $\mathbf{r}(\alpha)$ gives the third component of the "isospin" in the α direction. To verify this we first define this projection

$$\mathcal{H}_\alpha \equiv \mathbf{r}(\alpha)\cdot\mathbf{H} \tag{2.34}$$

or explicitly

$$\mathcal{H}_1 = \frac{1}{\sqrt{3}} H_1$$

$$\mathcal{H}_2 = -\left(\frac{1}{2\sqrt{3}} H_1 + \tfrac{1}{2}H_2\right) \tag{2.35}$$

$$\mathcal{H}_3 = -\frac{1}{2\sqrt{3}} H_1 + \tfrac{1}{2}H_2$$

Taking the scalar product of $\mathbf{r}(\alpha)$ with Eq. (2.17) (first replacing α by β in that equation) gives

$$[\mathcal{H}_\alpha, E_{\pm\beta}] = \pm\mathbf{r}(\alpha)\cdot\mathbf{r}(\beta)E_{\pm\beta} \tag{2.36}$$

Since $\mathbf{r}^2(\alpha) = 1/3$ while $\mathbf{r}(\alpha)\cdot\mathbf{r}(\beta) = -1/6$ for $\alpha \neq \beta$, we find

$$[\mathcal{H}_\alpha, E_{\pm\alpha}] = \pm\tfrac{1}{3}E_{\pm\alpha} \tag{2.37}$$

$$[\mathcal{H}_\alpha, E_{\pm\beta}] = \mp\tfrac{1}{6}E_{\pm\beta}, \quad \alpha \neq \beta \tag{2.38}$$

It is apparent from Eqs. (2.37) and (2.16) that $3\mathcal{H}_\alpha$ is the appropriately normalized third component of "isospin" in the α direction.

In addition to the ordinary isospin operator $\mathbf{T}$, we are led to define $\mathbf{U}$ and $\mathbf{V}$ spin:

$$U_{\pm} \equiv \sqrt{6}E_{\pm 3} \quad U_3 \equiv 3\mathcal{H}_3 \tag{2.39}$$

$$V_{\pm} \equiv \sqrt{6}E_{\pm 2} \quad V_3 \equiv 3\mathcal{H}_2 \tag{2.40}$$

The commutation rules are analogous to (2.33):

$$[U_+,U_-] = 2U_3 \quad [U_3,U_{\pm}] = \pm U_{\pm} \tag{2.41}$$

$$[V_+,V_-] = 2V_3 \quad [V_3,V_{\pm}] = \pm V_{\pm} \tag{2.42}$$

None of these subalgebras is an invariant subalgebra (9) since the operators in one subalgebra do not commute with those in another. [The algebra of $SU(3)$ is said to be *simple* since there is no invariant subalgebra.]

The great practical utility of the $SU(2)$ subgroups of $SU(3)$ having **T**, **U**, and **V** spin as generators has been emphasized by Levinson, Lipkin, and Meshkov (11,12). We shall make extensive use of this formalism in order to exploit the familiar features of $SU(2)$. The effect of the operators $T_{\pm}$, $U_{\pm}$, and $V_{\pm}$ is indicated in Fig. 2.4. The original commutation relations can be rewritten in terms of the **T**, **U**, and **V** operators. Making the definitions

$$I_{\pm}{}^{\alpha} = \sqrt{6}E_{\pm\alpha}, \quad I_{\pm}{}^{1} = T_{\pm}, \quad I_{\pm}{}^{2} = V_{\pm}, \quad I_{\pm}{}^{3} = U_{\pm}$$

$$I_z{}^{\alpha} = 3\mathcal{H}_{\alpha} \tag{2.43}$$

we find that Eqs. (2.15)–(2.17) can be written as

$$[I_{\pm}{}^{\alpha},I_{\pm}{}^{\beta}] = \mp\varepsilon_{\alpha\beta\gamma}I_{\mp}{}^{\gamma} \tag{2.44}$$

$$[I_{\pm}{}^{\alpha},I_{\mp}{}^{\beta}] = 2\delta_{\alpha\beta}I_z{}^{\alpha} \tag{2.45}$$

$$[I_z{}^{\alpha},I_{\pm}{}^{\beta}] = \pm 3\mathbf{r}(\alpha)\cdot\mathbf{r}(\beta)I_{\pm}{}^{\beta} \tag{2.46}$$

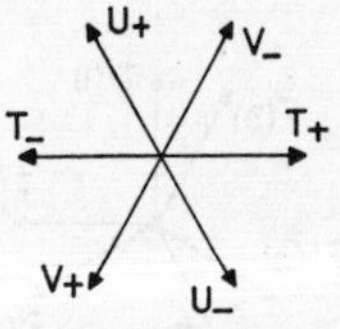

Fig. 2.4. The operators $T_{\pm}$, $U_{\pm}$, and $V_{\pm}$ change the eigenvalues of **H** by one lattice constant (cf. Fig. 2.4) in the direction shown.

Equation (2.46) can be simplified in the same way as Eq. (2.36). Equation (2.44) can also be summarized by

$$[T_+,U_+] = V_- \quad [U_+,V_+] = T_- \quad [V_+,T_+] = U_- \tag{2.47}$$

and the three relations obtained by Hermitian conjugation.

We next describe how one may construct for each of the $SU(2)$ subgroups linear combinations of H_1 and H_2 which are scalars. We have seen that $\mathcal{H}_\alpha = \mathbf{r}(\alpha)\cdot\mathbf{H}$ is the third component of the T, U, or V spin. Let us construct three vectors $\mathbf{r}'(\alpha)$ by rotating the three root vectors $\mathbf{r}(\alpha)$ counterclockwise by 90° (Fig. 2.5).

$$(r_1'(\alpha),r_2'(\alpha)) = (-r_2(\alpha),r_1(\alpha)) \tag{2.48}$$

$$\left.\begin{aligned} \mathbf{r}'(1) &= \left(0,\frac{1}{\sqrt{3}}\right) \\ \mathbf{r}'(2) &= \left(\frac{1}{2},-\frac{1}{2\sqrt{3}}\right) \\ \mathbf{r}'(3) &= \left(-\frac{1}{2},-\frac{1}{2\sqrt{3}}\right) \end{aligned}\right\} \qquad \mathbf{r}'(\alpha)\cdot\mathbf{r}(\alpha) = 0 \tag{2.49}$$

The quantities $\mathcal{H}_\alpha'$ are defined by the equality

$$\mathcal{H}_\alpha' \equiv \mathbf{r}'(\alpha)\cdot\mathbf{H} \tag{2.50}$$

Taking the scalar product of $\mathbf{r}'(\alpha)$ with both sides of Eq. (2.17) gives

$$[\mathcal{H}_\alpha',E_{\pm\alpha}] = 0 \tag{2.51}$$

In addition, all the $\mathcal{H}_\alpha$ and $\mathcal{H}_\beta'$ commute for all α and β. Therefore $\mathcal{H}_1'$ commutes with $\mathbf{T}$, $\mathcal{H}_2'$ commutes with $\mathbf{V}$, and $\mathcal{H}_3'$ commutes with $\mathbf{U}$. Figure 2.5 should be consulted to clarify the simple geometrical significance of this result.

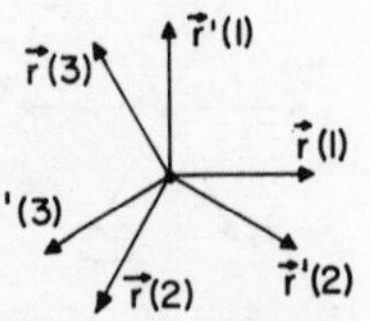

Fig. 2.5. The relation between the root vectors $\mathbf{r}(\alpha)$ and the set $\mathbf{r}'(\alpha)$ is shown.

The significance of these operators can be understood as follows. In detail, Eq. (2.50) is

$$\mathcal{H}_1' = \frac{1}{\sqrt{3}} H_2$$

$$\mathcal{H}_2' = \frac{1}{2} H_1 - \frac{1}{2\sqrt{3}} H_2 \tag{2.52}$$

$$\mathcal{H}_3' = -\left(\frac{1}{2} H_1 + \frac{1}{2\sqrt{3}} H_2\right)$$

It will be recalled that H_2 was introduced in order to describe the hypercharge quantum number. The specific relation is, however, model dependent. In the Sakata model, where the components of the basic triplet are identified with p, n, and Λ, the connection is

$$Y = 2H_2 + \tfrac{2}{3} \qquad \text{(Sakata model)} \tag{2.53}$$

while the identification of the eight baryons with the components of the regular representation (see below) leads to

$$Y = 2H_2 \qquad \text{(Eightfold way)} \tag{2.54}$$

In general a linear relation between Y and H_2 is called for. For brevity we discuss the $\mathcal{H}_j'$ for the case (2.54).

Comparing Eqs. (2.52) and (2.54) gives the following relation:

$$Y = 2\sqrt{3}\,\mathcal{H}_1' \tag{2.55}$$

Moreover, the electric charge is given by

$$Q = T_3 + \tfrac{1}{2}Y = -2\sqrt{3}\left(-\tfrac{1}{2}H_1 - \frac{1}{2\sqrt{3}} H_2\right) = -2\sqrt{3}\,\mathcal{H}_3' \tag{2.56}$$

The conserved quantity related to the 2-direction

$$Z \equiv 2\sqrt{3}\,\mathcal{H}_2' = Q - Y \tag{2.57}$$

is of course not independent of Q and Y. Thus far the "Z charge" has not been found to lead to any simplifications beyond the practice of describing states by means of Y and Q.

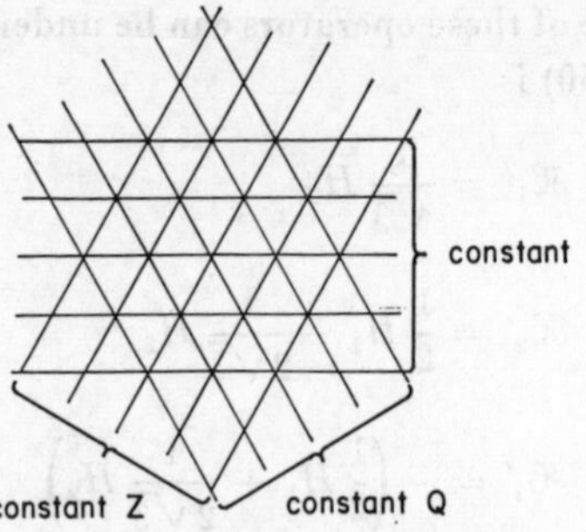

Fig. 2.6. Lines of constant charge Q, hypercharge Y, and $Z = Y - Q$ in the eigenvalue lattice are shown.

Equation (2.51) now shows that T, U, and V commute with Y, Q, and Z, respectively.

$$[\mathbf{T}, Y] = 0$$
$$[\mathbf{U}, Q] = 0 \qquad (2.58)$$
$$[\mathbf{V}, Z] = 0$$

Thus all members of a T-spin multiplet have the same hypercharge, all members of a U-spin multiplet have the same charge, and all members of a V-spin multiplet have the same value of $Z = Q - Y$. This result is indicated in Fig. 2.6. To emphasize the formal similarity of $\mathcal{H}_i$ and $\mathcal{H}_i{}'$ the lines of constant T_3, U_3, and V_3 are shown in Fig. 2.7.

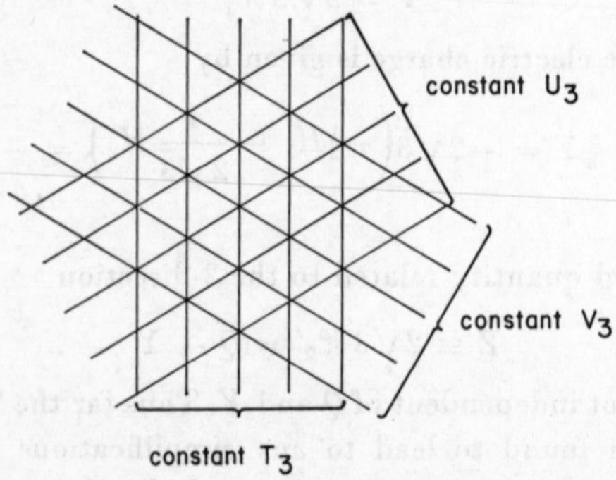

Fig. 2.7. Lines of constant T_3, U_3, and V_3 in the eigenvalue lattice are shown.

The explicit matrices representing Y, Q, and Z in the defining three-dimensional representation are

$$Y = \frac{1}{3}\begin{pmatrix} 1 & 0 & 0 \\ 0 & 1 & 0 \\ 0 & 0 & -2 \end{pmatrix}$$

$$Q = \frac{1}{3}\begin{pmatrix} 2 & 0 & 0 \\ 0 & -1 & 0 \\ 0 & 0 & -1 \end{pmatrix} \tag{2.59}$$

$$Z = \frac{1}{3}\begin{pmatrix} 1 & 0 & 0 \\ 0 & -2 & 0 \\ 0 & 0 & 1 \end{pmatrix}$$

It should be stressed that these forms follow from having imposed $Y = 2H_2$ on *all* representations. In particular, we note that if basic triplets exist, they must have fractional charges and hypercharges [Gell-Mann (13); Zweig (14)]. Whether or not such curious particles really exist, it is very useful for mathematical reasons to work with such triplets. [A variety of triplet theories have been discussed by Gursey, Lee, and Nauenberg (15).]

2.4 Reflection Symmetries of Weight Diagrams

It is useful to supplement the particular transformations (raising and lowering operations) of the $SU(2)$ subgroups discussed in the previous section. From the usual theory of angular momentum we know that a rotation by π about the 2-axis changes the sign of the eigenvalue m of T_3:

$$e^{i\pi T_2}\psi(T,m) = (-1)^{T+m}\psi(T,-m) \tag{2.60}$$

so that $\exp(i\pi T_2)$ is a "reflection" operator for the eigenvalue m. "Reflection" operators for the T, U, and V multiplets are defined by

$$\begin{aligned} R_T &= e^{i\pi T_2} \\ R_U &= e^{i\pi U_2} \\ R_V &= e^{i\pi V_2} \end{aligned} \tag{2.61}$$

It should be remembered that because of the double-valued character of the half-integral representations of $SU(2)$, the above operators are not ordinary reflection operators [explicitly, $R_T{}^2$ has eigenvalue $(-1)^{2T}$]. Nevertheless, we shall refer to the operators (2.61) as reflection operators for brevity. The present discussion follows that of de Swart (16); a somewhat different treatment has been given by MacFarlane, Sudarshan, and Dullemond (17).

Suppose we apply R_ν ($\nu = T, U$, or V) to an eigenfunction of $\mathbf{H}$, $\psi(\mathbf{m})$. We show now that $R_\nu\psi(\mathbf{m})$ is again an eigenfunction of $\mathbf{H}$, with eigenvalue obtained by reflection of $\mathbf{m}$ in the plane perpendicular to the root vectors $\mathbf{r}(\alpha)$ appropriate to the T, U, or V directions, respectively. Thus the existence of one state always implies the existence of others obtained by reflection (except in the special case in which the weight lies in the reflection plane).

In order to evaluate

$$R_T\mathbf{H}R_T{}^{-1} = e^{i\pi T_2}\mathbf{H}e^{-i\pi T_2} \tag{2.62}$$

and similar expressions one uses the standard operator identity:

$$e^{\lambda A}Be^{-\lambda A} = B + \lambda[A,B] + \frac{1}{2!}\lambda^2[A,[A,B]] + \cdots \tag{2.63}$$

Thus (2.62) is equal to

$$\mathbf{H} + i\pi[T_2,\mathbf{H}] + \frac{(i\pi)^2}{2!}[T_2,[T_2,\mathbf{H}]] + \frac{(i\pi)^3}{3!}[T_2,[T_2,[T_2,\mathbf{H}]]] + \cdots \tag{2.64}$$

The required commutators are

$$[T_2,\mathbf{H}] = i\mathbf{r}(1)T_1 \quad \text{and} \quad [T_2,[T_2,\mathbf{H}]] = \mathbf{r}(1)T_3 \tag{2.65}$$

so that further commutators give T_1 or T_3. Hence the series (2.64) sums to

$$\begin{aligned}\mathbf{H} + \left(\frac{(i\pi)^2}{2!} + \frac{(i\pi)^4}{4!} + \cdots\right)\mathbf{r}(1)T_3 - \mathbf{r}(1)\left(\pi - \frac{\pi^3}{3!} + \cdots\right)& \\ = \mathbf{H} - 2\mathbf{r}(1)T_3&\end{aligned} \tag{2.66}$$

The result can be written in a neater form upon noting that $\mathbf{r}(1)T_3$ equals $3\mathbf{r}(1)\cdot\mathbf{H}\mathbf{r}(1)$. We thus obtain

$$R_T \mathbf{H} R_T^{-1} = \mathbf{H} - 2\hat{\mathbf{r}}(1)\hat{\mathbf{r}}(1)\cdot\mathbf{H} \tag{2.67}$$

by introducing new root vectors of unit length. The analogous results for U and V spin are

$$\begin{aligned} R_V \mathbf{H} R_V^{-1} &= \mathbf{H} - 2\hat{r}(2)\hat{r}(2)\cdot\mathbf{H} \\ R_U \mathbf{H} R_U^{-1} &= \mathbf{H} - 2\hat{r}(3)\hat{r}(3)\cdot\mathbf{H} \end{aligned} \tag{2.68}$$

From the derivation (cf. Eq. 2.66) we see that the above results still hold if $R_\nu \to R_\nu^{-1}$. One finds finally

$$\begin{aligned} \mathbf{H} R_\nu \psi(\mathbf{m}) &= R_\nu[\mathbf{H} - 2\hat{r}(\nu)\hat{r}(\nu)\cdot\mathbf{H}]\psi(\mathbf{m}) \\ &= [\mathbf{m} - 2\hat{r}(\nu)(\hat{r}(\nu)\cdot\mathbf{m})]R_\nu\psi(\mathbf{m}) \end{aligned} \tag{2.69}$$

The geometrical construction for the reflection R_T is shown in Fig. 2.8. We have thus obtained the important result that *the weight diagram of any representation must have reflection symmetry in the planes orthogonal to the root vectors.* The weights of states of an irreducible representation connected by reflections are said to be *equivalent weights.*

It is also useful to notice the transformation properties of the raising and lowering operators:

$$\begin{aligned} R_T T_\pm R_T^{-1} &= -T_\mp \\ R_T U_\pm R_T^{-1} &= V_\mp \\ R_T V_\pm R_T^{-1} &= -U_\mp \end{aligned} \tag{2.70}$$

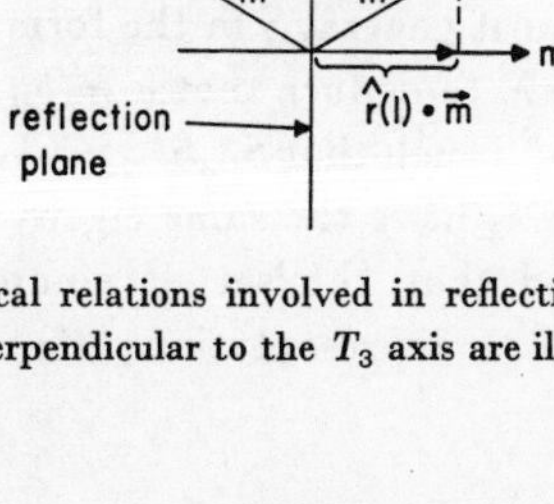

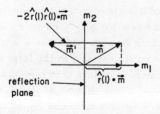

Fig. 2.8. The geometrical relations involved in reflecting the weight $\mathbf{m}$ in the plane perpendicular to the T_3 axis are illustrated.

and six other relations obtained by cyclic permutation in T, U, and V. Except for signs (which are not obvious since there is no unique rotation in $SU(2)$ corresponding to a given reflection) the results (2.70) can be guessed from Fig. 2.4. The results (2.70) can also be used to express a reflection in one plane in terms of compound reflections in the two remaining planes:

$$\begin{aligned} R_V &= R_T R_U{}^{-1} R_T{}^{-1} \\ R_U &= R_T R_V R_T{}^{-1} \end{aligned} \qquad (2.71)$$

Equations (2.71) should be supplemented by the relations obtained by cyclic permutation in T, U, and V.

2.5 The Complex Conjugate Representation 3*

In Section 2.2 a set of eight traceless 3 × 3 Hermitian generators were introduced and used to define the Lie algebra of $SU(3)$. An important fact is that there is an independent set of eight traceless 3 × 3 matrices satisfying this algebra. Previously we considered the infinitesimal transformation of the triplet ψ

$$\psi \to (1 + i\delta\boldsymbol{\alpha}\cdot\mathbf{G})\psi \qquad \mathbf{G} = \tfrac{1}{2}\boldsymbol{\lambda} \qquad (2.72)$$

In addition to the representation matrices (2.5) we may obtain a representation of $SU(3)$ by complex conjugation:

$$\psi^* \to (1 + i\delta\boldsymbol{\alpha}\cdot\mathbf{G}_c)\psi^* \qquad \mathbf{G}_c = -\tfrac{1}{2}\boldsymbol{\lambda}^* \qquad (2.73)$$

The question then arises whether the two representations are equivalent. In Chapter 1 we found that for $SU(2)$ the complex conjugate representation is equivalent to the defining representation. This is not the case for $SU(3)$, however. That is, there is no 3 × 3 matrix S which satisfies $S\boldsymbol{\lambda}S^{-1} = -\boldsymbol{\lambda}^*$. One way to show this is to write the most general S in the form $aI + \mathbf{b}\cdot\boldsymbol{\lambda}$, and use the properties of the λ_i to deduce that $a = b_i = 0$. More directly, for λ_8 the existence of S such that $S\lambda_8 S^{-1} = -\lambda_8$ would imply the contradiction that $\pm\lambda_8$ have the same eigenvalues.

Having established that the set of components $\psi_k \equiv (\psi^k)^*$, $(k = 1,2,3)$, generate a representation (**3***) distinctly different from the representation **3**, we discuss the question of constructing the corresponding raising and lowering operators. From the set of generators $\frac{1}{2}\boldsymbol{\lambda}^c = -\frac{1}{2}\boldsymbol{\lambda}^*$ (explicitly $\lambda^c_{2,5,7} = \lambda_{2,5,7}$; $\lambda^c_{1,3,4,6,8} = -\lambda_{1,3,4,6,8}$) one defines a set $E_\pm{}^c$, $H_j{}^c$ by Eqs. (2.18), with the λ_i replaced by $\lambda_i{}^c$. For instance, we have

$$E_{\pm 1}{}^c = \frac{1}{2\sqrt{6}}(\lambda_1{}^c \pm i\lambda_2{}^c) = \frac{1}{2\sqrt{6}}(-\lambda_1 \pm i\lambda_2) = -E_{\mp 1} \quad (2.74)$$

and of course, $H_j{}^c = -H_j$; the complete set is

$$E^c{}_{\pm\alpha} = -E_{\mp\alpha} \qquad H_j^c = -H_j \quad (2.75)$$

This set of operators, while quite natural, is not unavoidable nor even the most useful choice, as discussed below.

The weight diagram for the representation **3*** is clearly obtained by inversion of that for **3**, as shown in Fig. 2.9. For a general irreducible unitary representation D of $SU(3)$ with Hermitian generators **G** the generators of the complex conjugate representation can be taken to be $-\mathbf{G}^*$. D^* will be equivalent to D only if the weight diagram is left unaltered by inversion.

We have noted in Chapter 1 that by a judicious choice of phases in the set of basis functions generating the complex conjugate representation the usual Condon-Shortley formulas for the Clebsch-Gordan coefficients apply also to the complex conjugate basis. If we use the matrices (2.75) then this useful result is not true for any of the $SU(2)$ subgroups of $SU(3)$. For the three

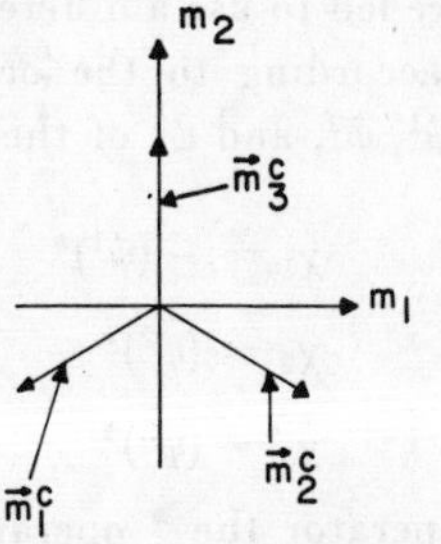

Fig. 2.9. The weight diagram for the complex conjugate representation **3*** is shown.

states in $\mathbf{3}(\psi^k)$ the Condon-Shortley phase convention holds for all the $SU(2)$ subgroups:

$$\begin{aligned} T_+\psi^2 &= \psi^1 \quad T_-\psi^1 = \psi^2 \\ U_+\psi^3 &= \psi^2 \quad U_-\psi^2 = \psi^3 \\ V_+\psi^1 &= \psi^3 \quad V_-\psi^3 = \psi^1 \end{aligned} \tag{2.76}$$

What are the analogous statements for the complex conjugate representation ψ_k, with components $(\psi_k)_l = \delta_{kl}\xi(x)$, where $\xi = \phi^*$ is the space–time wave function [cf. ψ^k preceding Eq. (2.9)]? The raising and lowering operators are

$$T_\pm{}^c = \sqrt{6}E^c{}_{\pm 1} = -\sqrt{6}E_{\mp 1} \tag{2.77}$$

with analogous relations for $U_{c\pm}$ and $V_{c\pm}$. We thus find

$$\begin{aligned} T_+{}^c\psi_1 &= -\psi_2 \qquad T_-{}^c\psi_2 = -\psi_1 \\ U_+{}^c\psi_2 &= -\psi_3 \qquad U_-{}^c\psi_3 = -\psi_2 \\ V_+{}^c\psi_3 &= -\psi_1 \qquad V_-{}^c\psi_1 = -\psi_3 \end{aligned} \tag{2.78}$$

so that, although the $T_\pm{}^c$, $U_\pm{}^c$, and $V_\pm{}^c$ act in the same direction in the weight diagram as do $T_\pm$, $U_\pm$, and $V_\pm$, the convenient $SU(2)$ phase convention has been lost.

It is clear, however, that the Condon-Shortley rules cannot be expected to hold since $\mathbf{3}^*$ contains the complex conjugate isotopic doublet (ψ_1,ψ_2), and the signs of this complex conjugate doublet were not chosen properly relative to the doublet (ψ^1,ψ^2) in $\mathbf{3}$ (see Eq. 1.29). Thus we are led to use a different set of basis functions (or field operators, according to the occasion) χ_1, χ_2, and χ_3, related to the basis ψ^1, ψ^2, and ψ^3 of the defining representation $\mathbf{3}$ as follows:

$$\begin{aligned} \chi_1 &= -(\psi^1)^* \\ \chi_2 &= (\psi^2)^* \\ \chi_3 &= (\psi^3)^* \end{aligned} \tag{2.79}$$

(When ψ is a field operator the * operation includes, of course, Hermitian conjugation.)

Let U^k be the elements of the matrix representation **3**

$$\psi^{k'} = U_{kl}\psi^l \tag{2.80}$$

so that the $\psi_k = (\psi^k)^*$ transform as

$$\psi_k' = U_{kl}^*\psi_l \tag{2.81}$$

Then the components of χ transform as

$$\begin{aligned}\chi_1' &= U_{11}^*\chi_1 - U_{12}^*\chi_2 - U_{13}^*\chi_3\\ \chi_2' &= -U_{21}^*\chi_1 + U_{22}^*\chi_2 + U_{23}^*\chi_3\\ \chi_3' &= -U_{31}^*\chi_1 + U_{32}^*\chi_2 + U_{33}^*\chi_3\end{aligned} \tag{2.82}$$

Specializing to infinitesimal transformations, the change $U_{12}^* \to -U_{12}^*$, $U_{13}^* \to -U_{13}^*$ requires $\lambda_1^c \to -\lambda_1^c$, $\lambda_2^c \to -\lambda_2^c$, $\lambda_4^c \to -\lambda_4^c$, and $\lambda_5^c \to -\lambda_5^c$. Thus the modified complex conjugate representation has generators

$$\begin{array}{llll} G_1^c = G_1 & G_2^c = -G_2 & G_3^c = -G_3 & G_4^c = G_4\\ G_5^c = -G_5 & G_6^c = -G_6 & G_7^c = G_7 & G_8^c = -G_8 \end{array} \tag{2.83}$$

with corresponding raising and lowering operators

$$\begin{array}{lll} E_{\pm 1}^c = E_{\mp 1} & E_{\pm 2}^c = E_{\mp 2} & E_{\pm 3}^c = -E_{\mp 3}\\ & H_i^c = -H_i & \end{array} \tag{2.84}$$

Identifying $T_\pm^c = \sqrt{6}E_{\pm 1}^c$, etc., we see that the Condon-Shortley phases are secured for the matrices of T and V spin but not for U spin. Nothing can be done about this, because of the commutation rules. One could transfer the minus signs to V spin by changing the minus sign in Eq. (2.79) from χ_1 to χ_2. Such a convention would seem meritorious since U spin has a more direct physical meaning than V spin, at present. However, tables of $SU(3)$ Clebsch-Gordan coefficients have been prepared (16, 18–19) using the conventions (2.84), so we shall adhere to this choice.

Suppose we have an irreducible representation $D = \exp(i\boldsymbol{\alpha}\cdot\mathbf{G})$

of dimension N, with basis functions $\phi(\mathrm{N}; T, T_3, Y)$. The complex conjugate representation D^* has the generators (2.75) rather than the desired convention given by (2.84). Thus a further unitary transformation SD^*S^{-1} is required to obtain (2.84). To discover an explicit form for S, first note that complex conjugation results in the generators

$$\begin{aligned} T_\pm{}^c &= -T_\mp \qquad & U_\pm{}^c &= -U_\mp \\ V_\pm{}^c &= -V_\mp \qquad & \mathbf{H}^c &= -\mathbf{H} \end{aligned} \tag{2.85}$$

The signs shown in (2.84) demand that the matrix S have the following properties:

$$\begin{aligned} ST_\pm S^{-1} &= -T_\pm \qquad & SV_\pm S^{-1} &= -V_\pm \\ SU_\pm S^{-1} &= U_\pm \qquad & S\mathbf{H}S^{-1} &= \mathbf{H} \end{aligned} \tag{2.86}$$

The last equality requires that S depend on $\mathbf{H}$. The next to last equality further shows that S should be a function of Q, the only combination of H_j commuting with $\mathbf{U}$. Now it is easy to see that an appropriate unitary S is

$$S = (-1)^Q \equiv \exp(i\pi Q) \qquad Q \equiv T_3 + \tfrac{1}{2}Y \tag{2.87}$$

since $T_\pm$ and $V_\pm$ change the charge by one unit. Here we suppose that Q is always given by $T_3 + \frac{1}{2}Y$, with Y given by (2.54), whether or not Q is integral, in order to obtain a single formula for all representations. If this convention is adhered to, then the elements of S are not, in general, real. For example, in the Sakata model Y had to be defined by Eq. (2.53) $2H_2 + \frac{2}{3}$ to obtain charges (1,0,0) for (p,n,Λ). With our convention (2.87) the three components of the triplet have "charges" $(2/3, -1/3, -1/3)$. (Further properties of such hypothetical triplets are discussed in Section 3.4.) To obtain a real S for **3** we then write $S \to S' = \eta S$ with $\eta = \exp(i\pi/3)$ so $S = \exp[i\pi(Q + \frac{1}{3})]$. The diagonal elements of S are $(-1,1,1)$. If we take the complex conjugate of the triplet (2.72) and multiply by S we obtain the triplet $\mathbf{3}^*$ of Eq. (2.79) whose generators have the desired form (2.84). Thus we have the relations

$$\psi(\mathbf{3}^*; TT_3Y) = \exp\,[i\pi(Q + \tfrac{1}{3})]\psi^*(\mathbf{3}; T, -T_3, -Y)$$
$$\psi(\mathbf{3}; TT_3Y) = \exp\,[i\pi(Q - \tfrac{1}{3})]\psi^*(\mathbf{3}^*; T, -T_3, -Y) \tag{2.88}$$

while for the regular representation **8** and all representations **N** contained in $\mathbf{8} \times \mathbf{8} \times \cdots \times \mathbf{8}$ (cf. Chapters 3 and 4)

$$\psi(\mathbf{N}^*; TT_3Y) = e^{i\pi Q}\psi^*(\mathbf{N}; T, -T_3, -Y) \tag{2.89}$$

We can obtain a deeper insight into the situation revealed by Eqs. (2.88) and (2.89) by classifying the representations of $SU(3)$ according to their *triality*.

For orientation, notice that in $SU(2)$ we can classify the representations according to whether $2j$ is even or odd. Consider the state of highest weight. Under a rotation by 2π the state is multiplied by $e^{2i\pi j}$ so that the representations fall into two classes according to whether $e^{2i\pi j} = \pm 1$. When we reduce direct products we find that odd × odd = even, even × odd = odd, and even × even = even. Alternatively, we can associate the number $d = 1$ with $2j$ = odd and $d = 0$ with $2j$ = even. [That is, $d = 2j$ (mod 2).] Then when multiplying representations we have $d_1 + d_2 = d_3$ (mod 2). In terms of basic doublets we say that odd powers $\psi, \psi \times \psi \times \psi, \ldots$ have "duality" 1 and even powers $\psi \times \psi, \psi \times \psi \times \psi \times \psi, \ldots$, have duality 0. Thus d is given by $e^{i\pi d}$, the eigenvalue of $e^{2i\pi J_z}$ applied to the state of highest weight.

In $SU(3)$ the representations fall into three classes of the types* contained in the direct products

$$(\mathbf{3})^{3n}, (\mathbf{3})^{3n+1}, (\mathbf{3})^{3n+2}; \quad n = 0, 1, 2, \ldots \tag{2.90}$$

The *triality* t is defined (mod 3) by writing the exponents occurring in Eq. (2.90) in the form $(3n + t)$. Thus the representation **3** has $t = 1$, $\mathbf{3} \times \mathbf{3} = \mathbf{6} + \mathbf{3}^*$ has $t = 2$, and $\mathbf{3} \times \mathbf{3} \times \mathbf{3} = \mathbf{10} + \mathbf{8} + \mathbf{8} + \mathbf{1}$ has $t = 0$. The three examples given suggest that $\eta = \exp\,(i\pi t/3)$. It is in fact clear that this choice renders the phase factor real in general:

$$S = \exp\,[i\pi(Q + t/3)]$$
$$\psi(\mathbf{N}^*; TT_3Y) = \exp\,[i\pi(Q + t/3)]\psi^*(\mathbf{N}; T, -T_3, -Y) \tag{2.91}$$

* The following discussion makes use of results obtained in Chapters 3 and 4.

This expression generalizes de Swart's result for the eightfold way ($t = 0$).

If we decompose the produce of representations having trialities t_1 and t_2 the resulting irreducible representations have triality $t_3 = t_1 + t_2$ (mod 3) in analogy to the $SU(2)$ case. For a proof of this statement see references 21 and 22. For our purposes this result is nearly obvious from the preceding examples.

Equations (2.88) and (2.89) illustrate how one can compute t. Apply the operator $\exp(2\pi i Y)$ to the state of highest weight in the reducible representation. The eigenvalue $\exp(2\pi i t/3)$ defines the triality (mod 3). As an illustration, note that for **3**, $\exp(2\pi i Y)$ gives $\exp(2\pi i/3)$. **3** × **3** then has eigenvalue $\exp(4\pi i/3)$ for its component of highest weight. Solving for t, we find $t = -1, 2, 5, \ldots$, i.e., $t = 2$ (mod 3).

Apparently the only representations realized in nature have triality zero. There seems to be no deep understanding of this fact.

A different approach to the triality concept has been given by Okubo et al. (23), who point out that the occurrence of fractional charge and hypercharge can be avoided if the group is not $SU(3)$ but $U(3)$. Charge and hypercharge are made integral by the redefinitions

$$Q' = Q + \tfrac{1}{3}t \qquad Y' = Y + \tfrac{2}{3}t \tag{2.92}$$

(cf. Eq. 2.91; for the integral character of Y' recall the relation $Q = T_3 + \frac{1}{2}Y$). Recall that in terms of the traceless generators $A_\nu{}^\mu$ of Eq. (2.27) Q and Y are given by

$$\begin{aligned} Q &= A_1{}^1 \\ Y &= A_1{}^1 + A_2{}^2 \end{aligned} \tag{2.93}$$

Defining the generators $B_\nu{}^\mu$ by

$$\begin{aligned} B_\nu{}^\mu &= A_\nu{}^\mu + \tfrac{1}{3}\delta_\nu{}^\mu \bar{t}; \\ \bar{t} &= B_1{}^1 + B_2{}^2 + B_3{}^3 \end{aligned} \tag{2.94}$$

where $\bar{t}$ may be shown (23) to have integral eigenvalues, we have

$$\begin{aligned} Q' &= B_1{}^1 \\ Y' &= B_1{}^1 + B_2{}^2 \end{aligned} \tag{2.95}$$

while T_3 is $\frac{1}{2}(A_1{}^1 - A_2{}^2)$ or $\frac{1}{2}(B_1{}^1 - B_2{}^2)$. The generators $B_\nu{}^\mu$ are simply those of $U(3)$. It will be noted that the operator $\bar{t}$ is truly additive and not defined merely mod 3.

2.6 The Regular Representation; The F and D Matrices

The traceless 3×3 Hermitian generators $\frac{1}{2}\lambda_i$ were used in Eqs. (2.22) and (2.23) to introduce the set of real coefficients f_{abc} and d_{abc} $(a,b,c = 1,\ldots,8)$. These coefficients have a number of useful properties which we now describe. First, we note that the f_{ijk} of $SU(3)$ are analogous to the ε_{ijk} of $SU(2)$. Recall that from the ε_{ijk} one can form a set of 3×3 Hermitian matrices $(t_i)_{jk} = -i\varepsilon_{ijk}$ that give a representation of the algebra of $SU(2)$, as indicated in Eqs. (1.35)–(1.37). Moreover, from the basic spinor ψ and the generators $\frac{1}{2}\boldsymbol{\tau}$, one can form a set of basis functions $\psi^\dagger\frac{1}{2}\boldsymbol{\tau}\psi$ transforming according to the regular representation of $SU(2)$. Analogous results hold for $SU(3)$.

We introduce the idea of the *regular representation* in a context more general than that of $SU(3)$. Suppose we have a set of N independent matrices M_a $(a = 1,\ldots N)$ subject to the following commutator structure

$$[M_a,M_b] = C_{ab}{}^c M_c \tag{2.96}$$

$(a,b,c = 1,\ldots,N)$. The *structure constants* $C_{ab}{}^c$ specify the characteristics of the algebra exhibited in this equation. When the M_a are generators of some continuous group of transformations, the $C_{ab}{}^c$ completely determine the local properties of that group. The structure constants $C_{ab}{}^c$ are antisymmetric in the lower indices:

$$C_{ab}{}^c = -C_{ba}{}^c \tag{2.97}$$

We now show that the C's themselves can be used to construct a set of $N \times N$ matrices satisfying the algebra of the M's. This set of N matrices built from the structure constants is called the regular representation of the algebra defined by Eq. (2.26).

The proof hinges on Jacobi's identity:

$$[M_a,[M_b,M_c]] + [M_b,[M_c,M_a]] + [M_c,[M_a,M_b]] = 0 \tag{2.98}$$

Using Eq. (2.96) to evaluate the commutators and making use of the independence of the M_i gives

$$C_{bc}{}^{m}C_{am}{}^{n} + C_{ca}{}^{m}C_{bm}{}^{n} + C_{ab}{}^{m}C_{cm}{}^{n} = 0 \tag{2.99}$$

If we now multiply by (-1), permute c and a in the second term and transfer the third term to the right-hand side, we obtain

$$C_{ac}{}^{m}C_{bm}{}^{n} - C_{bc}{}^{m}C_{am}{}^{n} = -C_{ab}{}^{m}C_{mc}{}^{n} \tag{2.100}$$

If we now define a set of N matrices R_a by

$$(R_a)_{bc} \equiv -C_{ab}{}^{c} \tag{2.101}$$

Eq. (2.100) can be rewritten as

$$(R_a)_{cm}(R_b)_{mn} - (R_b)_{cm}(R_a)_{mn} = C_{ab}{}^{m}(R_m)_{cn} \tag{2.102}$$

showing that a particular instance of Eq. (2.96) is $M_a = R_a$, with R_a defined in Eq. (2.101).

We apply this result to the structure constants if_{abc} of $SU(3)$. Since the f_{abc} are real and completely antisymmetric, the 8×8 matrices F_a defined by

$$(F_a)_{bc} \equiv (F^a)_{bc} \equiv -if_{abc} \tag{2.103}$$

are Hermitian. They naturally satisfy (2.26):

$$[F_a, F_b] = if_{abc}F_c = -F_{ab}{}^{c}F_c \tag{2.104}$$

(The writing of superscripts and subscripts on these matrices is only a matter of notational convenience.)

The "vector" matrix **F** is the analog of the matrix **t** encountered in $SU(2)$, the latter generating the rotations of the ordinary position vector **r** [see Eq. (1.38)]. This analogy leads us to define a *vector operator* in $SU(3)$ as follows. Suppose we have a set (of operators or $N \times N$ matrices) V_a $(a = 1,\ldots,8)$ whose commutators with the generators G_c (operators or $N \times N$ matrices) satisfy

$$[G_a, V_b] = if_{abc}V_c = -F_{ab}{}^{c}V_c \tag{2.105}$$

Then **V** is said to be a *vector operator*. This definition shows that under the transformation $\mathcal{O}_\alpha = \exp(i\boldsymbol{\alpha}\cdot\mathbf{G})$, $\mathbf{V}$ transforms according to the regular representation; we consider infinitesimal transformations:

$$\begin{aligned}\mathcal{O}_\alpha V_i \mathcal{O}_\alpha^{-1} &\simeq V_i + i\delta\alpha^k[G_k, V_i] \\ &= V_i - i\delta\alpha^k F_{ki}{}^j V_j \qquad (2.106) \\ &= [\delta_{ij} + i\delta\boldsymbol{\alpha}\cdot\mathbf{F}_{ij}]V_j\end{aligned}$$

i.e., $\mathbf{V} \to \exp(i\boldsymbol{\alpha}\cdot\mathbf{F})\mathbf{V}$ in analogy to $\mathbf{r} \to \exp(i\boldsymbol{\alpha}\cdot\mathbf{t})\mathbf{r}$ under spatial rotations.

The 3×3 generators λ_i can be used as Clebsch-Gordan coefficients to construct a set of functions (or operators) transforming as the regular representation. Suppose we have triplets ϕ, ψ transforming as $\phi \to (1 + i\delta\boldsymbol{\alpha}\cdot\boldsymbol{\lambda}/2)\phi$. Then experience with $SU(2)$ suggests that the eight quantities

$$V_k = \psi^\dagger \lambda_k \phi \qquad (2.107)$$

constitute a basis for the regular representation with matrices $\mathbf{F}$. The anticlimactic details follow:

$$\begin{aligned}V_k &\to \psi^\dagger(1 - i\delta\boldsymbol{\alpha}\cdot\boldsymbol{\lambda}/2)\lambda_k(1 + i\delta\boldsymbol{\alpha}\cdot\boldsymbol{\lambda}/2)\phi \\ &= V_k + i\delta\alpha^l\psi^\dagger[\lambda_k,\lambda_l]\phi/2 \qquad (2.108) \\ &= (\delta_{km} + i\delta\alpha^l F_{km}{}^l)V_m\end{aligned}$$

The V_k can be written in the form

$$V_k = (\lambda_k)_{ij}\psi_i{}^*\phi_j \qquad (2.109)$$

which displays the role of the $(\lambda_k)_{ij}$ as Clebsch-Gordan coefficients, which combine **3** and **3*** in the appropriate way to obtain the eight-dimensional regular representation. (The one-dimensional representation is found by constructing the inner product $\psi^\dagger\phi$.)

The above result can be generalized considerably. Consider "vectors" Ψ, Φ transforming via $1 + i\delta\boldsymbol{\alpha}\cdot\mathbf{G}$. Then the scalar product of a vector operator $\mathbf{V}$ automatically transforms as

$$\Psi^\dagger\mathbf{V}\Phi \to (1 + i\delta\boldsymbol{\alpha}\cdot\mathbf{F})\Psi^\dagger\mathbf{V}\Phi \qquad (2.110)$$

An especially important case occurs when **V** is just **F**, and Ψ and Φ are eight-component objects transforming as V_k in Eq. (2.108). In fact, the result holds whether or not the components of Ψ, Φ have their complex conjugate taken, as we are instructed to do in Eq. (2.110). This is true because the regular representation is equivalent to its complex conjugate. The particular regular representation $D = \exp(i\boldsymbol{\alpha}\cdot\mathbf{F})$ is even identical to its complex conjugate since $D^* = \exp(-i\boldsymbol{\alpha}\cdot\mathbf{F}^*) = D$, because $\mathbf{F}^* = -\mathbf{F}$.

Thus consider the "octets" A_a, B_a $(a = 1,\ldots,8)$ transforming as

$$\begin{aligned} A_a &\to (\delta_{ab} + i\delta\alpha_c F_{ab}{}^c)A_b \\ B_a &\to (\delta_{ab} + i\delta\alpha_c F_{ab}{}^c)B_b \end{aligned} \tag{2.111}$$

The linear combination V_c^F

$$V_c^F = (F_c)_{ab}A_aB_b \tag{2.112}$$

also transforms as

$$\mathbf{V}^F \to (1 + i\delta\boldsymbol{\alpha}\cdot\mathbf{F})\mathbf{V}^F \tag{2.113}$$

Therefore the coefficients f_{abc} are Clebsch-Gordan coefficients in the regular representation.

We now recall the symmetric real coefficients d_{abc}. Do these have any useful properties? From them we can form the real, symmetric 8×8 Hermitian matrices D_a:

$$(D_a)_{bc} \equiv d_{abc} \tag{2.114}$$

We now learn that **D** is a vector operator in the regular representation, i.e.,

$$[F_a, D_b] = -F_{ab}{}^c D_c \tag{2.115}$$

The proof of this and similar identities given below is based on a method described by Cutkosky (24). The appropriate D's and F's can be generated by the identity

$$[\lambda_a,\{\lambda_c,\lambda_b\}] = \{\lambda_b,[\lambda_a,\lambda_c]\} + \{[\lambda_a,\lambda_b],\lambda_c\} \tag{2.116}$$

One readily finds

$$D_{bc}{}^k F_{ak}{}^j = F_{ac}{}^k D_{bk}{}^j + F_{ab}{}^k D_{kc}{}^j \tag{2.117}$$

which can be written in the form (2.115) by permuting various indices.

According to the previous discussion the quantities

$$V_c^D = (D_c)_{ab} A_a B_b \tag{2.118}$$

where A_a and B_b transform as indicated in Eq. (2.111) also give a basis for the regular representation:

$$\mathbf{V}^D \rightarrow (1 + i\delta\boldsymbol{\alpha}\cdot\mathbf{F})\mathbf{V}^D \tag{2.119}$$

In the usual manner, the "dot product" of one vector with another is a scalar; whether these "vectors" are functions or vector operators is irrelevant. Thus the quantities $\mathbf{F}^2$, $\mathbf{D}^2$, and $\mathbf{F}\cdot\mathbf{D}$ commute with the F_i, and by Schur's Lemma are multiples of the unit matrix in the regular representation. In particular, we can show that

$$\begin{aligned} \text{Tr } F_a F_b &= \overline{\mathbf{F}}^2 \delta_{ab} \\ \text{Tr } D_a D_b &= \overline{\mathbf{D}}^2 \delta_{ab} \\ \text{Tr } F_a D_b &= 0 \end{aligned} \tag{2.120}$$

where $\overline{\mathbf{F}}^2$ and $\overline{\mathbf{D}}^2$ are the eigenvalues of the matrices $\mathbf{F}^2$ and $\mathbf{D}^2$. (Later we show that $\overline{\mathbf{F}}^2 = 3$ and $\overline{\mathbf{D}}^2 = 5/3$.) The proof consists of rewriting

$$\begin{aligned} \text{Tr } F_a F_b &= (F_a)_{ij}(F_b)_{ji} = (\mathbf{F}^2)_{ab} = \overline{\mathbf{F}}^2 \delta_{ab} \\ \text{Tr } D_a D_b &= (D_a)_{ij}(D_b)_{ji} = (\mathbf{D}^2)_{ab} = \overline{\mathbf{D}}^2 \delta_{ab} \end{aligned} \tag{2.121}$$

$$\text{Tr } F^a D^b = (F_a)_{ij}(D_b)_{ji} = 0 \tag{2.122}$$

the latter following from the symmetry of D and the antisymmetry of F in the ij indices.

The following trace properties are also useful:

$$\text{Tr } F^a = \text{Tr } D^a = 0 \tag{2.123}$$

The first of these relations is trivial. To prove the other, set $a = b$ in the anticommutator $\{\lambda_a, \lambda_b\}$ and sum on a. This gives

$$2\boldsymbol{\lambda}^2 = \tfrac{32}{3} I + 2 \sum_a D_{aa}{}^c \lambda_c \tag{2.124}$$

Since $\boldsymbol{\lambda}^2$ is proportional to I (it commutes with the λ_i), we see that

$$\lambda_c \operatorname{Tr} D^c = kI \tag{2.125}$$

where k is a constant. Multiplying by λ_a and taking the trace gives $2 \operatorname{Tr} D^a = k \operatorname{Tr} \lambda_a = 0$.

In addition to the commutators $[F_a,F_b]$, $[F_a,D_b]$ it is sometimes useful to know $[D_a,D_b]$. To obtain this one can begin from the identity

$$[\lambda_a,[\lambda_b,\lambda_c]] = \{\lambda_c,\{\lambda_a,\lambda_b\}\} - \{\lambda_b,\{\lambda_a,\lambda_c\}\} \tag{2.126}$$

Proceeding in a now familiar manner, one obtains

$$[D_a,D_b]_{cd} = -\tfrac{2}{3}(\delta_{ac}\delta_{bd} - \delta_{ad}\delta_{bc}) - F_{ab}{}^k(F_k)_{cd} \tag{2.127}$$

References

1. R. H. Dalitz, *Ann. Rev. Nucl. Sci.*, **13**, 339, (1963).
2. A. H. Rosenfeld, A. Barbaro-Galtieri, W. H. Barkas, P. L. Bastien, J. Kirz, and M. Roos, *Rev. Mod. Phys.*, **36**, 977 (1964).
3. P. Roman, *Theory of Elementary Particles*, North Holland Publ. Co., Amsterdam (1960), Chap. 12.
4. S. Sakata, *Progr. Theoret. Phys.*, **16**, 686 (1956).
5. M. Ikeda, S. Ogawa, and Y. Ohnuki, *Progr. Theoret. Phys. (Kyoto)*, **22**, 715 (1959); **Suppl. 19**, 44 (1961).
6. M. Gell-Mann, *Phys. Rev.*, **125**, 1067 (1962).
7. Y. Ne'eman, *Nucl. Phys.*, **26**, 222 (1961).
8. R. Behrends, J. Dreitlein, C. Fronsdal, and B. W. Lee, *Rev. Mod. Phys.*, **34**, 1 (1962).
9. M. Hamermesh, *Group Theory*, Addison-Wesley, Reading, Mass., 1962.
10. S. Okubo, *Progr. Theoret. Phys.*, **27**, 949 (1962).
11. C. A. Levinson, H. J. Lipkin, and S. Meshkov, *Phys. Rev. Letters*, **1**, 44 (1962).
12. H. J. Lipkin, *Lie Groups for Pedestrians*, Interscience, New York, 1965.
13. M. Gell-Mann, *Phys. Rev. Letters*, **8**, 214 (1964).
14. G. Zweig, CERN Rep. No. 8182/Th. 401 and 8419/Th. 412 (1964).
15. F. Gursey, T. D. Lee, and M. Nauenberg, *Phys. Rev.*, **135**, B467 (1964).
16. J. J. de Swart, *Rev. Mod. Phys.*, **35**, 916 (1963).
17. A. J. MacFarlane, E. C. G. Sudarshan, and C. Dullemond, *Nuovo Cimento*, **30**, 845 (1963).
18. P. Tarjanne, Carnegie Tech. Rept., NYO-9290, 9290A.
19. P. McNamee, and F. Chilton, *Rev. Mod. Phys.*, **36**, 1005 (1964).
20. L. C. Biedenharn and E. C. Fowler, unpublished.

21. G. E. Baird and L. C. Biedenharn, *Proceedings of the Coral Gables Conference on Symmetry Principles at High Energy*, ed., B. Kursunoglu, W. H. Freeman and Co., San Francisco, Calif., 1964.
22. C. R. Hagen and A. J. Macfarlane, *J. Math. Phys.*, **5**, 1335 (1964).
23. S. Okubo, C. Ryan, and R. E. Marshak, *Nuovo Cimento*, **34**, 759 (1964).
24. R. E. Cutkosky, *Ann. Phys.*, **23**, 415 (1963).

Chapter 3

Construction of Representations of $SU(3)$

3.1 Introduction

The irreducible representations of $SU(3)$ are found by decomposing Kronecker products of **3** and **3*** representations into irreducible constituents. Consider a product state composed of p functions ψ^k transforming like **3**, and q functions ϕ_k transforming like **3***:

$$\Phi^{\alpha\beta\ldots\nu}_{ab\ldots k} = \psi^\alpha(1)\psi^\beta(2)\ldots\psi^\nu(p)\phi_a(p+1)\ldots\phi_k(p+q) \quad (3.1)$$

The labels $1, 2, \ldots, p+q$ can be regarded as independent coordinates. This set of 3^{p+q} functions is a (reducible) tensor under $SU(3)$ transformations; we shall often denote the (reducible) representation generated by (3.1) by

$$(\mathbf{3})^p \times (\mathbf{3}^*)^q \quad (3.2)$$

For later reference, we note that the *highest weight* contained in the set (3.1) is*

$$\mathbf{M}(p,q) = p\mathbf{m}_H + q\mathbf{m}_H{}^* = \left(\frac{p+q}{2\sqrt{3}}, \frac{p-q}{6}\right) \quad (3.3)$$

which occurs for $\alpha = \beta = \cdots = \nu = 1$, $a = b = \cdots = k = 2$, where $\mathbf{m}_H$ and $\mathbf{m}_H{}^*$ are the highest weights of the representations **3** and **3***, respectively. Note that this state, which is the analogue of the "stretched" configuration occurring in the vector addition of angular momentum, is nondegenerate. The irreducible repre-

* To find the state of *highest weight*, first find the states with greatest H_1; among these choose the one with greatest H_2.

sentation to which this function belongs is called $D(p,q)$, or simply (p,q). When no confusion can arise, the representations are often referred to by their dimensionality. In the $D(p,q)$ notation the identity representation **1** is $D(0,0)$, **3** is by convention $D(1,0)$, and **3*** is $D(0,1)$. The importance of this notation is revealed by the following fact: by letting p and q range over the nonnegative integers the states of highest weight (3.3) in the product (3.2) run through all the irreducible representations of $SU(3)$.

As discussed in Chapter 2, the conservation of isospin (T) and hypercharge (Y) corresponds to invariance under a particular subgroup $SU(2)_T \times U(1)_Y$ of $SU(3)$. The third component of isospin T_3 was identified with $\sqrt{3}\,H_2$. There is more freedom in the assignment of Y but we shall adopt, subject to further discussion, the eightfold way assignment $Y = 2H_2$ [see Eqs. (2.53) and (2.54)]. The state of highest weight in $D(p,q)$ has $T = T_3$ for that state. Hence we find that the state of highest weight in the representation $D(p,q)$ has isospin and hypercharge given by

$$T_H = \tfrac{1}{2}(p + q), \quad Y_H = \tfrac{1}{3}(p - q) \tag{3.4}$$

the latter relation being specific to the eightfold way. In this scheme the only permitted representations having integral Y have p and q connected by $p - q = 3n$, n an integer. Hence the eightfold way excludes a large class of representations of $SU(3)$.*

There are two principal means of decomposing (3.2) into its irreducible constituents. One of these methods is a simple generalization of the raising-lowering operator technique so familiar in $SU(2)$. This procedure is elementary and provides a detailed understanding of the specific properties of the various representations (1–4). The second method, which involves the use of tensor analysis, is speedier but requires more subtle mathematical theorems for its justification (5–7). Therefore we shall

* The group of the eightfold way is the factor group $SU(3)/Z_3$, where Z_3 is the *center* of $SU(3)$. In exact analogy, the integral j (single-valued) representations of $SU(2)$ correspond to $SU(2)/Z_2$. In the latter case Z_2 is composed of $\pm I$, I the identity matrix.

describe the raising-lowering operator technique in some detail in Section 3.2. In Section 4.6 we shall describe, without complete proofs, how to use the tensor methods and the connection between the two approaches.

3.2 The Raising and Lowering Operator Technique

Under an infinitesimal transformation the tensor (3.1) transforms as

$$\Phi^{\alpha'\beta'\ldots\nu'}_{a'b'\ldots k'} = T^{\alpha'\beta'\ldots\nu';\,ab\ldots k}_{\alpha\beta\ldots\nu;\,a'b'\ldots k'}\,\Phi^{\alpha\beta\ldots\nu}_{ab\ldots k} \tag{3.5}$$

where the infinitesimal transformation coefficients are

$$\begin{aligned} T^{\alpha'\ldots k}_{\alpha\ldots k'} = {} & \delta_\alpha{}^{\alpha'}\delta_\beta{}^{\beta'}\cdots\delta_\nu{}^{\nu'}\delta_{a'}{}^{a}\delta_{b'}{}^{b}\cdots\delta_{k'}{}^{k} \\ & + i\,\frac{\delta\boldsymbol{\alpha}}{2}\cdot[\boldsymbol{\lambda}(1)_\alpha{}^{\alpha'}\delta_\beta{}^{\beta'}\cdots\delta_{k'}{}^{k} + \cdots \\ & + \boldsymbol{\lambda}(p)_\nu{}^{\nu'}\delta_\alpha{}^{\alpha'}\cdots\delta_\mu{}^{\mu'}\delta_{a'}{}^{a}\cdots\delta_{k'}{}^{k} \\ & + \boldsymbol{\lambda}^c(p+1)_{a'}{}^{a}\delta_\alpha{}^{\alpha'}\cdots\delta_\nu{}^{\nu'}\delta_{b'}{}^{b}\cdots\delta_{k'}{}^{k} \\ & + \delta_\alpha{}^{\alpha'}\cdots\delta_{j'}{}^{j}\boldsymbol{\lambda}_c(p+q)_{k'}{}^{k}] \end{aligned} \tag{3.6}$$

Here the distinction between upper and lower indices has been introduced to agree with the conventions of the tensor methods discussed below. The label a in $A_b{}^a$ stands for the row index while b is the column index for the matrix A. More succinctly, the transformation $T = 1 + i\delta\boldsymbol{\alpha}\cdot\mathbf{G}$ where

$$\mathbf{G} = \frac{1}{2}\left(\sum_{i=1}^{p}\boldsymbol{\lambda}(i) + \sum_{i=p+1}^{p+q}\boldsymbol{\lambda}^c(i)\right) \tag{3.7}$$

As discussed in Chapter 2, it is convenient to introduce a special phase convention in order that the Condon-Shortley phase convention may be used for two of the $SU(2)$ subgroups. Using this convention [cf. Eq. (2.79)], we convert (3.7) to the analogous relations for the raising and lowering operators:

$$T_{\pm} \equiv \sqrt{6}\left[\sum_{i=1}^{p} E_{\pm 1}(i) + \sum_{i=p+1}^{p+q} E_{\pm 1}{}^{c}(i)\right],$$

$$T_{\pm} = \sqrt{6}\left[\sum_{i=1}^{p} E_{\pm 1}(i) + \sum_{i=p+1}^{p+q} E_{\mp 1}(i)\right];$$

$$U_{\pm} \equiv \sqrt{6}\left[\sum_{i=1}^{p} E_{\pm 3}(i) + \sum_{i=p+1}^{p+q} E_{\pm 3}{}^{c}(i)\right],$$

$$U_{\pm} = \sqrt{6}\left[\sum_{i=1}^{p} E_{\pm 3}(i) - \sum_{i=p+1}^{p+q} E_{\mp 3}(i)\right];$$

$$V_{\pm} \equiv \sqrt{6}\left[\sum_{i=1}^{p} E_{\pm 2}(i) + \sum_{i=p+1}^{p+q} E_{\pm 2}{}^{c}\right], \tag{3.8}$$

$$V_{\pm} = \sqrt{6}\left[\sum_{i=1}^{p} E_{\pm 2}(i) + \sum_{i=p+1}^{p+q} E_{\mp 2}(i)\right];$$

$$\mathbf{H} = \sum_{i=1}^{p} \mathbf{H}(i) + \sum_{i=p+1}^{p+q} \mathbf{H}^{c}(i),$$

$$\mathbf{H} = \sum_{i=1}^{p} \mathbf{H}(i) - \sum_{i=p+1}^{p+q} \mathbf{H}(i).$$

We have presented the generators in mixed form (**T**, **U**, **V**, and **H**) since we find this convenient in applications. The last of Eqs. (3.8) exhibits the familiar feature that the eigenvalues of the diagonal operators (**H**) add in product states. Before giving a general discussion we shall illustrate the essential features of the procedure by a few examples. Our treatment is patterned after that described by Gasiorowicz (1), with some changes in conventions used.

First we consider the representation **3** × **3**, whose basis may be taken as

$$\psi^{\alpha\beta} = \psi^{\alpha}(1)\psi^{\beta}(2) \tag{3.9}$$

the transformation matrix being $\exp\left[\tfrac{1}{2}i\boldsymbol{\alpha}\cdot(\boldsymbol{\lambda}(1) + \boldsymbol{\lambda}(2))\right]$. The composite weight [corresponding to $\mathbf{H} = \mathbf{H}(1) + \mathbf{H}(2)$] for the state $\psi^{\alpha\beta}$ is hence

$$\mathbf{m}_{\alpha\beta} = \mathbf{m}_{\alpha}(1) + \mathbf{m}_{\beta}(2) \tag{3.10}$$

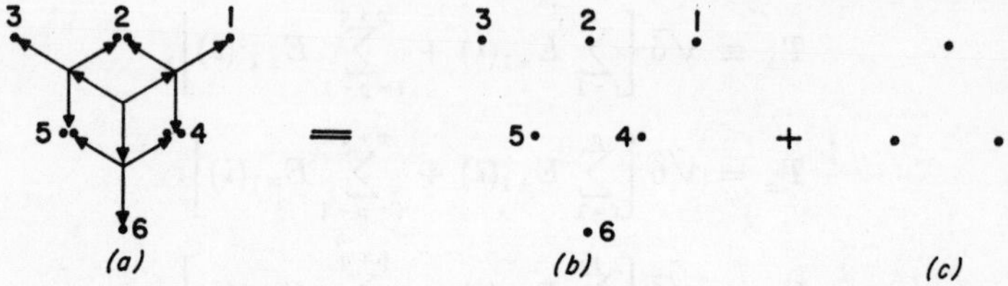

Fig. 3.1. Fig. (3.1*a*) illustrates the vector addition of the weight diagrams **3** × **3**; the number of dots at a site indicates the degeneracy at each site for the corresponding reducible representation. Figs. (3.1*b*) and (3.1*c*) show how **3** × **3** breaks up into the irreducible representations **6** and **3***.

The allowed weights can be found by "adding the weight diagrams" of the two representations (Fig. 3.1). The dots indicate the number of states having the same weight. The state of highest weight ψ^{11} is nondegenerate and has weight $2\mathbf{m}^1 = (1/\sqrt{3},\frac{1}{3})$ corresponding to $T_3 = T = 1$ and $Y = 1$ [cf. Eq. (3.4)]. The remaining members of the representation to which $\psi^{11} \equiv \Psi_1$ belongs are found by applying $T_\pm$, $U_\pm$, $V_\pm$. Since Ψ_1 is the $T_3 = 1$ member of a T-spin triplet we can obtain the remaining members of this triplet by applying T_-:

$$\begin{aligned} \Psi_2 &\equiv \frac{1}{\sqrt{2}} T_- \Psi_1 = \frac{1}{\sqrt{2}} (\psi^2(1)\psi^1(2) + \psi^1(1)\psi^2(2)) \\ \Psi_3 &\equiv \frac{1}{\sqrt{2}} T_- \Psi_2 = \psi^2(1)\psi^2(2). \end{aligned} \tag{3.11}$$

The various sites in the weight diagram are labeled in order as shown in Fig. 3.1*b*. To obtain further members of the representation we can, for instance, apply V_+ to Ψ_1, which state is the $V_3 = -1$ member of a V-spin triplet. Thus we find

$$\Psi_4 \equiv \frac{1}{\sqrt{2}} V_+ \Psi_1 = \frac{1}{\sqrt{2}} (\psi^1(1)\psi^3(2) + \psi^3(1)\psi^1(2)) \tag{3.12}$$

which is the $T_3 = 1/2$ member of a $T = 1/2$ doublet, the accompanying $T_3 = -1/2$ state being

$$\Psi_5 = T_- \Psi_4 = \frac{1}{\sqrt{2}} (\psi^2(1)\psi^3(2) + \psi^3(1)\psi^2(2)). \qquad (3.13)$$

The $V_3 = 1$ state Ψ_6, which clearly has $T = 0$, is given by

$$\Psi_6 = \frac{1}{\sqrt{2}} V_+ \Psi_4 = \psi^3(1)\psi^3(2) \qquad (3.14)$$

No new states can be generated by further operations in the group. This is most easily seen by observing that the operators $T_\pm$, $U_\pm$, $V_\pm$ are essentially permutation operators, and the functions Ψ_i ($i = 1$–6) exhaust the symmetric functions that can be formed from the nine states $\psi^\alpha(1)\psi^\beta(2)$.

The six-dimensional irreducible representation generated by Ψ_i ($i = 1$–6) is called $D(2,0)$ or just **6**. It is composed of a triplet, doublet, and singlet in any of the $SU(2)$ subgroups (see Fig. 3.1*b*).

The remaining three states independent of Ψ_2, Ψ_4, Ψ_5 and sites 2, 4, 5 form the basis for a three-dimensional representation isomorphic to **3***. At site 2 we form a function orthogonal to and therefore independent of Ψ_2:

$$\Phi_3 = \frac{1}{\sqrt{2}} (\psi^1(1)\psi^2(2) - \psi^2(1)\psi^1(2)) \qquad (3.15)$$

The sign has been chosen by the convention that the plus goes with the highest T_3 state of particle number one. Φ_3 clearly has $T = 0$; it is also the $V_3 = -1/2$ member of a V-spin doublet. The other member of this doublet,

$$\Phi_1 = V_+ \Phi_3 = \frac{1}{\sqrt{2}} (\psi^2(1)\psi^3(2) - \psi^3(1)\psi^2(2)) \qquad (3.16)$$

is orthogonal to Ψ_5. Φ_1 is the $T_3 = -1/2$ member of a T-spin doublet. The state Φ_2 given by

$$\Phi_2 = T_+ \Phi_1 = \frac{1}{\sqrt{2}} (\psi^1(1)\psi^3(2) - \psi^3(1)\psi^1(2)) \qquad (3.17)$$

has $T = T_3 = 1/2$, and is orthogonal to Ψ_4. The states Φ_i ($i = 1$–3) have the same weights as the ϕ_i ($i = 1$–3) used to define the representation **3***, and are transformed into each other in the same manner as the ϕ_i when the group operations are performed (see Fig. 3.1*c*). The numbering of states within an irreducible representation has been chosen in accord with the convention of de Swart (1).

The resultant decomposition

$$\mathbf{3} \times \mathbf{3} = \mathbf{6} + \mathbf{3}^*$$

or

$$D(1,0) \times D(1,0) = D(2,0) + D(0,1) \tag{3.18}$$

is seen to be accomplished simply by decomposing the second rank tensor ψ^{ij} into its symmetric and antisymmetric parts:

$$\psi^{\alpha\beta} = \psi^\alpha(1)\psi^\beta(2) = \frac{1}{\sqrt{2}}\left(\frac{\psi^\alpha(1)\psi^\beta(2) + \psi^\beta(1)\psi^\alpha(2)}{\sqrt{2}}\right) + \frac{1}{\sqrt{2}}\left(\frac{\psi^\alpha(1)\psi^\beta(2) - \psi^\beta(1)\psi^\alpha(2)}{\sqrt{2}}\right) \tag{3.19}$$

Next consider the more interesting case of $\mathbf{3} \times \mathbf{3}^*$, whose basis is

$$\psi_\beta{}^\alpha = \psi^\alpha(1)\phi_\beta(2)$$

Addition of the weight diagrams of **3** and **3*** leads to the allowed weights shown in Fig. 3.2*a*. It will be noted that the only degeneracy occurs at the center of the weight diagram. The highest weight is $\mathbf{M}(1,1) = (1/\sqrt{3},0)$. The state $\psi_2{}^1$ therefore has $T = T_3 = 1$, and $Y = 0$. The remaining members of the T-spin

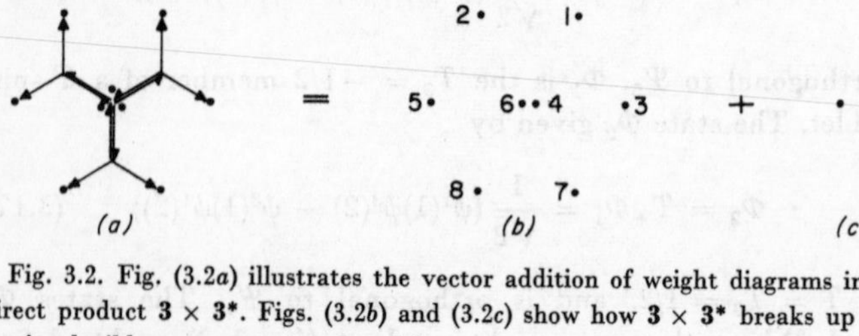

Fig. 3.2. Fig. (3.2*a*) illustrates the vector addition of weight diagrams in the direct product $\mathbf{3} \times \mathbf{3}^*$. Figs. (3.2*b*) and (3.2*c*) show how $\mathbf{3} \times \mathbf{3}^*$ breaks up into the irreducible representations **8** and **1**.

triplet are found by applying T_-. The triplet $T = 1$, $Y = 0$ has the wave functions (see Fig. 3.2*b* for the numbering convention)

$$\begin{aligned} \Psi_3 &= \psi^1\phi_2 & T_3 &= 1 \\ \Psi_4 &= \frac{1}{\sqrt{2}}(\psi^2\phi_2 + \psi^1\phi_1) & T_3 &= 0 \qquad Y = 0 \\ \Psi_5 &= \psi^2\phi_1 & T_3 &= -1 \end{aligned} \tag{3.20}$$

Ψ_5 is a member of a V-spin doublet with $V_3 = +1/2$. The $V_3 = -1/2$ member located at site 2 in Fig. 3.2*b* is found by applying V_-, with the result $\Psi_2 = \psi^2\phi_3$. This state, in turn, is the $T_3 = -1/2$ member of a T-spin doublet. Applying T_+ to Ψ_2 then gives Ψ_1:

$$\begin{aligned} \Psi_1 &= \psi^1\phi_3 & T_3 &= \tfrac{1}{2} \\ \Psi_2 &= \psi^2\phi_3 & T_3 &= -\tfrac{1}{2} \end{aligned} \qquad Y = 1 \tag{3.21}$$

In the same manner, we note that Ψ_3 is the $V_3 = -1/2$ member of another V-spin doublet, whose companion is $\Psi_8 = T_-\Psi_7$:

$$\begin{aligned} \Psi_7 &= \psi^3\phi_2 & T_3 &= \tfrac{1}{2} \\ \Psi_8 &= \psi^3\phi_1 & T_3 &= -\tfrac{1}{2} \end{aligned} \qquad Y = -1 \tag{3.22}$$

Thus far we have shown that all six states on the periphery belong to the same irreducible representation. It remains to investigate the threefold degeneracy at the center of the weight diagram. We have seen that T_+ or T_- applied to Ψ_5 and Ψ_3 lead to a state at the center, Ψ_4. The three independent functions with zero weight are $\psi^1\phi_1$, $\psi^2\phi_2$, and $\psi^3\phi_3$. The combination $\Psi_4 = (\psi^1\phi_1 + \psi^2\phi_2)/\sqrt{2}$ has been shown to belong to the same representation as the six states on the periphery of the weight diagram. Next note that Ψ_1 is the $T_3 = -1$ member of a V-spin triplet. The state $\Psi_\alpha \equiv V_+\Psi_1/\sqrt{2}$ is accordingly the $V_3 = 0$ member of the triplet:

$$\Psi_\alpha \equiv V_+\Psi_1/\sqrt{2} = \frac{1}{\sqrt{2}}(\psi^1\phi_1 + \psi^3\phi_3); \qquad V_3 = 0 \tag{3.23}$$

(Ψ_α is also obtained by applying V_- to Ψ_8.) Similarly Ψ_2 is the $U_3 = +1$ member of a U-spin triplet. Applying U_- leads to Ψ_β:

$$\Psi_\beta \equiv U_-\Psi_2/\sqrt{2} = \frac{1}{\sqrt{2}}(\psi^3\phi_3 - \psi^2\phi_2); \qquad U_3 = 0 \quad (3.24)$$

The minus sign can be traced to the sign conventions discussed in Section 2.5.

The functions Ψ_α, Ψ_β, and Ψ_4 are not independent. Extracting the component of Ψ_α parallel to Ψ_4 defines a new function χ_α, orthogonal to and independent of Ψ_4:

$$\Psi_\alpha = \Psi_4(\Psi_4,\Psi_\alpha) + \chi_\alpha = \tfrac{1}{2}\Psi_4 + \chi_\alpha$$

$$\chi_\alpha = \frac{1}{2\sqrt{2}}(\psi^1\phi_1 - \psi^2\phi_2 + 2\psi^3\phi_3) \quad (3.25)$$

A similar projection of Ψ_β yields $\chi_\beta = \chi_\alpha$:

$$\begin{aligned} \Psi_\beta &= \Psi_4(\Psi_4,\Psi_\beta) + \chi_\beta = -\tfrac{1}{2}\Psi_4 + \chi_\beta, \\ \chi_\beta &= \chi_\alpha \end{aligned} \quad (3.26)$$

Normalizing χ_α and defining a new function Ψ_6 we find

$$\Psi_6 \equiv \frac{2}{\sqrt{3}}\chi_\alpha = \frac{1}{\sqrt{6}}(\psi^1\phi_1 - \psi^2\phi_2 + 2\psi^3\phi_3) \quad (3.27)$$

$$\Psi_\alpha = \tfrac{1}{2}\Psi_4 + \frac{\sqrt{3}}{2}\Psi_6 \quad (3.28)$$

$$\Psi_\beta = -\tfrac{1}{2}\Psi_4 + \frac{\sqrt{3}}{2}\Psi_6 \quad (3.29)$$

The state Ψ_6, which was obtained by requiring it to be orthogonal to the $T = 1$, $T_3 = 0$ state Ψ_4, has $T = 0$. Note that (3.28) and (3.29) show how to express the central components of the U and V-spin triplets in terms of components of the T-spin triplet. This connection is very useful in applications.

We have now generated (by systematic application of all the group operations to the state of highest weight) an irreducible representation with eight basis functions Ψ_i ($i = 1$–8). This eight-dimensional representation will be shown to be the regular representation of $SU(3)$. It plays a central role in physical applications, as discussed in Section 3.4. The isospin–hypercharge composition of this representation [**8**; $D(1,1)$] is seen to coincide exactly with that of the collections of particles in Fig. 2.1, except for the extra, neutral vector meson which will be the subject of subsequent discussion. This correlation justifies the physical correspondence $Y = 2H_2$ of Eq. (2.54).

One independent function remains at the center of the weight diagram. Since it is inaccessible by the route of applying $SU(3)$ operations to members of the representation **8**, it belongs by definition to an inequivalent representation. The function orthogonal to Ψ_4 and Ψ_6 is

$$\Psi_0 = \frac{-1}{\sqrt{3}}[\psi^1(-\phi_1) + \psi^2\phi_2 + \psi^3\phi_3] \qquad T = Y = 0 \quad (3.30)$$

This $SU(3)$ scalar is simply the contraction of ψ^i and ϕ_j taking into account the extra minus sign introduced in the ϕ triplet to enforce the standard phase convention. (With the extra sign the metric tensor is no longer the Kronecker delta.)

In Table 3.1 the basis functions for the various subgroups $SU(2) \times U(1)$ have been given for the representation **8**. The signs have been chosen to maintain the standard phase conventions in all three $SU(2)$ subgroups. In parentheses the states have been expressed in terms of the usual baryon states, labeled by the quantum numbers of $SU(2)_T \times U(1)_Y$ appropriate to physical particles.

It is frequently useful to have at hand explicit expressions for the matrix elements of the generators in the representation **8**. These are easily found by referring to the weight diagram, which reveals the nonzero matrix elements, and using the results of the preceding calculation of the basis functions. Rather than write out 8×8 matrices having few nonzero entries, we employ an

TABLE 3.1

Composition of the Octet Wave Functions in Terms of the Constituents $\mathbf{3}(\psi^i)$ and $\mathbf{3}^*(\phi_j)$. Basis Functions May Be Labeled by the Quantum Numbers of any of the $SU(2) \times U(1)$ Subgroups. U- and V-Spin Multiplets Are Labeled in Terms of the T-Spin States, the Latter Labeled by the Familiar Baryons.

$SU(2)_T \times U(1)_Y$		$SU(2)_V \times U(1)_Z$		$SU(2)_U \times U(1)_Q$	
$T = 1/2$, $Y = 1$	$\Psi_1 = \psi^1\phi_3\ (p)$ $\Psi_2 = \psi^2\phi_3\ (n)$	$V = 1/2$, $Z = 1$	$\Psi_7\ (\Xi^0)$ $\Psi_3\ (\Sigma^+)$	$U = 1/2$, $Q = 1$	$\Psi_1\ (p)$ $-\Psi_3\ (-\Sigma^+)$
$T = 1$, $Y = 0$	$\Psi_3 = \psi^1\phi_2\ (\Sigma^+)$ $\Psi_4 = \frac{1}{\sqrt{2}}(\psi^2\phi_2 + \psi^1\phi_1)\ (\Sigma^0)$ $\Psi_5 = \psi^2\phi_1\ (\Sigma^-)$	$V = 1$, $Z = 0$	$\Psi_8\ (\Xi^-)$ $\Psi_\alpha\ \left(\tfrac{1}{2}\Sigma^0 + \frac{\sqrt{3}}{2}\Lambda\right)$ $\Psi_1\ (p)$	$V = 1$, $Q = 0$	$\Psi_2\ (n)$ $\Psi_\beta\ \left(-\tfrac{1}{2}\Sigma^0 + \frac{\sqrt{3}}{2}\Lambda\right)$ $-\Psi_7\ (-\Xi^0)$
$T = Y = 0$	$\Psi_6 = \frac{1}{\sqrt{6}}(\psi^1\phi_1 - \psi^2\phi_2 + 2\psi^3\phi_3)\ (\Lambda)$	$V = Z = 0$	$\Psi_{\alpha'} = \frac{\sqrt{3}}{2}\Psi_4 - \tfrac{1}{2}\Psi_6 = \left(\frac{\sqrt{3}}{2}\Sigma^0 - \tfrac{1}{2}\Lambda\right)$	$U = Q = 0$	$\Psi_{\beta'} = \frac{\sqrt{3}}{2}\Psi_4 + \tfrac{1}{2}\Psi_6 = \left(\frac{\sqrt{3}}{2}\Sigma^0 + \tfrac{1}{2}\Lambda\right)$
$T = 1/2$, $Y = -1$	$\Psi_7 = \psi^3\phi_2\ (\Xi^0)$ $\Psi_8 = \psi^3\phi_1\ (\Xi^-)$	$V = 1/2$, $Z = -1$	$\Psi_5\ (\Sigma^-)$ $\Psi_2\ (n)$	$U = 1/2$, $Q = -1$	$\Psi_5\ (\Sigma^-)$ $\Psi_8\ (\Xi^-)$

outer product notation, using $|i\rangle$ for Ψ_i ($i = 1$–8). The following results are easily found for the generators T_-, U_-, V_-, T_3, and Y. T_+, U_+, and V_+ are found by transposition of T_-, U_-, and V_-. $E_{\pm\alpha}$ and $\mathbf{H}$ are found by inserting the appropriate factors.

$$T_- = |2\rangle\langle 1| + |8\rangle\langle 7| + \sqrt{2}\,|4\rangle\langle 3| + \sqrt{2}\,|5\rangle\langle 4|;$$

$$V_- = |2\rangle\langle 5| + |3\rangle\langle 7| + \sqrt{2}\,|\alpha\rangle\langle 8| + \sqrt{2}\,|1\rangle\langle \alpha|,$$

$$V_- = |2\rangle\langle 5| + |3\rangle\langle 7| + \frac{1}{\sqrt{2}}\,|4\rangle\langle 8| + \frac{1}{\sqrt{2}}\,|1\rangle\langle 4|$$

$$+ \sqrt{\tfrac{3}{2}}\,|6\rangle\langle 8| + \sqrt{\tfrac{3}{2}}\,|1\rangle\langle 6|;$$

$$U_- = -|3\rangle\langle 1| + |8\rangle\langle 5| + \frac{1}{\sqrt{3}}\,|\beta\rangle\langle 2| - \frac{1}{\sqrt{3}}\,|7\rangle\langle \beta|, \quad (3.31)$$

$$U_- = -|3\rangle\langle 1| + |8\rangle\langle 5| - \frac{1}{2\sqrt{3}}\,|4\rangle\langle 2| + \frac{1}{2\sqrt{3}}\,|7\rangle\langle 4|$$

$$+ \tfrac{1}{2}|6\rangle\langle 2| - \tfrac{1}{2}|7\rangle\langle 6|$$

$$T_3 = \mathrm{diag}\,[\tfrac{1}{2}, -\tfrac{1}{2}, 1, 0, -1, 0, \tfrac{1}{2}, -\tfrac{1}{2}]$$

$$Y = \mathrm{diag}\,[1, 1, 0, 0, 0, 0, -1, -1]$$

The states numbered 1 through 8 correspond respectively to the particle states p, n, Σ^+, Σ^0, Σ^-, Λ^0, Ξ^0, Ξ^-. The members of the T-spin multiplets just named are related to each other by the standard phase convention.

The important ten-dimensional representation arises in the reduction $\mathbf{3} \times \mathbf{3} \times \mathbf{3}$. The latter representation has the basis $\xi^\alpha(1)\xi^\beta(2)\xi^\gamma(3)$, where ξ transforms as $\mathbf{3}$. Since $\mathbf{3} \times \mathbf{3} = \mathbf{6} + \mathbf{3}^*$, the product $\xi^\alpha(1)\xi^\beta(2)$ can be expressed in terms of the basis functions of the irreducible representations $\mathbf{6}$ and $\mathbf{3}^*$. The problem thus reduces to considering separately $\mathbf{3} \times \mathbf{3}^*$ and $\mathbf{3} \times \mathbf{6}$:

$$\mathbf{3} \times \mathbf{3} \times \mathbf{3} = (\mathbf{6} + \mathbf{3}^*) \times \mathbf{3} = \mathbf{6} \times \mathbf{3} + \mathbf{3}^* \times \mathbf{3} \quad (3.32)$$

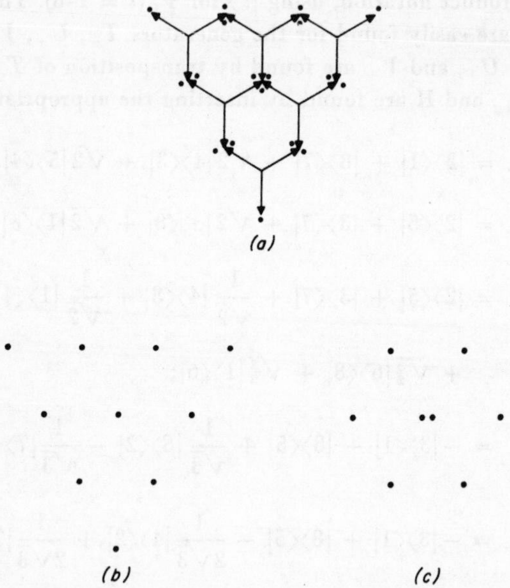

Fig. 3.3. Fig. (3.3*a*) illustrates the vector addition of weight diagrams in the direct product **3** × **6**. The breakup of **3** × **6** into **10** and **8** is illustrated in Figs. (3.3*b*) and (3.3*c*).

The weight diagram for the product representation **3** × **6** is shown in Fig. 3.3*a*. The state of highest weight, which has

$$\mathbf{M}(3,0) = \left(\frac{\sqrt{3}}{2}, \frac{1}{2}\right) \qquad T_3 = T = \frac{3}{2}, \qquad Y = 1 \tag{3.33}$$

belongs to a T-spin quartet. (This state is also the $V_3 = -3/2$ member of a V-spin quartet.) The basis functions ψ_α ($\alpha = 1,\ldots,6$) of the representation $D(2,0)$ were obtained in Eqs. (3.9–3.14). (To avoid confusion we denote the triplets by ξ instead of ψ.) Labeling the sites in the composite weight diagram as in Fig. 3.3*b*, the T-spin quartet belonging to the state Φ_1 of highest weight is

$$\Phi_1 = \psi^1\xi^1$$

$$\Phi_2 = \frac{1}{\sqrt{3}}\, T_-\Phi_1 = \sqrt{\tfrac{1}{3}}\,\psi^1\xi^2 + \sqrt{\tfrac{2}{3}}\psi^2\xi^1 \tag{3.34}$$

$$\Phi_3 = \tfrac{1}{2}T_-\Phi_2 = \sqrt{\tfrac{2}{3}}\psi^2\xi^2 + \sqrt{\tfrac{1}{3}}\psi^3\xi^1$$

$$\Phi_4 = \frac{1}{\sqrt{3}}\, T_-\Phi_3 = \psi^3\xi^2$$

in order of decreasing T_3. Applying V_+ to Φ_1 results in a $T_3 = T = 1$ state at site 5 in Fig. 3.3*b*. Applying T_- to Φ_5 twice results in the *T*-spin triplet:

$$\Phi_5 = \sqrt{\tfrac{1}{3}}\,\psi^1\xi^3 + \sqrt{\tfrac{2}{3}}\psi^4\xi^1$$

$$\Phi_6 = \frac{1}{\sqrt{3}}(\psi^2\xi^3 + \psi^5\xi^1 + \psi^4\xi^2) \tag{3.35}$$

$$\Phi_7 = \sqrt{\tfrac{1}{3}}\psi^3\xi^3 + \sqrt{\tfrac{2}{3}}\psi^5\xi^2$$

A *T*-spin doublet is reached by applying V_+ to Φ_5, and then applying T_-

$$\Phi_8 = \sqrt{\tfrac{1}{3}}\,\psi^6\xi^1 + \sqrt{\tfrac{2}{3}}\psi^4\xi^3$$
$$\Phi_9 = \sqrt{\tfrac{1}{3}}\,\psi^6\xi^2 + \sqrt{\tfrac{2}{3}}\psi^5\xi^3 \tag{3.36}$$

and finally a *T*-spin singlet Φ_{10} is reached by applying V_+ to Φ_8:

$$\Phi_{10} = \psi^6\xi^3 \tag{3.37}$$

The nature of the obtained functions is perhaps best exhibited by expressing Φ_i ($i = 1,\ldots,10$) completely in terms of the constituent triplets:

$$\Phi_1 = \xi^1(1)\xi^1(2)\xi^1(3)$$

$$\Phi_2 = \frac{1}{\sqrt{3}}(\xi^1(1)\xi^1(2)\xi^2(3) + \xi^1(1)\xi^2(2)\xi^1(3) + \xi^2(1)\xi^1(2)\xi^1(3))$$

$$\Phi_3 = \frac{1}{\sqrt{3}}(\xi^2(1)\xi^2(2)\xi^1(3) + \xi^1(1)\xi^2(2)\xi^2(3) + \xi^2(1)\xi^1(2)\xi^2(3))$$

$$\Phi_4 = \xi^2(1)\xi^2(2)\xi^2(3)$$

$$\Phi_5 = \frac{1}{\sqrt{3}}(\xi^1(1)\xi^1(2)\xi^3(3) + \xi^1(1)\xi^3(2)\xi^1(3) + \xi^3(1)\xi^1(2)\xi^1(3))$$

$$\Phi_6 = \frac{1}{\sqrt{6}}(\xi^1(1)\xi^2(2)\xi^3(3) + \xi^2(1)\xi^1(2)\xi^3(3) + \xi^2(1)\xi^3(2)\xi^1(3) + \xi^3(1)\xi^2(2)\xi^1(3) + \xi^1(1)\xi^3(2)\xi^2(3) + \xi^3(1)\xi^1(2)\xi^2(3))$$

$$\Phi_7 = \frac{1}{\sqrt{3}}(\xi^2(1)\xi^2(2)\xi^3(3) + \xi^2(1)\xi^3(2)\xi^2(3) + \xi^3(1)\xi^2(2)\xi^2(3))$$

$$\Phi_8 = \frac{1}{\sqrt{3}}(\xi^3(1)\xi^3(2)\xi^1(3) + \xi^1(1)\xi^3(2)\xi^3(3) + \xi^3(1)\xi^1(2)\xi^3(3))$$

$$\Phi_9 = \frac{1}{\sqrt{3}}(\xi^3(1)\xi^3(2)\xi^2(3) + \xi^2(1)\xi^3(2)\xi^3(3) + \xi^3(1)\xi^2(2)\xi^3(3))$$

$$\Phi_{10} = \xi^3(1)\xi^3(2)\xi^3(3) \tag{3.38}$$

The Φ_i exhaust the set of functions completely symmetrical under interchange of the coordinates α of the triplet functions $\xi(\alpha)$. This fact implies that we have found all the members of the irreducible representation $D(3,0)$, since the generators $E_{\pm\alpha} = E_{\pm\alpha}(1) + E_{\pm\alpha}(2) + E_{\pm\alpha}(3)$ are symmetrical under interchange of 1, 2, and 3, and can never change the symmetry of a function, even though the labels k of ξ^k are permuted by $E_{\pm\alpha}$. (Recall that we begin with the state of highest weight, which is completely symmetrical.)

The representation **10** ($D(3,0)$) is completely symmetrical with regard to T, U, and V-spin. As discussed in Section 3.4, its isospin–hypercharge content coincides with the observed set of $P_{3/2}$ meson–baryon resonances.

The generators, expressed in terms of the outer product notation explained after Eq. (3.31), are given by

$$\begin{aligned} T_- &= \sqrt{3}\,|2\rangle\langle 1| + 2|3\rangle\langle 2| + \sqrt{3}\,|4\rangle\langle 3| \\ &\quad + \sqrt{2}\,|6\rangle\langle 5| + \sqrt{2}\,|7\rangle\langle 6| + |9\rangle\langle 8| \\ U_- &= \sqrt{3}\,|9\rangle\langle 10| + 2|7\rangle\langle 9| + \sqrt{3}\,|4\rangle\langle 7| \\ &\quad + \sqrt{2}\,|6\rangle\langle 8| + \sqrt{2}\,|3\rangle\langle 6| + |2\rangle\langle 5| \\ V_- &= \sqrt{3}\,|8\rangle\langle 10| + 2|5\rangle\langle 8| + \sqrt{3}\,|1\rangle\langle 5| \\ &\quad + \sqrt{2}\,|6\rangle\langle 9| + \sqrt{2}\,|2\rangle\langle 6| + |3\rangle\langle 7| \end{aligned} \tag{3.39}$$

The rest of the reduction of **6** × **3** follows easily. Separating off the sites of **10** (Fig. 3.3*b*) from Fig. 3.3*a* leaves the weight diagram of $D(1,1)$, Fig. 3.3*c*. Taking that combination of functions at site 5 orthogonal to Φ_5 gives the state of highest weight of the eight-dimensional representation:

$$\begin{aligned} \chi_3 &\equiv \sqrt{\tfrac{2}{3}}\,\psi^1\xi^3 - \sqrt{\tfrac{1}{3}}\,\psi^4\xi^1 \\ &= \frac{1}{\sqrt{6}}\,(2\xi^1(1)\xi^1(2)\xi^3(3) - \xi^1(1)\xi^3(2)\xi^1(3) - \xi^3(1)\xi^1(2)\xi^1(3)) \end{aligned} \tag{3.40}$$

Clearly there is an arbitrary overall phase. We have chosen the phase so that plus one goes with the left-hand state ψ with the highest weight. We shall not quote the remaining seven functions associated with (3.40). Note that (3.40) is symmetrical in coordinates 1 and 2 [$\psi^k = \psi^k(1,2)$ is symmetrical]. The symmetry in the pairs (1,3) and (2,3) though "mixed" is preserved by the group operations, and is best analyzed using Young diagrams. [The eight-dimensional representation obtained from **3*** × **3** in (3.32) is antisymmetrical in 1 and 2.]

The complete reduction is therefore

$$\mathbf{3} \times \mathbf{3} \times \mathbf{3} = \mathbf{10} + \mathbf{8} + \mathbf{8} + \mathbf{1} \tag{3.41}$$

Note that the two eight-dimensional representations, though completely indistinguishable under $SU(3)$ transformations (action on the basis function labels) can be distinguished by symmetry properties outside the group, in this case permutations of the coordinates which distinguish one triplet ξ from another. We shall often have occasion to distinguish among $SU(3)$-identical basis functions in this manner.

3.3 Casimir Operators for $SU(3)$

We are now in a position to discuss the so-called *Casimir operators* for $SU(3)$. For orientation, note that in $SU(2)$ the eigenvalues of $\mathbf{J}^2$ (square of the "angular momentum") are used to distinguish the various irreducible representations from each other. Within an irreducible representation $\mathbf{J}^2 = j(j+1)I$, where j takes on any one of the values $0, 1/2, 1, 3/2, \ldots$ $\mathbf{J}^2$ is the Casimir operator for $SU(2)$. In $SU(3)$ there are two independent quantities that commute with all the generators and so are proportional to the identity within an irreducible representation. One of these operators is clearly $\mathbf{G}^2$. However, let us proceed in a more systematic manner. We have already noted that there are two independent ways to couple two sets of functions transforming as **8** to get another basis transforming in the same way. (That there are only two ways will be proved in Section 3.6.) The sets V_c^F and V_c^D of Eqs. (2.101) and (2.107) are clearly independent since they are orthogonal. Thus, given a third basis set C_c transforming as **8** we can form a scalar from **A**, **B**, **C** in two independent ways

$$S_F = (F_c)_{ab} A_a B_b C_c$$
$$S_D = (D_c)_{ab} A_a B_b C_c \tag{3.42}$$

In $SU(2)$ there is only one analogous invariant, $\varepsilon_{ijk} A_i B_j C_k = \mathbf{A} \cdot (\mathbf{B} \times \mathbf{C})$.

In analogous fashion we can construct from an irreducible representation of the generators G_a satisfying (2.26) two independent vector operators

$$\mathcal{O}_F{}^a = (F^a)_{bc} G_b G_c$$
$$\mathcal{O}_D{}^a = (D^a)_{bc} G_b G_c \tag{3.43}$$

Then the quantities

$$
\begin{aligned}
C_2' &= (F^a)_{bc} G_a G_b G_c \\
C_3 &= (D^a)_{bc} G_a G_b G_c
\end{aligned} \tag{3.44}
$$

commute with all the G_k and by Schur's Lemma are multiples of the identity within an irreducible representation of $SU(3)$. The eigenvalues of these *Casimir operators* are used to characterize the various representations.

Previously it was noted that $\mathbf{G}^2$ is a Casimir operator. In fact it coincides with C_2' up to a constant factor. To show this, note that in C_2' we can replace $G_b G_c$ by $\frac{1}{2}[G_b, G_c]$ because of the anti-symmetry of $(F^a)_{bc}$ in the lower indices. Hence

$$
\begin{aligned}
C_2' &= \tfrac{1}{2}(F^a)_{bc} G_a [G_b, G_c] = -\tfrac{1}{2}(F^a)_{bc}(F^d)_{bc} G_a G_d \\
&= \tfrac{1}{2} \operatorname{Tr}(F^a F^d) \cdot G_a G_d = \tfrac{3}{2}\mathbf{G}^2
\end{aligned} \tag{3.45}
$$

on using Eq. (2.109), anticipating the precise value of $\mathbf{F}^2$. Since $\mathbf{G}^2$ is of simpler structure we shall use it instead of the equivalent form C_2' of Eq. (3.45). Thus we take our definition of the Casimir operators to be:

$$
\begin{aligned}
C_2 &= \mathbf{G}^2 = G_a G_a \\
C_3 &= d_{abc} G_a G_b G_c
\end{aligned} \tag{3.46}
$$

The evaluation of C_2 is easily accomplished by converting it to the basis of the $E_{\pm\alpha}$, $\mathbf{H}$ and applying C_2 to the state of highest weight $\mathbf{M}$ of the irreducible representation in question. Using the correspondence (2.18) ($\frac{1}{2}\boldsymbol{\lambda} \to \mathbf{G}$) we find

$$
C_2 = 3\left\{H_1{}^2 + H_2{}^2 + \sum_{i=1}^{3} (E_i E_{-i} + E_{-i} E_i)\right\} \tag{3.47}
$$

We recall that for the state $\psi(\mathbf{M})$ of highest weight $\mathbf{M}$

$$
E_1 \psi(\mathbf{M}) = E_{-2}\psi(\mathbf{M}) = E_{-3}\psi(\mathbf{M}) = 0 \tag{3.48}
$$

Using the commutator $[E_\alpha, E_{-\alpha}] = \mathbf{r}(\alpha) \cdot \mathbf{H}$ we then find

$$
\begin{aligned}
C_2\psi(\mathbf{M}) &= 3\{H_1{}^2 + H_2{}^2 + E_1E_{-1} + E_{-2}E_2 + E_{-3}E_3\}\psi(\mathbf{M}) \\
&= 3\{M_1{}^2 + M_2{}^2 + [E_1,E_{-1}] + [E_{-2},E_2] + [E_{-3},E_3]\}\psi(\mathbf{M}) \\
&= 3\{M_1{}^2 + M_2{}^2 + [\mathbf{r}(1) - \mathbf{r}(2) - \mathbf{r}(3)]\cdot\mathbf{M}\}\psi(\mathbf{M}) \\
&= 3\left\{M_1{}^2 + M_2{}^2 + \frac{2}{\sqrt{3}}M_1\right\}\psi(\mathbf{M}) \qquad (3.49)
\end{aligned}
$$

Substitution of $M_1 = \sqrt{3}(p+q)/6$, $M_2 = (p-q)/6$ now yields

$$C_2(p,q) = \tfrac{1}{3}(p^2 + q^2 + pq + 3(p+q)) \qquad (3.50)$$

The values of C_2 for various representations of moderately low dimension can be found in Table 3.2.

TABLE 3.2

Dimensionality and Values of the Casimir Operators for Some Low-Dimensional Representations (p,q) of $SU(3)$.

(p,q)	(0,0)	(1,0)	(1,1)	(2,0)	(2,1)	(2,2)	(3,0)	(3,1)	(3,2)	(3,3)	(4,0)	(4,1)
Dimension	1	3	8	6	15	27	10	24	42	64	15	35
C_2	0	4/3	3	10/3	16/3	8	6	25/3	34/3	15	28/3	12
C_3	0	10/9	0	35/9	28/9	0	9	80/9	55/9	0	154/9	18

The evaluation of C_3 is somewhat more involved. For the details we refer the reader to the paper of Baird and Biedenharn (9), which also considers analogous constructions for the group $SU(n)$. In terms of our notation their result is

$$C_3(p,q) = \tfrac{1}{18}(p-q)(2p+q+3)(2q+p+3) \qquad (3.51)$$

Clearly either the pair (p,q) or C_2, C_3 can be used to characterize a representation. Note that C_2 is symmetrical in (p,q) while C_3 is antisymmetrical. Thus the sign of C_3 distinguishes a representation $D(p,q)$ from its complex conjugate equivalent $D^*(q,p)$. For $p = q$, $C_3 = 0$, and $D(p,p)$ is equivalent to $D^*(p,p)$. C_3 vanishes only for those representations which are equivalent to their complex conjugate.

We can now complete the evaluation of Tr F^aF^b and Tr D^aD^b

begun in Eq. (2.109). Since $\mathbf{F}^2 = 3$, from Eq. (3.50) with $p = q = 1$, we find

$$\mathrm{Tr}\, F_a F_b = 3\delta_{ab} \tag{3.52}$$

We can evaluate $\mathrm{Tr}\, D_a D_b$ by writing out Eq. (2.116) for $[D_a, D_b]$ in full

$$D_{ack} D_{bkd} - D_{bck} D_{akd} = -\tfrac{2}{3}(\delta_{ac}\delta_{bd} - \delta_{ad}\delta_{bc}) - (F^k)_{ab}(F^k)_{cd} \tag{3.53}$$

Setting $b = c$ and summing on b gives

$$\mathrm{Tr}\, D_a D_d = \mathrm{Tr}\, D_k \cdot D_{akd} + \tfrac{14}{3}\delta_{ad} - (\mathbf{F}^2)_{ad} = \tfrac{5}{3}\delta_{ad} \tag{3.54}$$

which reduces to

$$\mathrm{Tr}\, D_a D_b = \tfrac{5}{3}\delta_{ab} \tag{3.55}$$

taking into account the fact that D has vanishing trace.

For reference we also express C_2 in terms of the generators $A_\nu{}^\mu$ defined in Eq. (2.27). In terms of these quantities it is easy to construct scalars by complete contraction, e.g.,

$$\begin{aligned} (A,A) &\equiv A_\nu{}^\mu A_\mu{}^\nu \\ (A,A,A) &\equiv A_\nu{}^\mu A_\lambda{}^\nu A_\mu{}^\lambda \end{aligned} \tag{3.56}$$

and so forth, commute with all the $A_\nu{}^\mu$ and so qualify as Casimir operators. (Contractions of products of A's greater than 3 gives scalars that are not independent of the above.)

The connection of the $A_\nu{}^\mu$ to the Hermitian generators G_k is

$$\begin{aligned} &A_2{}^1 = G_1 - iG_2, \quad A_3{}^1 = G_4 - iG_5, \\ &A_3{}^2 = G_6 - iG_7 \quad A_1{}^1 = G_3 + \frac{1}{\sqrt{3}} G_8 = Q, \\ &A_2{}^2 = -G_3 + \frac{1}{\sqrt{3}} G_8 = -Q + Y \equiv -Z, \\ &A_3{}^3 = -\frac{2}{\sqrt{3}} G_8 = -Y; \quad A_1{}^2 = (A_2{}^1)^\dagger, \qquad \text{etc.} \end{aligned} \tag{3.57}$$

Expanding $A_\nu{}^\mu A_\mu{}^\nu$ in terms of its constituents leads, after application of the commutation rules for the G_a, to the result

$$(A,A) = 2C_2 \tag{3.58}$$

A similar method of constructing the Casimir operators for $SU(n)$ has been given by Klein (8). An essentially equivalent procedure has been described by Biedenharn (9).

3.4 Physical Interpretation of the Representations

An unsatisfactory feature of the theory as developed up to this point is its avoidance of a basic question: why is the Sakata model wrong? Why must we use the more complicated assignments of the eightfold way? One wonders why no $SU(3)$ triplets have been observed, since objects of this type were used to *define* the group. From the point of view of bootstrap theories based on dispersion relations, the realization of a given representation by means of particles or resonances is purely a dynamical question. However, the poor numerical accuracy that characterizes such calculations prevents the exclusion of the Sakata model on this basis. On the other hand, the traditions of field theory suggest that one attempt to associate actual particle fields with the defining representation **3**. There are quite a number of ways to do this; since there is no experimental hint that any of these schemes is correct we only mention the most economical model (10, 11), which employs only one field. Our reason for doing this is that practical calculations are often clarified by the use of these probably fictitious particles. The properties of this field must be such that the properties of the observed multiplets are reproduced. Recalling the relations

$$\begin{aligned} \mathbf{3} \times \mathbf{3}^* &= \mathbf{8} + \mathbf{1} \\ \mathbf{3} \times \mathbf{3} \times \mathbf{3} &= \mathbf{10} + \mathbf{8} + \mathbf{8} + \mathbf{1} \end{aligned} \tag{3.59}$$

suggests that the baryon octet and decuplet be composed of three spin 1/2 Dirac particles q while the pseudoscalar and vector meson octets are made up from q and anti-q. We follow Gell-Mann (10) in calling these (presently hypothetical) particles *quarks*. The restriction to one field requires the quarks to have baryon number 1/3. Thus instead of Sakata's (p,n,Λ) triplet we have

$$q = \begin{pmatrix} q_1 \\ q_2 \\ q_3 \end{pmatrix} \tag{3.60}$$

where (q_1,q_2) still make up a T-spin doublet and q_3 a T-spin singlet. However, the joint requirements that baryons transform as qqq imposes the eightfold way relations $Y = 2H_2$, $T_3 = \sqrt{3}\,H_1$ on the quark quantum numbers. The quantum numbers of q_i are listed in Table 3.3. The discovery of such bizarre objects would

TABLE 3.3

Quantum Numbers of the Components of the Quark Field (*a*) and of Some Products (*b*).

(*a*)

	Q	Y	T_3	B
q_1	2/3	1/3	1/2	1/3
q_2	−1/3	1/3	−1/2	1/3
q_3	−1/3	−2/3	0	1/3

(*b*)

	Q	T_3	Y	B
$\bar{q}_1 q_2$	−1	−1	0	0
$\bar{q}_2 q_3$	0	1/2	−1	0
$\bar{q}_3 q_1$	1	1/2	1	0

surely be an exciting event. At the time of writing no such particles have been discovered with mass less than several nucleon masses.

Whether or not quarks exist, they are extremely useful and suggestive in calculations. We exhibit this by constructing the appropriate field operator for the P-meson octet transforming according to the hermitian regular representation **F**. The appropriate set of linear combinations of $q_i^* q_j$ transforming in this way is given by $P_a = \bar{q}\lambda_a q/\sqrt{2}$, $a = 1, \ldots, 8$. The eight components of P_a are given explicitly by

$$
\begin{aligned}
P_1 &= \frac{1}{\sqrt{2}}(\bar{q}_1 q_2 + \bar{q}_2 q_1) & P_5 &= \frac{i}{\sqrt{2}}(\bar{q}_3 q_1 - \bar{q}_1 q_3) \\
P_2 &= \frac{i}{\sqrt{2}}(\bar{q}_2 q_1 - \bar{q}_1 q_2) & P_6 &= \frac{1}{\sqrt{2}}(\bar{q}_2 q_3 + \bar{q}_3 q_2) \\
P_3 &= \frac{1}{\sqrt{2}}(\bar{q}_1 q_1 - \bar{q}_2 q_2) & P_7 &= \frac{i}{\sqrt{2}}(\bar{q}_3 q_2 - \bar{q}_2 q_3) \\
P_4 &= \frac{1}{\sqrt{2}}(\bar{q}_1 q_3 + \bar{q}_3 q_1) & P_8 &= \frac{1}{\sqrt{6}}(\bar{q}_1 q_1 + \bar{q}_2 q_2 - 2\bar{q}_3 q_3)
\end{aligned}
\tag{3.61}
$$

The P_i have zero baryon number. P_8 is clearly an isosinglet with zero hypercharge. P_3 has $T_3 = Y = 0$; it has opposite symmetry to P_8 and has isospin 1. P_8 and P_3 clearly correspond to π^0 and η. Inspection of Table 3.3 suggests in addition the following identifications:

$$
\begin{aligned}
\bar{q}_2 q_1 &= \pi^+, & \bar{q}_1 q_2 &= (\pi^+)^* = \pi^- \\
\bar{q}_3 q_1 &= K^+, & \bar{q}_1 q_3 &= (K^+)^* = K^- \\
\bar{q}_2 q_3 &= K^0, & \bar{q}_3 q_2 &= (K^0)^* = \overline{K^0}
\end{aligned}
\tag{3.62}
$$

The combination of P-meson fields transforming via the generators $\mathbf{F}$ is therefore

$$
\mathbf{P} = \begin{pmatrix} (\pi^+ + \pi^-)/\sqrt{2} \\ i(\pi^+ - \pi^-)/\sqrt{2} \\ \pi^0 \\ (K^+ + K^-)/\sqrt{2} \\ i(K^+ - K^-)/\sqrt{2} \\ (K^0 + \overline{K^0})/\sqrt{2} \\ i(K^0 - \overline{K^0})/\sqrt{2} \\ \eta \end{pmatrix} \qquad \mathbf{P}^* = \mathbf{P} \tag{3.63}
$$

Notice that **P** is self-conjugate: $P_a^* = P_a$. When q is subject to the transformation $q \to \exp(i\boldsymbol{\alpha}\cdot\boldsymbol{\lambda}/2)q$, P undergoes the transformation $\mathbf{P} \to \exp(i\boldsymbol{\alpha}\cdot\mathbf{F})\mathbf{P}$. In this case the complex conjugate representation $\exp(-i\boldsymbol{\alpha}\cdot\mathbf{F}^*)$ is identical to the original one since $\mathbf{F}^* = -\mathbf{F}$. The underlying quark fields may now be abandoned in favor of the "physical" fields P_a. For the vector meson octet we substitute $\pi^\pm \to \rho^\pm$, $\pi^0 \to \rho^0$, $K^\pm \to K^{*\pm}$, $K^0 \to K^{0*}$, $\overline{K^0} \to \overline{K^0}{}^*$, $\eta \to \phi_0$. However, the baryon octet is not self-conjugate and it is convenient to make the following definition of the baryon octet B_a transforming as (3.63):

$$\mathbf{B} = \begin{pmatrix} (\Sigma^+ + \Sigma^-)/\sqrt{2} \\ i(\Sigma^+ - \Sigma^-)/\sqrt{2} \\ \Sigma^0 \\ (p - \Xi^-)/\sqrt{2} \\ i(p + \Xi^-)/\sqrt{2} \\ (n + \Xi^0)/\sqrt{2} \\ i(n - \Xi^0)/\sqrt{2} \\ \Lambda \end{pmatrix} \tag{3.64}$$

In (3.64) Ξ^- is quite independent of p, in contrast to the pair K^+, K^- in (3.63). The sign on Ξ^- has been chosen so that the customary isospin doublet (Ξ^0, Ξ^-) enters in the $SU(2)$-invariant couplings. The above fields now agree with the conventions of Eq. (1.52). In particular, $\Sigma^\pm = (\Sigma_1 \pm i\Sigma_2)/\sqrt{2}$ destroy the indicated particles, etc. As mentioned at the end of Chapter 1, the operators in Eqs. (3.63) and (3.64) do not create multiplets having the useful standard phase relation. This problem will be discussed shortly.

First, however, we indicate the connection of the above approach with the commonly used 3×3 matrix representation, which arises naturally when one uses tensor analysis for the construction of irreducible representations. We may define traceless

3×3 Hermitian matrices by contracting **P** or **B** with $\boldsymbol{\lambda}$: $\mathscr{P} = \sum_a P_a\lambda_a/\sqrt{2}$, $\mathscr{B} = \sum_a B_a\lambda_a/\sqrt{2}$

$$\mathscr{P} = \begin{pmatrix} \dfrac{\sqrt{3}\pi^0 + \eta}{\sqrt{6}} & \pi^+ & K^+ \\ \pi^- & \dfrac{-\sqrt{3}\pi^0 + \eta}{\sqrt{6}} & K^0 \\ K^- & \overline{K^0} & \dfrac{-2}{\sqrt{6}}\eta \end{pmatrix} \tag{3.65}$$

$$\mathscr{B} = \begin{pmatrix} \dfrac{\sqrt{3}\Sigma^0 + \Lambda^0}{\sqrt{6}} & \Sigma^+ & p \\ \Sigma^- & \dfrac{-\sqrt{3}\Sigma^0 + \Lambda}{\sqrt{6}} & n \\ -\Xi^- & \Xi^0 & \dfrac{-2}{\sqrt{6}}\Lambda \end{pmatrix}$$

It is easily verified that the transformation of $\mathscr{P}$ by the 3×3 matrix $U = \exp(i\boldsymbol{\alpha}\cdot\boldsymbol{\lambda}/2)$:

$$\mathscr{P} \to \mathscr{P}' = U\mathscr{P}U^{-1} \tag{3.66}$$

agrees with the relations

$$\begin{aligned} P_a' &= (\delta_{ab} + i\delta\boldsymbol{\alpha}\cdot\mathbf{F}_{ab})P_b \\ \mathscr{P}' &= \sum_a P_a'\lambda_a/\sqrt{2} \end{aligned} \tag{3.67}$$

The conjugate $\overline{\mathscr{P}}$ is defined to include Hermitian conjugation of both the fields P_a and the matrix $\boldsymbol{\lambda}$; hence $\overline{\mathscr{P}} = \mathscr{P}$ for the meson matrix and $\overline{\mathscr{B}}$ is given by

$$\overline{\mathscr{B}} = \begin{pmatrix} \dfrac{\sqrt{3}\overline{\Sigma^0} + \overline{\Lambda}}{\sqrt{6}} & \overline{\Sigma^-} & -\overline{\Xi^-} \\ \overline{\Sigma^+} & \dfrac{-\sqrt{3}\overline{\Sigma^0} + \overline{\Lambda}}{\sqrt{6}} & \overline{\Xi^0} \\ \overline{p} & \overline{n} & \dfrac{-2}{\sqrt{6}}\overline{\Lambda} \end{pmatrix} \tag{3.68}$$

Under charge conjugation the matrix $\mathscr{P}$ is simply changed into its transpose. This operation is also the same as reflecting in the origin of the weight diagram. The latter is not the same as charge conjugation for $\mathfrak{B}$ but is sometimes a useful concept nevertheless. We define the R-transformation by

$$\mathscr{P} \underset{R}{\rightarrow} \mathscr{P}^T \qquad \mathfrak{B} \underset{R}{\rightarrow} \mathfrak{B}^T \tag{3.69}$$

This transformation (defined more generally below) does *not* belong to those of $SU(3)$. (In particular the strong interactions are definitely not invariant under "R-conjugation".) To demonstrate this for, say, the matrix $\mathscr{P}$ we can ask whether there exists any V which transposes $\mathscr{P}$:

$$V\mathscr{P}V^{-1} \overset{?}{=} \mathscr{P}^T \tag{3.70}$$

If this were the case, then

$$V\lambda_i V^{-1} = \lambda_i{}^T = \lambda_i{}^* \tag{3.71}$$

For $i = 1, 3, 4, 6, 8$ we have $\lambda_i{}^* = \lambda_i$ and for $i = 2, 5, 7$, $\lambda_i{}^* = -\lambda_i$. Thus V must simultaneously satisfy

$$\begin{aligned} [V,\lambda_i] &= 0 \qquad i = 1, 3, 4, 6, 8 \\ \{V,\lambda_i\} &= 0 \qquad i = 2, 5, 7 \end{aligned} \tag{3.72}$$

The most general 3×3 matrix V can be written in the form

$$V = aI + \mathbf{b}\cdot\boldsymbol{\lambda} \tag{3.73}$$

where a and b_i $(i = 1,\ldots,8)$ are complex numbers. We now show that (3.72) implies $a = b_i = 0$. For $i = 2, 5, 7$ we have

$$2a\lambda_i + b_j\{\lambda_i,\lambda_j\} = 0 \tag{3.74}$$

while for $i = 1, 3, 4, 6, 8$ one finds

$$b_j[\lambda_j,\lambda_i] = 0 \tag{3.75}$$

Taking the trace of Eq. (3.74) gives $b_i = 0$, $i = 2, 5, 7$. Eq. (3.75) implies that $b_j f_{jkl} = 0$. Taking successively $k = 1, 3, 4, 6$, and noting nonzero values of f_{ijk}, shows that $b_3 = b_1 = b_6 = b_4 = 0$.

To eliminate b_8 we note that now $b_j f_{jkl} = b_8 f_{8kl}$, so that taking $(k,l) = (6,7)$ completes the proof that $\mathbf{b} = 0$. Eq. (3.74) reduces to $2a\lambda_i = 0$ which in turn implies that a vanishes. A similar proof can be given for the inequivalence of **3** and **3***. In that case one proceeds as above, in showing that no 3×3 matrix V exists such that $V\lambda_i V^{-1} = -\lambda_i^*$. [Cf. the discussion following Eq. (2.73).]

We now discuss the identification of state vectors with the components of irreducible representations of $SU(3)$. For this purpose, it is useful to employ phase conventions different from those used in the preceding discussion of field operators, as has been mentioned several times. Thus, in the following discussion particle symbols always refer to states having the standard phase relation. Hence, the states Ψ_i ($i = 1$–8) of Section 3.2 can be identified with the following sets of physical states:

$$|B_i\rangle = \begin{bmatrix} |p\rangle \\ |n\rangle \\ |\Sigma^+\rangle \\ |\Sigma^0\rangle \\ |\Sigma^-\rangle \\ |\Lambda\rangle \\ |\Xi^0\rangle \\ |\Xi^-\rangle \end{bmatrix} \qquad |P_i\rangle = \begin{bmatrix} |K^+\rangle \\ |K^0\rangle \\ |\pi^+\rangle \\ |\pi^0\rangle \\ |\pi^-\rangle \\ |\eta\rangle \\ |\overline{K^0}\rangle \\ |K^-\rangle \end{bmatrix} \qquad |V_i\rangle = \begin{bmatrix} |K^{+*}\rangle \\ |K^{0*}\rangle \\ |\rho^+\rangle \\ |\rho^0\rangle \\ |\rho^-\rangle \\ |\phi_0\rangle \\ |\overline{K^0}{}^*\rangle \\ |K^{-*}\rangle \end{bmatrix}, \tag{3.76}$$

provided one is rather tolerant of the obvious nondegeneracy of the masses. (See Fig. 3.4, for example.) The fact that the strongly interacting particles (3.76) fit so neatly into the regular representation of $SU(3)$ is surely astonishing and beautiful. There are, of course, many other implications of the presumed invariance of the strong interactions which must be satisfied, at least approximately, if the symmetry is to be believed. These other relations are the subject of later chapters. The identification of particles with the basis functions of irreducible representations is a necessary preliminary for such applications.

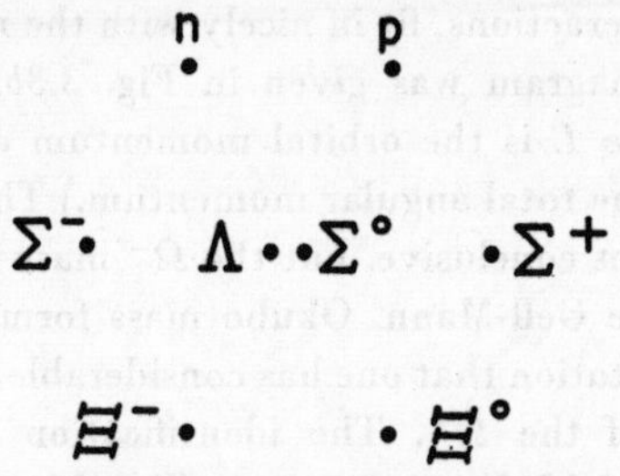

Fig. 3.4. The baryon octet is the prime example of the correspondence of observed low-lying particles with the regular representations of $SU(3)$.

One can also group the particle states (3.76) into V- or U-spin multiplets; for instance, the sets (Σ^+, Ξ^0), (n, Σ^-), $(p, \frac{1}{2}(\Sigma^0 + \sqrt{3}\,\Lambda), \Xi^-)$, and $\frac{1}{2}(-\Sigma^0 + \sqrt{3}\,\Lambda)$ give V-spin doublets, a triplet, and a singlet. If desired, appropriate field operators for U- or V-spin may be constructed as was done in Section 1.4 for ordinary T-spin. For completeness we give the relation between the *operators* appearing in (3.64) and the corresponding *states* in (3.76). Recalling the discussion of Chapter 1, we note the connection

$$\begin{bmatrix} |p\rangle \\ |n\rangle \\ |\Sigma^+\rangle \\ |\Sigma^0\rangle \\ |\Sigma^-\rangle \\ |\Lambda\rangle \\ |\Xi^0\rangle \\ |\Xi^-\rangle \end{bmatrix} = \begin{bmatrix} p \\ n \\ -\Sigma^+ \\ \Sigma^0 \\ \Sigma^- \\ \Lambda \\ \Xi^0 \\ \Xi^- \end{bmatrix}^* \times |0\rangle; \qquad \begin{bmatrix} |K^+\rangle \\ |K^0\rangle \\ |\pi^+\rangle \\ |\pi^0\rangle \\ |\pi^-\rangle \\ |\eta\rangle \\ |\overline{K^0}\rangle \\ |K^-\rangle \end{bmatrix} = \begin{bmatrix} K^+ \\ K^0 \\ -\pi^+ \\ \pi^0 \\ \pi^- \\ \eta \\ \overline{K^0} \\ -K^- \end{bmatrix}^* \times |0\rangle \qquad (3.77)$$

In (3.77) $|0\rangle$ stands for the vacuum state and the asterisk denotes Hermitian conjugation of the components of the column matrix.

The set of $P_{3/2}$ baryon resonances and the so-called Ω^-, stable under strong interactions, fit in nicely with the representation **10**, whose weight diagram was given in Fig. 3.3*b*. (Notation: $P_{3/2}$ means L_J, where L is the orbital momentum of the meson and baryon, and J the total angular momentum.) The spin and parity of Ω^- are not yet conclusive, but the Ω^- mass is so close to that predicted by the Gell-Mann, Okubo mass formula (see Chap. 6) for this representation that one has considerable confidence in this interpretation of the Ω^-. The identification of the $N^*(1238)$ quartet, the $Y_1^*(1385)$ triplet, the $\Xi^*(1430)$ doublet and the $\Omega^-(1585)$ singlet with the sites in the **10** weight diagram follows upon comparison of Figs. 2.2*a* and 3.3*b*. (The number in parentheses following a particle name is the mass, in MeV.) From 1 to 10 the states are N^{*++}, N^{*+}, N^{*0}, N^{*-}, Y_1^{*+}, Y_1^{*0}, Y_1^{*-}, Ξ^{*0}, Ξ^{*-}, and Ω^-. The reader may prefer the less cumbersome but equally arbitrary nomenclature described by Chew et al (12).

Extremely important theoretical support for the above picture arises from the natural way in which the existence of the $P_{3/2}$ decuplet can be understood in terms of a simple dynamical model. The elucidation of such connections between symmetries and dynamics is under active investigation at the moment. The general ideas of the dynamical approach are sketched in Chapter 7.

There are a large number of additional resonances, mainly of higher energy and higher spin than the "low-lying" states discussed above. There is also a $T = 0$ $\pi\Sigma$ resonance at 1405 MeV (apparently $S_{1/2}$) which can be (and according to dynamical calculations, should be) considered to be a unitary singlet. There is a $D_{3/2}$ state at 1520 MeV that may also be a unitary singlet. We shall defer discussion of the possible existence of other representations to subsequent chapters. We only mention here that there is substantial, though not unambiguous, evidence for a $D_{3/2}$ octet of meson–baryon resonances including the 1512-MeV πN maximum (see Glashow and Rosenfeld (13)).

3.5 The Reduction of 8 × 8

In this section we work out in detail the basis functions of the irreducible representations contained (14) in **8** × **8**. The result is of prime interest in applications and is sufficiently complicated to illuminate the general analysis of representations.

For clarity we label the first set by the baryon labels and the second by the pseudoscalar mesons. The sixty-four states $B_i P_j$ $(i,j = 1,\ldots,8)$ corresponding to the sets of Eq. (3.76) generate a reducible representation; the state of highest weight being $\Sigma^+\pi^+$. Adding the octet weight diagrams gives rise to Fig. 3.5; the degeneracy at a given site is indicated by the attached number. All the states belonging to the same representation as $\Sigma^+\pi^+$ can be obtained by applying $T_\pm$ and $V_\pm$ to $\Sigma^+\pi^+$ and all the states obtained thereby. (The use of $U_\pm$ along with its minus signs can be easily avoided.) Applying T_- to $\Sigma^+\pi^+$ generates a $T = 2$ quintet $(\Sigma\pi)_2$. The following conventions are adopted with respect to the isospin wave functions: the baryon is particle "number one" and stands on the left while the meson is particle two and stands on the right. The isospin T wave function formed from baryon and meson is written $(BP)_T$, where the T_3 value usually does not need to be specified. The sign convention is as

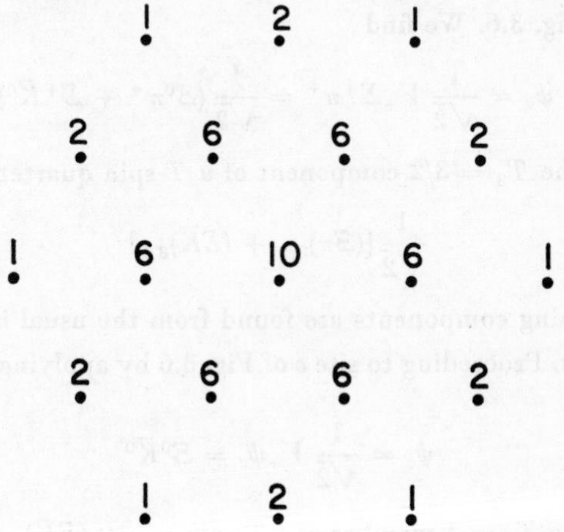

Fig. 3.5. Vector addition of the octet weight diagrams gives the degeneracies indicated. (The central site has $Y = T_3 = 0$.)

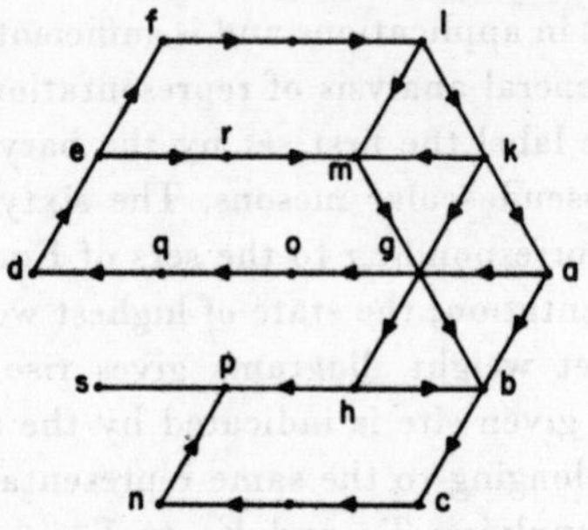

Fig. 3.6. This diagram shows the paths followed in separating the representation 27 from the 64-dimensional reducible representation 8 × 8. Site *a* is the (non-degenerate) state of highest weight.

follows: particle number one having the highest charge is always given a positive Clebsch-Gordan coefficient. For example, the $T_3 = 1/2$ state in the multiplet $(N\pi)_{1/2}$ is $(p\pi^0 - \sqrt{2}\, n\pi^+)/\sqrt{3}$, while that in $(\Sigma K)_{1/2}$ is $(\sqrt{2}\Sigma^+ K^0 - \Sigma^0 K^+)/\sqrt{3}$.

$\Sigma^+\pi^+$ is also the $V_3 = -1$ member of a V-spin triplet. Applying $V_+/\sqrt{2}$ to $\Sigma^+\pi^+ \equiv \psi_a$ then gives the normalized state ψ_b at site b of Fig. 3.6. We find

$$\psi_b = \frac{1}{\sqrt{2}} V_+ \Sigma^+\pi^+ = \frac{1}{\sqrt{2}} (\Xi^0\pi^+ + \Sigma^+\bar{K}^0) \tag{3.78}$$

which is the $T_3 = 3/2$ component of a T-spin quartet

$$\frac{1}{\sqrt{2}} [(\Xi\pi)_{3/2} + (\Sigma\bar{K})_{3/2}] \tag{3.79}$$

the remaining components are found from the usual isospin considerations. Proceeding to site c of Fig. 3.6 by applying $V_+/\sqrt{2}$ to ψ_b yields

$$\psi_c = \frac{1}{\sqrt{2}} V_+\psi_c = \Xi^0\bar{K}^0 \tag{3.80}$$

which is the $T_3 = 1$ member of a T-spin triplet $(\Xi\bar{K})_1$. Going now to site d, to which belongs the $V = 1$ state $\psi_d = \Sigma^-\pi^-$, we obtain a function ψ_e with $T_3 = -T = -3/2$

$$\psi_e = \frac{1}{\sqrt{2}} V_- \Sigma^- \pi^- = \frac{1}{\sqrt{2}} (n\pi^- + \Sigma^- K^0) \tag{3.81}$$

one member of the $T = 3/2$ quartet $[(N\pi)_{3/2} + (\Sigma K)_{3/2}]/\sqrt{2}$. Promoting ψ_e again by $V_-/\sqrt{2}$ yields

$$\psi_f = \frac{1}{\sqrt{2}} V_- \psi_e = nK^0 \tag{3.82}$$

and the associated triplet $(NK)_1$.

We next ask whether the other independent state at site b, $[(\Sigma\bar{K})_{3/2} - (\Xi\pi)_{3/2}]/\sqrt{2}$ (note sign convention), belongs to the same representation as ψ_b. To see that this is not the case we go from a to b along the paths agh and $aghb$. Neglecting normalization factors, along path agh we have

$$\begin{aligned}\phi_b \equiv U_- T_- \psi_a &= [U_-, T_-]\psi_a + T_- U_- \psi_a \\ &= -V_+ \psi_a + 0 \propto \psi_b\end{aligned} \tag{3.83}$$

Similarly, along path $aghb$ we end up with the function

$$\chi_b \equiv T_+ V_+ T_- \psi_a = T_+ T_- V_+ \psi_a \propto \psi_b \tag{3.84}$$

since T_- commutes with V_+ and ψ_b is an eigenfunction of $T_+ T_-$. A slight extension of this argument shows that no path can generate a function at b independent of ψ_b. Hence, by using the Weyl reflections, the boundary points e, k, and l of Fig. 3.6 have only one state belonging to the same irreducible representation as ψ_a. This result can be generalized; the boundary of the weight diagram of an irreducible representation is nondegenerate.

Thus any more functions belonging to ψ_a's representation must lie within the boundary. We start at point k, where $\psi_k = (p\pi^+ + \Sigma^+ K^+)/\sqrt{2}$ has $V_3 = -V = -3/2$, and create a state at site g:

$$\begin{aligned}\psi_g' = \frac{1}{\sqrt{3}} V_+ \psi_k = \frac{1}{\sqrt{6}} \Big[p\bar{K}^0 + \Xi^0 K^+ &+ \frac{1}{\sqrt{2}} (\Sigma^+ \pi^0 + \Sigma^0 \pi^+) \\ &+ \sqrt{\tfrac{3}{2}} (\Lambda^0 \pi^+ + \Sigma^+ \eta) \Big]\end{aligned} \tag{3.85}$$

This function is independent of, but not orthogonal to, the $T_3 = 1$ member of the $(\Sigma\pi)_2$ multiplet. Orthogonalization gives

$$\phi_g = \frac{1}{\sqrt{10}}[\sqrt{2}(p\bar{K}^0 + \Xi^0 K^+) + \sqrt{3}(\Lambda\pi^+ + \Sigma^+\eta)] \quad (3.86)$$

a $T = T_3 = 1$ function. By reflection symmetry, the route bg will not give a function at g independent of ψ_g and ϕ_g. Nor is the route lmg independent of lkg, because $V_+U_- = U_-V_+$. Furthermore, the route kmg is equal to a combination of kg and kag, since $T_-U_- = V_+ + U_-T_-$.

As these results are general, we state them graphically in terms of the parallelograms of Fig. 3.7. Consider going from points 1 to 2 in (*a*) and (*b*). In case (*a*) we have 120° turns; the operator products corresponding to paths A and B are T_-V_+ and V_+T_-, respectively. Clearly, we can rotate the figure by 120° and 240° and obtain the same result. If, however, we turn by 240° as in Fig. 3.7*b*, the paths A and B do not yield the same result. Path A involves U_-T_- while B stands for T_-U_-. Since $[T_-,U_-] = V_+$, we see that

$$\text{path } A + \text{path } (12) = \text{path } B \quad (3.87)$$

(The latter results apply also for parallelograms rotated by 120° and 240°.) The $T = 1$ multiplet associated with ϕ_g is

$$\frac{1}{\sqrt{10}}\{\sqrt{2}[(N\bar{K})_1 + (\Xi K)_1] + \sqrt{3}[(\Lambda\pi)_1 + (\Sigma\eta)_1]\} \quad (3.88)$$

Fig. 3.7. Sites 1, 2, *A*, and *B* are occupied sites in a weight diagram. Going from 1 to 2 (using the appropriate operators) through *A* or *B* gives the same result for paths of type (*a*) and a different result for paths of type (*b*).

Next we apply V_+ to the state pK^+ at site l. Since pK^+ is the $V_3 = -2$ member of a V-spin quintet we find

$$\psi_m = \tfrac{1}{2}V_+(pK^+) = \frac{1}{2\sqrt{2}}[p\pi^0 + \sqrt{3}p\eta + \Sigma^0K^+ + \sqrt{3}\Lambda K^+] \tag{3.89}$$

This state does not have a definite T-spin. We find a $T = T_3 = 1/2$ state by removing from ψ_m its projection onto the $T_3 = 1/2$ member of the $T = 3/2$ state at site m, $[(N\pi)_{3/2} + (\Sigma K)_{3/2}]/\sqrt{2}$. The result is the doublet

$$\frac{1}{\sqrt{20}}[3(N\eta) + 3(\Lambda K) + (N\pi)_{1/2} + (\Sigma K)_{1/2}] \tag{3.90}$$

Similarly proceeding from n to o or from g to h by $V_\pm$ and orthogonalizing to the $Y = -1$, $T = 3/2$ multiplet (3.79) we obtain a $T = 1/2$, $Y = -1$ doublet

$$\frac{1}{\sqrt{20}}[3(\Lambda\bar{K}) + 3(\Xi\eta) - (\Xi\pi)_{1/2} - (\Sigma\bar{K})_{1/2}] \tag{3.91}$$

It is now clear that the inner octagon (sites *mghpqr*) of Fig. 3.6 is doubly degenerate with states attached to the state of highest weight. We now have to find out what states belong to this representation at the origin O of the weight diagram. There is only one more, obtained by going from the $V_3 = -1$ state (3.89) to the origin. The result of applying V_+ to (3.89) is a superposition of $T = 0$, 1, and 2 components. Extracting the $T = 1$ and 2 parts already found gives the $Y = 0$ isosinglet

$$\sqrt{\tfrac{3}{20}}\left[(N\bar{K})_0 + (\Xi K)_0 + \frac{3}{\sqrt{2}}(\Lambda\eta)_0 - \frac{1}{\sqrt{6}}(\Sigma\pi)_0\right] \tag{3.92}$$

By reflection symmetry, no other approach to the origin gives anything new.

We summarize the wave functions of the 27-dimensional irreducible representation $D(2,2)$ in Table 3.4. The degeneracy of the weight diagram of **27** is shown in Fig. 3.8.

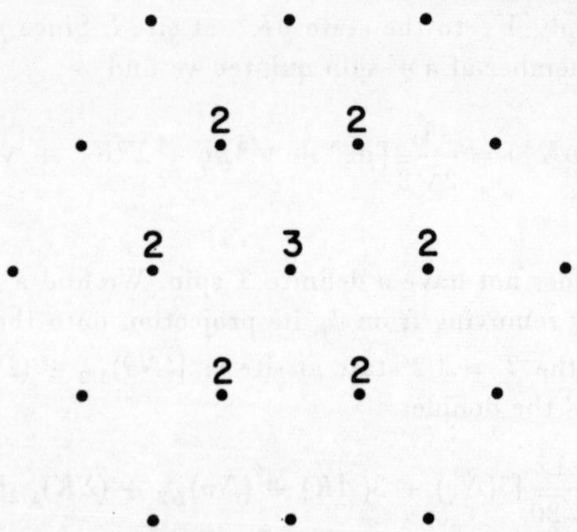

Fig. 3.8. The degeneracy of the weight diagram for the irreducible representation 27 is shown.

Removing the number of independent states of the representation 27 of Fig. 3.8 from those of Fig. 3.5 reveals that the remaining state of highest weight occurs at site k of Fig. 3.6. Orthogonalizing to the member of 27 at k, $(pK^+ + \Sigma^+K^+)/\sqrt{2}$, gives the state $(\Sigma^+K^+ - pK^+)/\sqrt{2}$, the topmost member of the $T = 3/2$ quartet

$$[(\Sigma K)_{3/2} - (NK)_{3/2}]/\sqrt{2} \tag{3.93}$$

Going from site k to site g gives the $T_3 = 1$ member of the T-spin triplet

$$\frac{1}{\sqrt{12}}[\sqrt{2}(\Xi^\circ K)_1 - \sqrt{2}(N\bar{K})_1 + \sqrt{3}(\Sigma\eta)_1 - \sqrt{3}(\Lambda\pi)_1 + \sqrt{2}(\Sigma\pi)_1] \tag{3.94}$$

Continuing in the V_+ direction gives a T-spin doublet and a T-spin singlet

$$\frac{1}{\sqrt{12}}[\sqrt{3}(\Sigma K)_{1/2} + \sqrt{3}(\Xi\pi)_{1/2} + \sqrt{3}(\Xi\eta)_{1/2} - \sqrt{3}(\Lambda K)] \tag{3.95}$$

$$(\Xi\bar{K})_0 \tag{3.96}$$

The ten independent states contained in the multiplets (3.93)–

(3.96) form a basis for the representation **10.** As seen in Section 3.2, the weights of this representation are nondegenerate. [This result actually obtains for all triangular representations; the latter are of the form $D(n,0)$ or $D(0,n)$. The state of highest weight also has highest hypercharge. The top boundary is flat and reflection invariance implies a triangular shape. The nondegeneracy follows from the observation that only one completely symmetrical function can be formed from n ξ's at each site, the generators being permutation operators working inward from the state of highest weight.] One can make sure that the state at site b does not belong to the above representation by using the rules of Fig. 3.7. The path kab, which gives zero, is equivalent to kgb. Thus b can't be reached from k through g. Further considerations of the same nature show that no path leads from k to b.

Having removed **27** and **10** from **8** × **8**, we remove the representation attached to the state of next highest weight, at site b. Again one obtains ten functions, belonging to the representation **10*** [or $D(0,3)$], whose weight diagram is obtained from that of **10** by reflection in the origin. As the calculation is essentially the same as for **10**, we omit the details and give the result in Table 3.4.

Removal of the states of **27**, **10**, and **10*** from the weight diagram of Fig. 3.5 leaves us with Fig. 3.9. The latter clearly

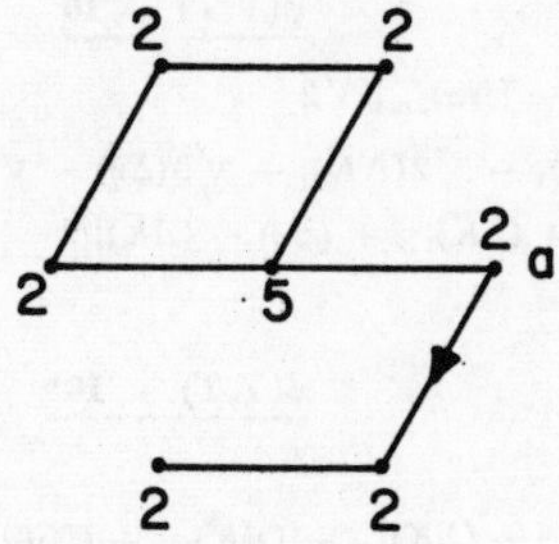

Fig. 3.9. After the representations **27**, **10**, and **10*** have been removed from **8** × **8**, the residual independent functions have the weights shown (with degeneracy indicated). The lines indicate the paths followed in rearranging these functions to form two 8-dimensional and one 1-dimensional irreducible representation.

indicates that two octets and a singlet remain. We therefore have obtained the reduction

$$8 \times 8 = 27 + 10 + 10^* + 8_1 + 8_2 + 1 \qquad (3.97)$$

where the indices 1 and 2 label the two independent eight-dimensional representations, whose $SU(3)$ transformation properties are identical.

TABLE 3.4

Wave Functions of the Irreducible Representations Contained in 8 × 8 in Terms of Isospin-Hypercharge Components.

Y	T	ψ
		$\psi(Y,T)$ **27**
2	1	$(NK)_1$
1	3/2	$[(N\pi)_{3/2} + (\Sigma K)_{3/2}]/\sqrt{2}$
1	1/2	$[3(N\eta) + (\Lambda K) + (N\pi)_{1/2} - (\Sigma K)_{1/2}]/\sqrt{20}$
0	2	$(\Sigma\pi)_2$
0	1	$[\sqrt{2}(N\bar{K})_1 + \sqrt{2}(\Xi K)_1 + \sqrt{3}(\Lambda\pi) + \sqrt{3}(\Sigma\eta)]/\sqrt{10}$
0	0	$[\sqrt{6}(N\bar{K})_0 - \sqrt{6}(\Xi K)_0 + 3\sqrt{3}(\Lambda\eta) - (\Sigma\pi)_0]/\sqrt{40}$
−1	3/2	$[(\Xi\pi)_{3/2} + (\Sigma\bar{K})_{3/2}]/\sqrt{2}$
−1	1/2	$[3(\Lambda\bar{K}) + 3(\Xi\eta) - (\Xi\pi)_{1/2} + (\Sigma\bar{K})_{1/2}]/\sqrt{20}$
−2	1	$(\Xi\bar{K})_1$
		$\psi(Y,T)$ **10**
1	3/2	$[(\Sigma K)_{3/2} - (N\pi)_{3/2}]/\sqrt{2}$
0	1	$[\sqrt{2}(\Xi K)_1 - \sqrt{2}(N\bar{K})_1 + \sqrt{3}(\Sigma\eta) - \sqrt{3}(\Lambda\pi) + \sqrt{2}(\Sigma\pi)_1]/\sqrt{12}$
−1	1/2	$[(\Xi\pi)_{1/2} + (\Sigma\bar{K})_{1/2} + (\Xi\eta) - (\Lambda\bar{K})]/2$
−2	0	$(\Xi\bar{K})_0$
		$\psi(Y,T)$ **10***
2	0	$-(NK)_0$
1	1/2	$[-(N\pi)_{1/2} - (\Sigma K)_{1/2} - (\Lambda K)_{1/2} + (N\eta)]/\sqrt{2}$
0	1	$[\sqrt{2}(N\bar{K})_1 - \sqrt{2}(\Sigma\pi)_1 - \sqrt{2}(\Xi K)_1 + \sqrt{3}(\Sigma\eta) - \sqrt{3}(\Lambda\pi)]/\sqrt{12}$
−1	3/2	$[(\Sigma\bar{K})_{3/2} - (\Xi\pi)_{3/2}]/\sqrt{2}$

(continued)

TABLE 3.4—*cont.*

Y	T	ψ
		$\psi(Y,T)$ $\mathbf{8}_1$
1	1/2	$[-3(\Sigma K)_{1/2}+3(N\pi)_{1/2}-(N\eta)-(\Lambda K)]/2\sqrt{5}$
0	1	$[\sqrt{2}(\Sigma\eta)+\sqrt{2}(\Lambda\pi)-\sqrt{3}(\Xi K)_1-\sqrt{3}(NK)_1]/\sqrt{10}$
0	0	$[-\sqrt{6}(\Sigma\pi)_0+(N\bar{K})_0-(\Xi K)_0-\sqrt{2}(\Lambda\eta)]/\sqrt{10}$
−1	1/2	$[3(\Sigma\bar{K})_{1/2}-(\Xi\eta)-3(\Xi\pi)_{1/2}-(\Lambda\bar{K})]/2\sqrt{5}$
		$\psi(Y,T)$ $\mathbf{8}_2$
1	1/2	$[(\Sigma K)_{1/2}+(N\pi)_{1/2}+(N\eta)-(\Lambda K)]/2$
0	1	$[2(\Sigma\pi)_1+(N\bar{K})_1-(\Xi K)_1]/\sqrt{6}$
0	0	$[(N\bar{K})_0+(\Xi K)_0]/\sqrt{2}$
−1	1/2	$[(\Sigma\bar{K})_{1/2}+(\Xi\pi)_{1/2}+(\Lambda\bar{K})-(\Xi\eta)]/2$
		$Y=T=0$ $\mathbf{1}$
		$\psi=1/4[2(N\bar{K})_0-(\Xi K)_0+\sqrt{6}(\Sigma\pi)_0-2(\Lambda\eta)]$

To obtain the wave functions of the two octets we begin once more at the site of highest weight, here labeled a in Fig. 3.9. From the six independent states $\Sigma^+\pi^0, \Sigma^0\pi^+, p\bar{K}^0, \Xi^0\Sigma^+, \Sigma^+\eta$, and $\Lambda\pi^+$ belonging to this site, we form two orthogonal states also orthogonal to the four $Y=0$, $T_3=1$ states belonging to 27, 10, and 10*. Expressing the latter in terms of symmetric and antisymmetric combinations [here $S(x,y)$ means $x+y$ and $A(x,y)$ means $x-y$)]

$$\psi(\mathbf{27}, T=2)=S(\Sigma^+\pi^0,\Sigma^0\pi^+)/\sqrt{2}$$

$$\psi(\mathbf{27}, T=1)=[\sqrt{2}S(p\bar{K}^0,\Xi^0K^+)+\sqrt{3}S(\Sigma^+\eta,\Lambda\pi^+)]/\sqrt{10}$$

$$\psi(\mathbf{10}, T=1)=[-\sqrt{2}A(p\bar{K}^0,\Xi^0K^+)+\sqrt{3}A(\Sigma^+\eta,\Lambda\pi^+)+A(\Sigma^+\pi^0,\Sigma^0\pi^+)]/\sqrt{10} \quad (3.98)$$

$$\psi(\mathbf{10^*}, T=1)=[\sqrt{2}A(p\bar{K}^0,\Xi^0K^+)+\sqrt{3}A(\Sigma^+\eta,\Lambda\pi^+)-A(\Sigma^+\pi^0,\Sigma^0\pi^+)]/\sqrt{10}$$

we see immediately that the appropriate functions are proportional to $\sqrt{2}S(\Sigma^+\eta,\Lambda\pi^+) - \sqrt{3}S(\Xi^0K^+,p\bar{K}^0)$ and $\sqrt{2}A(\Sigma^+\pi^0,\Sigma^0\pi^+) + A(p\bar{K}^0,\Xi^0K^+)$. The two octets then have states of highest weight

$$\begin{aligned} \psi_{8_1}{}^H &= [\sqrt{2}(\Sigma^+\eta + \Lambda\pi^+) - \sqrt{3}(\Xi^0K^+ + p\bar{K}^0)]/\sqrt{10} \\ \psi_{8_2}{}^H &= [\sqrt{2}(\Sigma^+\pi^0 - \Sigma^0\pi^+) + (p\bar{K}^0 - \Xi^0K^+)]/\sqrt{6} \end{aligned} \tag{3.99}$$

and corresponding $Y = 0$, T-spin triplets

$$\begin{aligned} \psi_{8_1}(T = 1) &= [\sqrt{2}(\Sigma\eta)_1 + \sqrt{2}(\Lambda\pi)_1 - \sqrt{3}(\Xi K)_1 \\ &\qquad - \sqrt{3}(N\bar{K})_1]/\sqrt{10} \\ \psi_{8_2}(T = 1) &= [2(\Sigma\pi)_1 + (N\bar{K})_1 - (\Xi K)_1]/\sqrt{6} \end{aligned} \tag{3.100}$$

Proceeding in a now overly familiar manner along the directions indicated in Fig. 3.9 we obtain the wave functions for 8_1 and 8_2 given in Table 3.4.

Now only one state remains, the unitary singlet $Y = T = 0$ state. It must be a linear combination of $(\Sigma\pi)_0$, $(N\bar{K})_0$, $(\Lambda\eta)$, and $(\Xi K)_0$ orthogonal to the three other states of the same weight having $T = Y = 0$. A brief, tedious calculation gives

$$\psi(0,0) = \tfrac{1}{4}[2(N\bar{K})_0 - 2(\Xi K)_0 + \sqrt{6}(\Sigma\pi)_0 - \sqrt{2}\Lambda\eta] \tag{3.101}$$

All these results are collected in Table 3.4.

In Section 2.6 we showed how to construct two independent octets (transforming via the Hermitian generators F_i) from two octets A_a and B_b. These functions ($f_{abc}A_bB_c$ and $d_{abc}A_bB_c$) transform in the same way under $SU(3)$ transformations, but have different symmetry under the exchange $A \leftrightarrow B$. The present analysis proves that there are no more ways to construct octets out of two octets.

The irreducible representations obtained in the reduction of $\mathbf{8} \times \mathbf{8}$ have a further useful symmetry which we now discuss in detail. We define the R-transformation by the following substitutions of *states*:

$$\begin{array}{llll} p \leftrightarrow \Xi^-, & n \leftrightarrow \Xi^0, & \Lambda \leftrightarrow \Lambda, & \Sigma^0 \leftrightarrow \Sigma^0 \\ K^+ \leftrightarrow K^-, & K^0 \leftrightarrow \bar{K}^0, & \eta \leftrightarrow \eta, & \pi^0 \leftrightarrow \pi^0 \end{array} \tag{3.102}$$

Thus in this example R is essentially the operation of inversion in the octet weight diagram. (More generally, it is *defined* as such an inversion.) The operation (3.102) can be used to distinguish the representations $\mathbf{8}_1$ and $\mathbf{8}_2$. Explicitly we have the following simple result

$$\begin{aligned} R\psi_{27}(Y,T,T_3) &= \psi_{27}(-Y,T,-T_3) \\ R\psi_{10}(Y,T,T_3) &= \psi_{10}{}^*(-Y,T,-T_3) \\ R\psi_{8_1}(Y,T,T_3) &= \psi_{8_1}(-Y,T,-T_3) \\ R\psi_{8_2}(Y,T,T_3) &= -\psi_{8_2}(-Y,T,-T_3) \\ R\psi_1(0,0,0) &= \psi_1(0,0,0) \end{aligned} \tag{3.103}$$

Thus when we apply R to a component of an irreducible representation contained in $\mathbf{8} \times \mathbf{8}$ we obtain a wave function with inverted weight. Notice that R interchanges **10** and **10***. For the self-conjugate representations $D(2,2)$, $D(1,1)$, and $D(0,0)$ (**27**, $\mathbf{8}_1$, and $\mathbf{8}_2$, and **1**) the state at the center of the weight diagram is an eigenfunction of R. The eigenvalue is 1 for **27**, $\mathbf{8}_1$, and **1** but -1 for $\mathbf{8}_2$. In this way we can use the R transformation, which lies outside the group $SU(3)$, to distinguish among representations which are otherwise equivalent.

Even though R does not belong to the group, one can ask whether the strong interactions are invariant under R. There are many indications that this is not the case. For instance, transitions of the type $8_1 \to 8_2$ in PB elastic scattering would be forbidden if R were conserved. However it is possible that in meson processes the R-violating baryons are sufficiently unimportant that a limited R symmetry is valid. This possibility has been discussed by Bronzan and Low (15).

References

1. S. Gasiorowicz, *Argonne National Laboratory Report ANL-6729* (1963), unpublished.
2. J. J. de Swart, *Rev. Mod. Phys.*, **35**, 916 (1963).
3. R. Behrends, C. Fronsdal, J. Dreitlein, and B. W. Lee, *Rev. Mod. Phys.*, **34**, 1 (1962).
4. P. Tarjanne, *Carnegie Institute of Technology Report NYO9290, 9290A*.
5. A. R. Edmonds, *Proc. Roy. Soc.* (*London*), **A268**, 567 (1962).
6. M. A. Rashid, *Nuovo Cimento*, **26**, 118 (1962).
7. M. Hamermesh, *Group Theory*, Addison-Wesley, Reading, Mass., 1962, Chap. 10.
8. A. Klein, *J. Math. Phys.*, **4**, 1283 (1963).
9. G. E. Baird and L. C. Biedenharn, *J. Math. Phys.*, **4**, 1449 (1963); **5**, 1723 (1964).
10. M. Gell-Mann, *Phys. Letters*, **8**, 214 (1964).
11. G. Zweig, *CERN Rept. Th. 401 and Th. 412* (1964).
12. G. F. Chew, M. Gell-Mann, and A. H. Rosenfeld, *Sci. Am.*, **210** (No. 2), 74 (1964).
13. S. L. Glashow and A. H. Rosenfeld, *Phys. Rev. Letters*, **10**, 192 (1963).
14. S. L. Glashow and J. J. Sakurai, *Nuovo Cimento*, **25**, 337 (1962).
15. J. B. Bronzan and F. E. Low, *Phys. Rev. Letters*, **12**, 522 (1964).

Chapter 4

General Properties of Representations of $SU(3)$

4.1 Introduction

The previous chapter was concerned with the explicit and detailed discussion of those low-dimensional representations of special physical interest. Although more extensive results are not often necessary in physical applications, some readers will wish to obtain a deeper understanding of the properties of the group. To obtain a panoramic view of the representations of $SU(3)$ (here one might as well study $SU(n)$ in general) there is no substitute for the use of the symmetric group and its calculus of Young diagrams. The symmetry properties of various specific representations were noted in Chapter 3. We shall summarize a few of the most useful methods and results obtained by this technique in Section 4.6. The reader is directed to Weyl's *Classical Groups* (1) for an extensive development of the subject, although it may be easier to begin with Chapter 10 of Hamermesh's book on *Group Theory* (2). A series of papers by Baird and Biedenharn (3, 4) develops the theory of representations of $SU(n)$ in the "explicit manner preferred by physicists." Further references will be given in Section 4.3.

Other topics we shall not describe in full generality concern the form and multiplicity of the eigenvalue lattices corresponding to the various representations of $SU(3)$. However, much can be said from our previous analysis. First of all, the Weyl reflection invariance (Chap. 2) shows that the weight diagram has to be invariant under 120° rotations. Our analysis of the reduction of

8×8 also shows generally that the boundary is nondegenerate and convex. We also learned that for fixed Y, as one proceeds in from the boundary one generally encounters a new independent function for each step inwards, corresponding to a sequence of isospin states of eigenvalue $T, T-1, T-2, \ldots$. Analogous remarks holds for the U- and V-spin directions except that if one writes the independent functions at a site in terms of the subgroup $SU(2)_T \times U(1)_Y$ then these functions are linear combinations of the U- or V-spin eigenfunctions. This detail does not affect the counting of independent states. Thus, as one proceeds inwards from the boundary along any of the lattice translation (root) vectors the degeneracy of the site increases by one. What we shall not prove is that the process terminates after the last layer assumes a triangular shape. The eigenvalue lattice may be viewed as a truncated pyramid, the top of which is a triangle. Consider the weight diagram of the representation $D(p,q)$. The state of highest weight has $Y = (p-q)/3$ and $T = (p+q)/2$. It is easily seen that one can take q steps in the U_+ direction and p steps in the V_+ direction (the state of highest weight belongs to a U-spin multiplet of dimension $q+1$ and a V-spin multiplet of dimension $p+1$). This is illustrated in Fig. 4.1 for the special

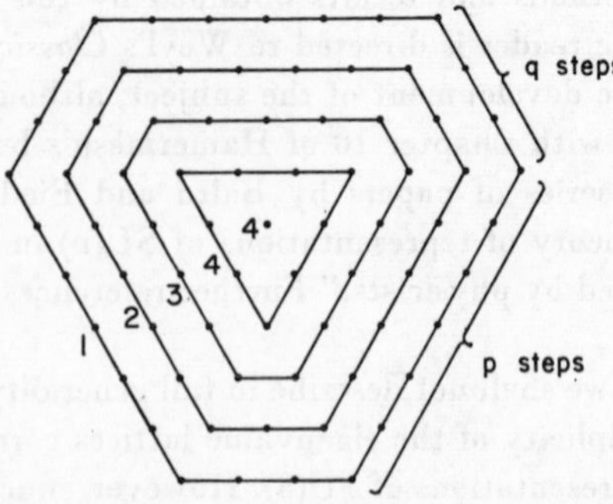

Fig. 4.1. The degeneracy of the sites for the representation $D(6,3)$ is shown to illustrate the rule that the degeneracy increases by one as one follows contour lines inward until a triangular contour is reached.

case $p = 6$, $q = 3$. Given this fact it is easy to compute the dimensionality $d(p,q)$ of the irreducible representation

$$d(p,q) = \tfrac{1}{2}(p + 1)(q + 1)(p + q + 2) \tag{4.1}$$

Later we shall prove this formula using tensor methods. For a detailed description of the structure of eigenvalue lattices the reader is referred to Gasiorowicz (5), Cutkosky (6) and Behrends et al. (7).

In order to give a unique matrix representation of an irreducible representation one has to make a fairly elaborate set of phase conventions. These have been described in Section 3.5. In brief, we agree to use the eigenvalues (T, T_3, Y) of the isospin-hypercharge subgroup to label the basis functions. The Condon-Shortley phase convention is enforced for the T- and V-spin operators. Biedenharn (4, 8) and Racah (9) have given explicitly the effect of applying V_- to a given state $\phi(T, T_3, Y)$ belonging to $D(p,q)$

$$\begin{aligned} V_-\phi(T,T_3,Y) = a_+\phi(T + \tfrac{1}{2}, T_3 + \tfrac{1}{2}, Y + 1) \\ + a_-\phi(T - \tfrac{1}{2}, T_3 + \tfrac{1}{2}, Y + 1), \end{aligned} \tag{4.2}$$

$$a_+ = \left\{\frac{(T + T_3 + 1)[\frac{1}{3}(p - q) + T + \frac{1}{2}Y + 1] \times [\frac{1}{3}(p + 2q) + T + \frac{1}{2}Y + 2][\frac{1}{3}(2p + q) - T - \frac{1}{2}Y]}{2(T + 1)(2T + 1)}\right\}^{1/2}$$

$$a_- = \left\{\frac{(T - T_3)[\frac{1}{3}(q - p) + T - \frac{1}{2}Y] \times [\frac{1}{3}(p + 2q) - T + \frac{1}{2}Y + 1][\frac{1}{3}(2p + q) + T - \frac{1}{2}Y + 1]}{2T(2T + 1)}\right\}^{1/2}$$

Along with the commutation rules and the usual matrix elements of the $T_\pm$ operators, this result completely defines the representation matrices.

4.2 *SU*(3) Clebsch-Gordan Coefficients

In this section we describe the properties of the $SU(3)$ Clebsch-Gordan coefficients, following closely the review of de Swart (10).

Special cases have already been given in Chapter 3. Suppose we have two irreducible representations $D(p_1,q_1)$ and $D(p_2,q_2)$ generated by the sets of basis functions $\phi_{\nu_1}{}^{(\mu_1)}$ and $\phi_{\nu_2}{}^{(\mu_2)}$, respectively. Here the labels μ_j specify the representation and ν_j the particular basis function within the representation. Thus ν includes the quantum numbers T, T_3, Y, while μ stands for the values of the two Casimir operators C_2 and C_3, or equivalently the pair (p,q). The dimensions of the representations are denoted by d_1 and d_2 [cf. Eq. (4.1)]. The product $\phi_{\nu_1}{}^{(\mu_1)}\phi_{\nu_2}{}^{(\mu_2)}$ generates a reducible (except in the trivial case in which one of the representations is the trivial one) representation. In the usual way one splits the (d_1d_2)-dimensional space spanned by $\phi_{\nu_1}{}^{(\mu_1)}\phi_{\nu_2}{}^{(\mu_2)}$ into irreducible invariant subspaces by forming suitable linear combinations:

$$\Phi(\mu\gamma\nu;\mu_1\mu_2) = \sum_{\nu_1\nu_2} \begin{pmatrix} \mu_1 & \mu_2 & \mu_\gamma \\ \nu_1 & \nu_2 & \nu \end{pmatrix} \phi_{\nu_1}{}^{(\mu_1)}\phi_{\nu_2}{}^{(\mu_2)} \tag{4.3}$$

Here μ describes the irreducible representation thus obtained and ν the composite quantum numbers (T, T_3, Y). The label γ distinguishes independent but $SU(3)$-equivalent representations; for example, in reducing $\mathbf{8} \times \mathbf{8}$ we found two eight-dimensional representations which could be distinguished by their symmetry properties [cf. Eq. (3.103) or Sec. 2.6]. Hence, in the Clebsch-Gordan series for $SU(3)$,

$$D(p_1,q_1) \times D(p_2,q_2) = \sum_{P,Q} n(P,Q) D(P,Q), \tag{4.4}$$

the positive (or zero) integers $n(P,Q)$ can be greater than unity, in contrast to the well-known vector-addition rule for $SU(2)$.

The analysis of the preceding chapter suggests that we may express the set Φ usefully in terms of a sum of various isospin wave functions. Clearly we can proceed in two steps. For given values of the additive quantum numbers $T_z = T_{1z} + T_{2z}$ and $Y = Y_1 + Y_2$ we first construct eigenfunctions of $T(\mathbf{T} = \mathbf{T}_1 + \mathbf{T}_2)$ using the usual $SU(2)$ Clebsch-Gordan coefficients [the notation of Rose (11) is used]:

$$\chi\begin{pmatrix} \mu_1 & \mu_2 \\ T_1Y_1 & T_2Y_2 \end{pmatrix}; TT_zY\Big) = \sum_{T_{1z}T_{2z}} C(T_1T_2T;T_{1z}T_{2z}T_{3z})\phi_{\nu_1}{}^{(\mu_1)}\phi_{\nu_2}{}^{(\mu_2)} \tag{4.5}$$

Then we superpose the various $\chi[\nu = (T, T_z, Y)$ fixed] to obtain eigenfunctions of C_2, C_3:

$$\Phi(\mu\gamma\nu;\mu_1\mu_2) = \sum_{\substack{T_1Y_1\\T_2Y_2}} \left(\begin{matrix} \mu_1 & \mu_2 \\ T_1Y_1 & T_2Y_2 \end{matrix}\middle| \begin{matrix} \mu\gamma \\ TY \end{matrix}\right) \chi\begin{pmatrix} \mu_1 & \mu_2 \\ T_1Y_1 & T_2Y_2 \end{pmatrix}; TT_zY\Big) \tag{4.6}$$

In practice, the *isoscalar factors* (12)

$$\left(\begin{matrix} \mu_1 & \mu_2 \\ T_1Y_1 & T_2Y_2 \end{matrix}\middle| \begin{matrix} \mu\gamma \\ TY \end{matrix}\right) \tag{4.7}$$

(so named because they are independent of the azimuthal quantum numbers) are found by starting from the unique state of highest weight, for which (4.7) is defined to be +1, and applying the raising and lowering operators as described in Chapter 3. The coefficients of the isospin wave functions in Table 3.4 are the isoscalar factors for the reduction **8** × **8**. We have thus found that the $SU(3)$ Clebsch-Gordan coefficients factor as follows:

$$\begin{pmatrix} \mu_1 & \mu_2 & \mu_\gamma \\ \nu_1 & \nu_2 & \nu \end{pmatrix} = C(T_1T_2T;T_{1z}T_{2z}T_z)\left(\begin{matrix} \mu_1 & \mu_2 \\ T_1Y_1 & T_2Y_2 \end{matrix}\middle| \begin{matrix} \mu_\gamma \\ TY \end{matrix}\right) \tag{4.8}$$

As the $SU(2)$ Clebsch-Gordan coefficients are widely available, we can devote our attention to the isoscalar factors. First we note that they can be chosen real, since the matrices $T_\pm$, $V_\pm$, $U_\pm$ are real (of course the $SU(2)$ Clebsch-Gordan coefficients are real).

If we suppose that the functions appearing in Eq. (4.3) are orthonormal (in particular the independent functions distinguished by the label γ should be orthogonal), then the $SU(3)$ Clebsch-Gordan coefficients form a real orthogonal matrix (unitarity and reality). Thus we can invert (4.3) simply by writing

$$\phi_{\nu_1}{}^{(\mu_1)}\phi_{\nu_2}{}^{(\mu_2)} = \sum_{\mu\gamma\nu} \begin{pmatrix} \mu_1 & \mu_2 & \mu_\gamma \\ \nu_1 & \nu_2 & \nu \end{pmatrix} \Phi(\mu\gamma\nu;\mu_1\mu_2) \tag{4.9}$$

Here we have made use of the orthogonality relations:

$$\sum_{\nu_1\nu_2}\begin{pmatrix}\mu_1 & \mu_2 & \mu_\gamma \\ \nu_1 & \nu_2 & \nu\end{pmatrix}\begin{pmatrix}\mu_1 & \mu_2 & \mu'_{\gamma'} \\ \nu_1 & \nu_2 & \nu'\end{pmatrix} = \delta_{\mu\mu'}\delta_{\gamma\gamma'}\delta_{\nu\nu'} \tag{4.10}$$

$$\sum_{\mu\gamma\nu}\begin{pmatrix}\mu_1 & \mu_2 & \mu_\gamma \\ \nu_1 & \nu_2 & \nu\end{pmatrix}\begin{pmatrix}\mu_1 & \mu_2 & \mu_\gamma \\ \nu_1' & \nu_2' & \nu\end{pmatrix} = \delta_{\nu_1\nu_1'}\delta_{\nu_2\nu_2'} \tag{4.11}$$

Because of the similar relations for the $SU(2)$ Clebsch-Gordan coefficients (11) these equations can be simplified to the following orthogonality relations among the isoscalar factors:

$$\sum_{T_1T_2\,Y_1Y_2}\left(\begin{matrix}\mu_1 & \mu_2 \\ T_1Y_1 & T_2Y_2\end{matrix}\middle|\begin{matrix}\mu_\gamma \\ TY\end{matrix}\right)\left(\begin{matrix}\mu_1 & \mu_2 \\ T_1Y_1 & T_2Y_2\end{matrix}\middle|\begin{matrix}\mu'_{\gamma'} \\ TY'\end{matrix}\right) = \delta_{\mu\mu'}\delta_{\gamma\gamma'}\delta_{YY'} \tag{4.12}$$

$$\sum_{\mu\nu Y}\left(\begin{matrix}\mu_1 & \mu_2 \\ T_1Y_1 & T_2Y_2\end{matrix}\middle|\begin{matrix}\mu_\gamma \\ TY\end{matrix}\right)\left(\begin{matrix}\mu_1 & \mu_2 \\ T_1'Y_1' & T_2'Y_2'\end{matrix}\middle|\begin{matrix}\mu_\gamma \\ TY\end{matrix}\right) = \delta_{T_1T_1'}\delta_{T_2T_2'}\delta_{Y_1Y_1'}\delta_{Y_2Y_2'} \tag{4.13}$$

4.3 Orthogonality Properties of the Representation Matrices

Consider the d_μ basis functions $|\phi_\nu^{(\mu)}\rangle$ of the irreducible representation μ. To be definite, we consider the functions $|\phi_\nu^{(\mu)}\rangle$ to be quantum-mechanical *state vectors* and define the representation matrices by analogy to Eq. (1.83).

$$|\phi'_\nu{}^{(\mu)}\rangle = \mathcal{O}(\boldsymbol{\alpha})\,|\phi_\nu^{(\mu)}\rangle = \sum_\lambda |\phi_\lambda^{(\mu)}\rangle\, D_{\lambda\nu}^{(\mu)}(\boldsymbol{\alpha}) \tag{4.14}$$

By virtue of the compactness of $SU(3)$ the matrices $D^{(\mu)}(\boldsymbol{\alpha})$ induced by the unitary operator $\mathcal{O}(\boldsymbol{\alpha})$ may always be taken as unitary and finite-dimensional. As in Chapter 1, we may introduce a *field operator* $\phi_\nu^{(\mu)}$ whose adjoint creates the state vector $|\phi_\nu^{(\mu)}\rangle$. Thus $\phi_\nu^{(\mu)\dagger}$ transforms as

$$\mathcal{O}(\boldsymbol{\alpha})\phi_\nu^{(\mu)\dagger}\mathcal{O}^{-1}(\boldsymbol{\alpha}) = \sum_\lambda \phi_\lambda^{(\mu)\dagger} D_{\lambda\nu}^{(\mu)}(\boldsymbol{\alpha}) \tag{4.15}$$

that is, the column vector $\boldsymbol{\phi}^{(\mu)}$, composed of the $\phi_\nu^{(\mu)}$, transforms as

$$\boldsymbol{\phi}^{(\mu)} \to \boldsymbol{\phi}^{(\mu)'} = [D^{(\mu)}(\boldsymbol{\alpha})]^{-1}\boldsymbol{\phi}^{(\mu)} \tag{4.16}$$

If we write $\mathcal{O}(\boldsymbol{\alpha})$ in the form $\exp(i\boldsymbol{\alpha}\cdot\mathbf{G})$, where $\mathbf{G}$ is the Hermitian unitary spin operator, then the matrix $D^{(\mu)}$ is given by

$$D_{\lambda\nu}^{(\mu)}(\boldsymbol{\alpha}) = \langle\phi_\lambda^{(\mu)}|\exp(i\boldsymbol{\alpha}\cdot\mathbf{G})|\phi_\nu^{(\mu)}\rangle \tag{4.17}$$

This result is most easily seen by expanding (4.14) for infinitesimal $\boldsymbol{\alpha}$. Writing the unitary matrix (4.17) in the form ($G^{(\mu)} = G^{(\mu)\dagger}$ is a Hermitian $d_\mu \times d_\mu$ matrix)

$$D^{(\mu)}(\boldsymbol{\alpha}) = \exp(i\boldsymbol{\alpha}\cdot\mathbf{G}^{(\mu)}) \tag{4.18}$$

we note that the transformation property (4.16) of the field operator becomes

$$\boldsymbol{\phi}^{(\mu)} \rightarrow \exp(-i\boldsymbol{\alpha}\cdot\mathbf{G}^{(\mu)})\boldsymbol{\phi}^{(\mu)} \tag{4.19}$$

The usual orthogonality relations for the representation matrices of finite groups hold for compact groups with an appropriate definition of volume element (2). The density function $d\rho$ will depend on the eight real parameters (for instance, $\boldsymbol{\alpha}$) specifying an $SU(3)$ transformation. The normalization can then be chosen so that

$$\int d\rho(\boldsymbol{\alpha})D_{ik}^{(\mu)}(\boldsymbol{\alpha})D_{jl}^{(\nu)*}(\boldsymbol{\alpha}) = \frac{1}{d_\mu}\,\delta_{\mu\nu}\delta_{ij}\delta_{kl} \tag{4.20}$$

where d_μ is the dimension of the representation $D^{(\mu)}$. The unitarity condition is, of course, expressed by

$$\sum_j D_{ij}^{(\mu)}(\boldsymbol{\alpha})D_{kj}^{(\mu)*}(\boldsymbol{\alpha}) = \delta_{ik} \tag{4.21}$$

A useful alternate form for the Clebsch-Gordan series will now be proved. We subject (4.9) to the transformation $\mathcal{O}(\boldsymbol{\alpha})$, obtaining

$$\sum_{\nu_1'\nu_2'} \phi_{\nu_1'}^{(\mu_1)}\phi_{\nu_2'}^{(\mu_2)}D_{\nu_1'\nu_1}^{(\mu_1)}D_{\nu_2'\nu_2}^{(\mu_2)} = \sum_{\mu\gamma\nu\nu'}\begin{pmatrix}\mu_1 & \mu_2 & \mu_\gamma\\ \nu_1 & \nu_2 & \nu\end{pmatrix}D_{\nu'\nu}^{(\mu\gamma)}\Phi(\mu\gamma\nu';\mu_1\mu_2) \tag{4.22}$$

Now using (4.3) to express $\Phi(\mu\gamma\nu';\mu_1\mu_2)$ in terms of the $\phi_{\nu_1'}^{(\mu_1)}\phi_{\nu_2'}^{(\mu_2)}$

and taking advantage of the orthogonality of the basis functions gives explicitly the reduction of the direct product $D^{(\mu_1)} \times D^{(\mu_2)}$:

$$D_{\nu_1'\nu_1}{}^{(\mu_1)} D_{\nu_2'\nu_2}{}^{(\mu_2)} = \sum_{\mu\gamma\nu\nu'} \begin{pmatrix} \mu_1 & \mu_2 & \mu_\gamma \\ \nu_1 & \nu_2 & \nu \end{pmatrix} \begin{pmatrix} \mu_1 & \mu_2 & \mu_\gamma \\ \nu_1' & \nu_2' & \nu' \end{pmatrix} D_{\nu'\nu}{}^{(\mu_\gamma)} \quad (4.23)$$

Similar relations are well known in the study of the rotation group.

Tables of isoscalar factors are given in Appendix 1.

4.4 Irreducible Tensors; Wigner-Eckart Theorem for $SU(3)$

An *irreducible tensor operator* $T_\nu{}^{(\mu)}$ transforming according to the irreducible representation (μ) is defined in the usual way by

$$\mathcal{O}(\boldsymbol{\alpha}) T_\nu{}^{(\mu)} \mathcal{O}(\boldsymbol{\alpha})^{-1} = \sum_\lambda T_\lambda{}^{(\mu)} D_{\lambda\nu}{}^{(\mu)}(\boldsymbol{\alpha}) \quad (4.24)$$

where the index ν labels the various components of the tensor $\mathbf{T}^{(\mu)}$. Sometimes it is useful to convert (4.24) to the equivalent infinitesimal form, as was done for the vector operator defined in Eq. (2.94). In that example $(\mu) = \mathbf{8}$ and ν runs from 1 to 8.

A Wigner-Eckart theorem similar to that for $SU(2)$ [cf. Eq. (1.84)] holds in $SU(3)$. The proof is very similar to that given for the former group [see, for example, Tinkham (13), Chap. 5]. Consider the matrix element of the irreducible tensor operator $T_\nu{}^{(\mu)}$ between states $|\phi_{\nu_1}{}^{(\mu_1)}\rangle$, $|\phi_{\nu_2}{}^{(\mu_2)}\rangle$ transforming according to the irreducible representations $D^{(\mu_1)}$, $D^{(\mu_2)}$. The theorem states that this matrix element is given by

$$\langle \phi_{\nu_2}{}^{(\mu_2)} | \, T_\nu{}^{(\mu)} \, | \phi_{\nu_1}{}^{(\mu_1)} \rangle = \sum_\gamma \begin{pmatrix} \mu_1 & \mu & \mu_{2\gamma} \\ \nu_1 & \nu & \nu_2 \end{pmatrix} \langle \mu_2 \| \, T^{(\mu)} \, \| \mu_1 \rangle_\gamma \quad (4.25)$$

where the reduced matrix element $\langle \mu_2 \| \, T^{(\mu)} \, \| \mu_1 \rangle_\gamma$ depends only on the representations involved. All the dependence on the quantum numbers ν_1, ν_2, ν is given by the $SU(3)$ Clebsch-Gordan coefficient. The number of terms in the sum is equal to the number of times the representation $D^{(\mu_2)}$ is contained in the reduction of $D^{(\mu_1)} \times D^{(\mu)}$. The left-hand side of (4.25) is equal to

$$\langle(\mathcal{O}(\boldsymbol{\alpha})\phi_{\nu_2}{}^{(\mu_2)})|\ \mathcal{O}(\boldsymbol{\alpha})T_\nu{}^{(\mu)}\mathcal{O}(\boldsymbol{\alpha})^{-1}\ |\mathcal{O}(\boldsymbol{\alpha})\phi_{\nu_1}{}^{(\mu_1)}\rangle$$
$$= \sum_{\nu_1'\nu_2'\nu'} D_{\nu_2'\nu_2}{}^{(\mu_2)*} D_{\nu_1'\nu_1}{}^{(\mu_1)} D_{\nu'\nu}{}^{(\mu)} \langle\phi_{\nu_2'}{}^{(\mu_2)}|\ T_{\nu'}{}^{(\mu)}\ |\phi_{\nu_1}{}^{(\mu_1)}\rangle \tag{4.26}$$

on using (4.14) and (4.24). The matrix elements involved are merely numbers independent of the group parameters $\boldsymbol{\alpha}$. In order to use the orthogonality theorem to advantage, we use Eq. (4.23) to express (4.26) in terms of products of two representation matrices:

$$\sum_{\substack{\nu_1'\nu_2'\nu' \\ \lambda\rho\sigma\gamma}} D_{\nu_2'\nu_2}{}^{(\mu_2)*} D_{\rho\sigma}{}^{(\lambda\gamma)} \begin{pmatrix} \mu_1 & \mu & \lambda_\gamma \\ \nu_1 & \nu & \sigma \end{pmatrix} \begin{pmatrix} \mu_1 & \mu & \lambda_\gamma \\ \nu_1' & \nu' & \rho \end{pmatrix} \times \langle\phi_{\nu_2'}{}^{(\mu_2)}|\ T_{\nu'}{}^{(\mu)}\ |\phi_{\nu_1'}{}^{(\mu_1)}\rangle \tag{4.27}$$

We now integrate over the parameter-space using the group weight function; from Eq. (4.20) we find $\lambda = \mu_2$, $\rho = \nu_2'$, $\sigma = \nu_2$ in the sum

$$\langle\phi_{\nu_2}{}^{(\mu_2)}|\ T_\nu{}^{(\mu)}\ |\phi_{\nu_1}{}^{(\mu_1)}\rangle$$
$$= \sum_\gamma \begin{pmatrix} \mu_1 & \mu & \mu_{2\gamma} \\ \nu_1 & \nu & \nu_2 \end{pmatrix} \frac{1}{d_\mu} \sum_{\nu_1'\nu_2'\nu} \begin{pmatrix} \mu_1 & \mu_2 & \mu_{2\gamma} \\ \nu_1' & \nu' & \nu_2' \end{pmatrix} \times \langle\phi_{\nu_2'}{}^{(\mu_2)}|\ T_{\nu'}{}^{(\mu)}\ |\phi_{\nu_1'}{}^{(\mu)}\rangle \tag{4.28}$$

Equation (4.28) clearly has the form promised in Eq. (4.25).

Note that two independent constants are required to give all the matrix elements of a vector operator in the regular representation. The reader will notice the connection with the discussion of Section 2.6. Lurie and MacFarlane (14) have given explicit expressions for all nonvanishing matrix elements of the vector operator.

4.5 Symmetry Properties of the *SU*(3) Clebsch-Gordan Coefficients

In practical applications, one often has to pay attention to conceptually simple but time-consuming questions involving the symmetry properties of generalized Clebsch-Gordan coefficients. For example, if one adds up unitary spins in different order the result is essentially the same although some extra minus signs may appear. Recalling the conventions made in Section 4.2, we note that

$$\begin{pmatrix} \mu_1 & \mu_2 & \mu_\gamma \\ \nu_1 & \nu_2 & \nu \end{pmatrix} = \xi_1 \begin{pmatrix} \mu_2 & \mu_1 & \mu_\gamma \\ \nu_2 & \nu_1 & \nu \end{pmatrix} \tag{4.29}$$

where ξ_1 is ± 1 and may be found most directly by explicit inspection of the functions. As ξ_1 is independent of ν_1, ν_2, and ν, its value may be found from the state of highest weight in the representation μ_γ.

By utilizing familiar symmetry properties of the $SU(2)$ Clebsch-Gordan coefficient, relations between the isoscalar factors are obtained. Employing the relation

$$C(T_1 T_2 T; T_{1z} T_{2z}) = (-1)^{T_1+T_2-T} C(T_2 T_1 T; T_{2z} T_{1z}) \tag{4.30}$$

we obtain from (4.29) the result

$$\left(\begin{matrix} \mu_1 & \mu_2 \\ T_1 Y_1 & T_2 Y_2 \end{matrix} \middle| \begin{matrix} \mu_\gamma \\ TY \end{matrix} \right) = \xi_1 (-1)^{T_1+T_2-T} \left(\begin{matrix} \mu_2 & \mu_1 \\ T_2 Y_2 & T_1 Y_1 \end{matrix} \middle| \begin{matrix} \mu_\gamma \\ TY \end{matrix} \right) \tag{4.31}$$

As a by-product of (4.31) we obtain the special result

$$\left(\begin{matrix} \mu_1 & \mu_1 \\ T_1 Y_1 & T_1 Y_1 \end{matrix} \middle| \begin{matrix} \mu_\gamma \\ TY \end{matrix} \right) = 0 \qquad \begin{matrix} \xi_1 = 1, & 2T_1 - T = \text{odd} \\ \xi_1 = -1, & 2T_1 - T = \text{even} \end{matrix} \tag{4.32}$$

In addition to (4.31), the following results involving the complex conjugate representations have been derived by de Swart (10) for irreducible representations occurring in the eightfold way. When only one representation occurs more than once (label γ), we are given the relation

$$\begin{pmatrix} \mu_1 & \mu_2 & \mu_\gamma \\ \nu_1 & \nu_2 & \nu_3 \end{pmatrix} = \xi_2 (-1)^{T_{1z}+\frac{1}{2}Y_1} \left(\frac{d}{d_2} \right)^{\frac{1}{2}} \begin{pmatrix} \mu_1 & \mu^* & \mu_{2\gamma'}{}^* \\ \nu_1 & -\nu_3 & -\nu_2 \end{pmatrix} \tag{4.33}$$

where the symbol $-\nu$ denotes the set $(T, -T_3, -Y)$ if ν stands for (T, T_3, Y). The $SU(2)$ relation

$$C(T_1 T_2 T; T_{1z} T_{2z} T_z) = (-1)^{T_1 - T_{1z}} \left(\frac{2T+1}{2T_2+1}\right)^{1/2} C(T_1 T T_2; T_{1z}, -T_{3z}, -T_{2z}) \quad (4.34)$$

permits the simplification of (4.33) to an expression for the isoscalar factors

$$\left(\begin{matrix} \mu_1 & \mu_2 \\ T_1 Y_1 & T_2 Y_2 \end{matrix} \middle| \begin{matrix} \mu_\gamma \\ TY \end{matrix}\right) = \xi_2 (-1)^{T_1 + \frac{1}{2} Y_1} \left[\frac{(2T_2+1)d}{(2T+1)d_2}\right]^{1/2} \left(\begin{matrix} \mu_1 & \mu^* \\ T_1 Y_1 & T - Y \end{matrix} \middle| \begin{matrix} \mu_{2\gamma'}{}^* \\ T_2, -Y_2 \end{matrix}\right) \quad (4.35)$$

A simpler relation is given by

$$\begin{pmatrix} \mu_1 & \mu_2 & \mu_\gamma \\ \nu_1 & \nu_2 & \nu \end{pmatrix} = \xi_3 \begin{pmatrix} \mu_1{}^* & \mu_2{}^* & \mu_\gamma{}^* \\ -\nu_1 & -\nu_2 & -\nu_3 \end{pmatrix} \quad (4.36)$$

This may be reduced to the following relation between isoscalar factors

$$\left(\begin{matrix} \mu_1 & \mu_2 \\ T_1 Y_1 & T_2 Y_2 \end{matrix} \middle| \begin{matrix} \mu_\gamma \\ TY \end{matrix}\right) = \xi_3 (-1)^{T_1 + T_2 - T} \left(\begin{matrix} \mu_1{}^* & \mu_2{}^* \\ T_1 - Y_1 & T_2 - Y_2 \end{matrix} \middle| \begin{matrix} \mu_\gamma{}^* \\ T - Y \end{matrix}\right) \quad (4.37)$$

on using

$$C(T_1 T_2 T; T_{1z} T_{2z} T_z) = (-1)^{T_1 + T_2 - T} C(T_1 T_2 T; -T_{1z}, -T_{2z}, -T_z) \quad (4.38)$$

The phase factors ξ_1, ξ_2, ξ_3 have been given by de Swart (10) for the decompositions **8** × **8**, **8** × **10**, **8** × **27**, **8** × **10***, **10** × **10**, **10** × **10***, and **10*** × **10***. They are reproduced in Table 4.1.

TABLE 4.1
Phase Factors Involved in the Symmetry Properties of the $SU(3)$ Clebsch-Gordan Coefficients.

μ_1	μ_2	μ_3	ξ_1	ξ_2	ξ_3	μ_1	μ_2	μ_3	ξ_1	ξ_2	ξ_3
8	8	27	1	−1	1	8	10*	35*	1	−1	1
		10	−1	−1	1			27	−1	−1	1
		10*	−1	1	1			10*	−1	−1	−1
		8_1	1	1	1			8	1	−1	−1
		8_2	−1	−1	−1						
		1	1	−1	1	10	10	28	1	1	1
8	10	35	1	−1	1			35	−1	−1	1
		27	−1	1	1			27	1	1	1
		10	−1	−1	−1			10*	−1	−1	1
		8	1	1	−1						
8	27	64	1	−1	1	10	10*	64	1	1	1
		35	−1	−1	1			27	−1	1	−1
		35*	−1	1	1			8	1	1	1
		27_1	1	1	1			1	−1	1	−1
		27_2	−1	−1	−1	10*	10*	28*	1	−1	1
		10	1	−1	−1			35*	−1	−1	1
		10*	1	1	−1			27	1	−1	1
		8	1	−1	1			10	−1	−1	1

4.6 Construction of Representations by Tensor Analysis

In Chapter 3 we described how one constructs irreducible representations by reducing the direct product $(\mathbf{3})^p \times (\mathbf{3}^*)^q$. Although the use of the two three-dimensional representations in this manner is economical, it is not essential since $\mathbf{3}^*$ is the antisymmetrical combination of two $\mathbf{3}$'s. Hence we could obtain the same representations (and some additional ones) by studying $(\mathbf{3})^{p+2q}$ at the expense of introducing a greater number of functions. We can further consider the problem of reducing $(\mathbf{3})^N$ as a special case of the general linear transformation on three component objects. In fact, it is no more difficult to study the general linear group in n dimensions $GL(n)$, defined by the transformation law on n objects ψ^i

$$\psi^{i'} = a_j{}^i \psi^j \tag{4.39}$$

for an arbitrary complex matrix a. Tensors with respect to $GL(n)$ are defined as usual by (r factors)

$$T'^{\alpha\beta\cdots\nu} = a_a{}^\alpha a_b{}^\beta \cdots a_n{}^\nu T^{ab\cdots n} \tag{4.40}$$

The representation $a \times a \times \cdots \times a$ (r times) is reducible. The irreducible tensors, which generate the irreducible representations, are constructed by applying the Young symmetrizers to the tensors T. The crucial facts that make the symmetrized tensors irreducible tensors are two: (*1*) the index permutations commute with the transformation (4.40); (*2*) for general $a_j{}^i$, no other operation commutes with the transformation. In this way the theory of the symmetric group is seen to be of direct relevance for the representation theory of $GL(n)$ and its various subgroups. This theory is developed fully in Chapter 10 of the book by Hamermesh (2). Only a few salient points are reviewed here. A succinct summary of the properties of Young diagrams, tableaux, and symmetrizers may be found in Appendix D of the book by Messiah (15). The main point of interest is that when the transformation matrices in (4.39) are required to be unitary and unimodular, the representations irreducible for $GL(n)$ remain irreducible for $SU(n)$. (This is not the case for the subgroup $O(n)$, the orthogonal group in n dimensions.)

The rth rank tensors of (4.40) span an n^r-dimensional vector space. Let us represent Eq. (4.40) symbolically by

$$T' = AT \tag{4.41}$$

and any permutation of the indices by P. Then one easily finds

$$\begin{aligned} PT' &= PAT \\ &= APT \end{aligned} \tag{4.42}$$

Hence sums and products of P's will also commute with the transformations of $GL(n)$. The n^r-dimensional vector space is decomposed into invariant, irreducible subspaces by the Young symmetrizers, projection operators $\mathscr{P}_\alpha$ obeying

$$\begin{aligned} \mathscr{P}_\alpha \mathscr{P}_\beta &= \delta_{\alpha\beta}\mathscr{P}_\alpha \\ \sum \mathscr{P}_\alpha &= I \end{aligned} \tag{4.43}$$

With each symmetrizer (not defined here) we can associate a so-called Young diagram.

We reexamine the examples of Chapter 3, paying special attention to the symmetry properties. The simplest case of all is the familiar process of representing a second-rank tensor as the sum of its symmetric and antisymmetric parts (Eq. 3.19)

$$\psi^i(1)\psi^j(2) = \tfrac{1}{2}(\psi^i(1)\psi^j(2) + \psi^j(1)\psi^i(2)) + \tfrac{1}{2}(\psi^i(1)\psi^j(2) - \psi^j(1)\psi^i(2)) \tag{4.44}$$

which for $SU(n)$ corresponds to the reduction of $\mathbf{n} \times \mathbf{n}$ into irreducible representations of dimension $\frac{1}{2}n(n+1)$ and $\frac{1}{2}n(n-1)$ (for example, $\mathbf{3} \times \mathbf{3} = \mathbf{6} + \mathbf{3}^*$). In the reduction of $\mathbf{3} \times \mathbf{3} \times \mathbf{3}$ it was found that the resulting representation **10** was completely symmetrical, while the two **8** representations have mixed symmetry and the 1-dimensional representation is the completely antisymmetric combination of $\psi^i\psi^j\psi^k$. The mixed symmetry of Eq. (3.40) (and of all the associated basis functions) is that of the operations of antisymmetrization of $\psi^i(1)\psi^j(2)\psi^k(3)$ in labels 1 and 3 followed by symmetrization in labels 1 and 2.

Thus, using the antisymmetrical tensor ε_{ijk} ($\equiv \varepsilon^{ijk}$), we can convert two **3** representations ψ^i to one $\mathbf{3}^*(\xi_i)$ by contraction

$$\xi_i = \varepsilon_{ijk}\psi^j\psi^k \tag{4.45}$$

or two $\mathbf{3}^*$ representations (ξ_j) to one $\mathbf{3}(\psi^i)$

$$\psi^i = \varepsilon^{ijk}\xi_j\xi_k \tag{4.46}$$

Here we are distinguishing upper indices (contravariant vectors $\sim\mathbf{3}$) from lower indices (covariant vectors $\sim\mathbf{3}^*$). This is useful because the operation of contraction of an upper with a lower index reduces the rank of a mixed tensor [see Eq. (3.5)] by two. The basic example is the formation of a scalar

$$\xi_i\psi^i = \delta_j{}^i\xi_i\psi^j = \xi_1\psi^1 + \xi_2\psi^2 + \xi_3\psi^3 \tag{4.47}$$

[Note: In tensor analysis it is convenient to forgo the Condon-Shortley phase convention; thus $\xi_i = (\xi^i)^*$. Alternatively (16) one can use the phase convention (2.79) for $\mathbf{3}^*$ and compensate by contracting with $g_j{}^i = \mathrm{diag}\,(-1,1,1)$ instead of the Kronecker delta; cf. Eq. (3.29).]

Using the unitary-unimodular property of the transformation matrices a, one easily verifies that the tensors

$$\delta_j{}^i \qquad \varepsilon_{ijk} \qquad \varepsilon^{ijk} \tag{4.48}$$

are unaltered by $SU(3)$ transformations. Alternatively, these operations (contraction and antisymmetrization) commute with the $SU(3)$ transformations on the mixed tensors and can be used to reduce the typical mixed tensor Eq. (3.1). The latter has p upper and q lower indices. Contraction with $\delta_\alpha{}^a$ results in a tensor with $p - 1$ upper and $q - 1$ lower indices:

$$\Phi'{}^{\beta\ldots\nu}_{b\ldots k} = \delta_\alpha{}^a \Phi{}^{\alpha\beta\ldots\nu}_{ab\ldots k} \tag{4.49}$$

The antisymmetric tensors ε^{ijk} and ε_{ijk} are used to raise and lower indices; for example,

$$\Phi''{}^{\alpha\beta\ldots\nu\omega}_{c\ldots k} = \varepsilon^{\omega ab}\Phi^{\alpha\beta\ldots\nu}_{ab\ldots k} \tag{4.50}$$

has $p + 1$ upper and $q - 2$ lower indices and

$$\Phi'''{}^{\gamma\ldots\nu}_{ab\ldots kl} = \varepsilon_{l\alpha\beta}\Phi^{\alpha\beta\ldots\nu}_{ab\ldots k} \tag{4.51}$$

has $p - 2$ upper and $q + 1$ lower indices.

The tensor Φ is surely not irreducible since the operations (4.49)–(4.51) yield tensors having transformation properties distinct from the original tensor Φ. If, however, we modify Φ to a form in which the operations (4.49)–(4.51) yield zero, then we shall have obtained an irreducible tensor. The procedure is then to add terms to Φ in order to obtain a new tensor which is totally symmetric in the upper indices and also in the lower indices, as well as traceless. (By virtue of the symmetry condition, the trace is defined on only one pair of indices: $\mathrm{Tr}\,\Phi = \sum_a \Phi^{\alpha\beta\ldots\nu}_{ab\ldots k}$.)

We shall now prove the dimension formula (4.1) by counting the number of independent components possessed by a tensor having the special properties mentioned in the preceding paragraph. First ignore the trace condition. For a fixed set of lower indices there are $\frac{1}{2}(p + 1)(p + 2)$ independent components. To show this we arrange the indices of a given tensor from left to right in order of increasing value. This avoids overcounting that might otherwise occur due to the symmetry of the tensor. Suppose that there are n ones (n can be any one of the sequence $0, 1, \ldots, p$). The remaining $p - n$ places are occupied by 2's and 3's. There can be no two's, one two, etc., up to $(p - n)$ two's, i.e., a total of $(p - n + 1)$ possibilities. The total number of independent upper index components is thus

$$N_u = \sum_{n=0}^{p} (p - n + 1) = \tfrac{1}{2}(p + 1)(p + 2) \tag{4.52}$$

In exactly the same way the number of independent lower index components is

$$N_l = \tfrac{1}{2}(q + 1)(q + 2) \tag{4.53}$$

The corresponding symmetrized tensor Φ_s therefore has $N_u N_l = \frac{1}{4}(p + 1)(q + 1)(p + 2)(q + 2)$ independent components. Suppose Φ_s is further required to have zero trace. The trace is a symmetric tensor with $p - 1$ upper and $q - 1$ lower indices. All the $N_t = \frac{1}{4}pq(p + 1)(q + 1)$ components of Φ_s must vanish. Hence the dimensionality of the associated representation is

$$d(p,q) = N_u N_l - N_t = \tfrac{1}{2}(p + 1)(q + 1)(p + q + 2) \tag{4.54}$$

The regular representation **8** has components given by

$$T^i{}_j = \psi^i(1)\psi_j(2) - \tfrac{1}{3}\delta^i{}_j(\psi,\psi) \tag{4.55}$$

where $(\psi,\psi) = \psi_i\psi^i$. We can also regard $T^i{}_j$ as a traceless 3×3 matrix (rows associated with i and columns with j).

For example, if ψ^i is associated with the quark field q^i and ψ_i with $\bar{q}_j$, (4.55) is equivalent to

$$T = \begin{pmatrix} \frac{1}{3}(2\bar{q}_1q_1 - \bar{q}_2q_2 - \bar{q}_3q_3) & \bar{q}_2q_1 & \bar{q}_3q_1 \\ \bar{q}_1q_2 & \frac{1}{3}(2\bar{q}_2q_2 - \bar{q}_1q_1 - \bar{q}_3q_3) & \bar{q}_3q_2 \\ \bar{q}_1q_3 & \bar{q}_2q_3 & \frac{1}{3}(2\bar{q}_3q_3 - \bar{q}_1q_1 - \bar{q}_2q_2) \end{pmatrix} \tag{4.56}$$

Making the identifications of Eqs. (3.61), (3.62), and (4.56) reduces to the matrix $\mathscr{P}$ of Eq. (3.65) previously derived from a different point of view.

The ten-dimensional representation is the completely symmetrized product of $\psi^i(1)\psi^j(2)\psi^k(3)$ [cf. Eq. (3.38)].

Next we give a simple example illustrating the reduction of direct products of irreducible representations. The direct product **3** × **8** has the set of basis functions

$$\phi^i T^j{}_k \tag{4.57}$$

where $T^j{}_j = 0$ by (4.55).

We wish to express (4.57), which is *not* traceless and does not have definite symmetry properties in upper indices, as a sum of terms having these desired properties. One proceeds in two steps:

$$\begin{aligned}\phi^i T^j{}_k &= \tfrac{1}{2}(\phi^i T^j{}_k + \phi^j T^i{}_k) + \tfrac{1}{2}(\phi^i T^j{}_k - \phi^j T^i{}_k)\\ &= [\tfrac{1}{2}(\phi^i T^j{}_k + \phi^j T^i{}_k) - \tfrac{1}{8}(\delta^i{}_k\phi^l T^j{}_l + \delta^j{}_k\phi^l T^i{}_l)]\\ &\quad + [\tfrac{1}{2}(\phi^i T^j{}_k - \phi^j T^i{}_k) - \tfrac{1}{4}(\delta^i{}_k\phi^l T^j{}_l - \delta^j{}_k\phi^l T^i{}_l)]\\ &\quad + [\tfrac{3}{8}\delta^i{}_k\phi^l T^j{}_l - \tfrac{1}{8}\delta^j{}_k\phi^l T^i{}_l]\end{aligned} \tag{4.58}$$

The three terms in square brackets are traceless tensors. The first is symmetric in its upper indices and hence gives rise to $D(2,1)$, or **15**. The second term is antisymmetric in i and j; there are six independent components. Denoting it by $A^{ij}{}_k$, one sees that its independent components can be put in one–one correspondence with the tensor $\phi_{lk} = \varepsilon_{lij}A^{ij}{}_k + \varepsilon_{kij}A^{ij}{}_l$, a symmetric covariant tensor of rank 2. Thus the representation generated by $A^{ij}{}_k$ is $D(0,2)$, or **6***. Similarly, the last term corresponds to $D(1,0)$, or **3**. This example should remind the reader that although a given representation *can* be obtained by symmetrization of the primeval tensor Φ, tensors of more complicated symmetry give rise to the same representation. A good exercise is to reduce **8** × **8** using this technique. The lazy reader will find the details given in Okubo's notes (17).

A simple prescription for reducing direct products (using tensors) has been given by Coleman (18). A graphical method has been given by Speiser (19) [see also de Swart (10)]. Further details on the analysis of representations using tensor analysis can be found in references 1–4, 7, 16, and 17.

We conclude by giving the definition of a mixed rank-two-tensor operator in the present context. This operator corresponds to the "vector operator" defined by Eq. (2.101). The eight $SU(3)$ generators transforming as Eq. (4.55) were given in Eq. (2.27). The corresponding commutation rules were given in Eq. (2.29). The mixed tensor operator of rank 2 hence satisfies (by definition)

$$[A^i{}_j, T^k{}_l] = \delta^i{}_l T^k{}_j - \delta^k{}_j T^i{}_l \qquad (4.59)$$

(This definition holds also if we do not require $T^k{}_l$ to be traceless; in any event $T^k{}_k$ commutes with the $A^i{}_j$ and is a multiple of the identity.)

Contraction of two such tensors on one index yields another tensor of the same type; thus $U^i{}_j = S^i{}_k T^k{}_j$ satisfies (4.59) with $T \rightarrow U$. Further $U^i{}_i$ is a scalar within an irreducible representation. Thus we note that the operators

$$(A \cdot A) = A^i{}_j A^j{}_i; \quad (A \cdot A \cdot A) = A^i{}_j A^j{}_k A^k{}_i; \quad \text{etc.} \qquad (4.60)$$

all transform as scalars. Since only two Casimir operators exist for the group $SU(3)$, one expects that only two of the sequence (4.60) are independent. In fact all "powers" of A higher than the second and third of (4.60) can be expressed in terms of the latter two (17).

An alternative form of the Wigner-Eckart theorem for the octet operator of $SU(3)$ is given by Okubo's formula for the traceless tensor $T^i{}_j$: Within an irreducible representation $T^i{}_j$ has the form (17, 20)

$$T^i{}_j = a(p,q)A^i{}_j + b(p,q)[A^i{}_k A^k{}_j - \tfrac{1}{3}\delta^i{}_j(A \cdot A)] \qquad (4.61)$$

where $a(p,q)$ and $b(p,q)$ depend on the representation.

References

1. H. Weyl, *Classical Groups*, Princeton University Press, Princeton, New Jersey, 1946.
2. M. Hamermesh, *Group Theory*, Addison-Wesley, Reading, Mass., 1962.

3. L. C. Biedenharn, *J. Math. Phys.*, **4**, 436 (1963).
4. G. E. Baird and L. C. Biedenharn, *J. Math. Phys.*, **4**, 1449 (1963); **5**, 1723 (1964); **5**, 1730 (1964).
5. S. Gasiorowicz, Argonne Natl. Lab. Rept. ANL 6729 (1962), unpublished.
6. R. E. Cutkosky, *Ann. Rev. Nucl. Sci.*, **14**, 175 (1964).
7. R. E. Behrends, J. Dreitlein, C. Fronsdal, and B. W. Lee, *Rev. Mod. Phys.*, **34**, 1 (1962).
8. L. C. Biedenharn, *Phys. Letters*, **3**, 69 (1962).
9. G. Racah, in *Group Theoretical Concepts and Methods in Elementary Particle Physics*, F. Gursey, Ed., Gordon and Breach, New York, 1964.
10. J. J. de Swart, *Rev. Mod. Phys.*, **35**, 916 (1963).
11. M. E. Rose, *Elementary Theory of Angular Momentum*, Wiley, New York, 1957.
12. A. R. Edmonds, *Proc. Roy. Soc.* (*London*), **A268**, 567 (1962).
13. M. Tinkham, *Group Theory and Quantum Mechanics*, McGraw-Hill, New York, 1964.
14. D. Lurie and A. J. MacFarlane, *J. Math. Phys.*, **5**, 565 (1964).
15. A. Messiah, *Quantum Mechanics*, North-Holland Publ. Co., Amsterdam, 1963, Vol. II.
16. N. Mukunda and L. K. Pandit, *J. Math. Phys.*, **6**, 746 (1965).
17. S. Okubo, *Lectures on Unitary Symmetry*, University of Rochester, 1964, unpublished.
18. S. Coleman, *J. Math. Phys.*, **5**, 1343 (1964).
19. D. Speiser, in *Group Theoretical Concepts and Methods in Elementary Particle Physics*, F. Gursey, Ed., Gordon and Breach, New York, 1964.
20. S. Okubo, *Prog. Theoret. Phys.* (*Kyoto*), **27**, 949 (1962).

Chapter 5

$SU(3)$-Invariant Vertices and Amplitudes

5.1 Construction of Invariant Couplings

Using the results of the preceding sections, it is relatively simple to construct interactions among the various unitary multiplets which are invariant under the transformations of $SU(3)$. First we derive the Yukawa couplings of the pseudoscalar meson octet P_a to the baryon octet B_b $(a,b = 1,\ldots,8)$. (Clearly these considerations hold for the more general PBB vertex.) In Section 2.5 we found that there are two independent sets of functions transforming according to the regular representation, $\bar{B}F^kB$ and $\bar{B}D^kB$ (where the B_a and P_a transform via the "Hermitian" regular representation, and are given explicitly in Eqs. (3.63) and (3.64)). We can form invariants by contracting these expressions with the pseudoscalar meson octet P_k. (That these are the only invariants can be seen from the fact that the identity representation occurs only twice in **8** × **8** × **8**, since **8** × **10**, **8** × **10***, and **8** × **27** do not contain **1**.)

Inserting the Dirac matrix γ_5 to account for the pseudoscalar character of the mesons, the interaction Hamiltonian density has the form

$$\mathcal{H}_{PBB} = g_1\bar{B}\gamma_5 D^a B P_a + g_2\bar{B}\gamma_5 F^a B P_a \tag{5.1}$$

so that only two independent coupling parameters enter. This should be compared with the relatively unrestrictive result obtained using isospin invariance, Eq. (1.51).

It is customary to introduce a "mixing parameter" α which measures the relative strength of the symmetric and antisymmetric couplings (D and F types, respectively) by

$$g_1 = 2g\alpha$$
$$g_2 = 2g(1 - \alpha) \tag{5.2}$$

so that (5.1) has the form

$$\mathcal{H} = 2g\bar{B}\gamma_5[\alpha\mathbf{D} + (1 - \alpha)\mathbf{F}]B\cdot\mathbf{P} \tag{5.3}$$

The overall strength is measured by g, which turns out to be just the usual π–N coupling constant $g^2/4\pi \cong 15$. This result, as well as expressions for all the coupling constants of Eq. (1.51), can be found by writing out (5.3) in detail.

As an illustration of this, we extract from (5.3) the πN component. From Eq. (3.36) it is clear that P_1, P_2, P_3, and $B_4, \ldots B_7$ are the only components giving rise to the πN interaction. Consider the **F** terms in (5.3). Omitting γ_5 again for notational ease, the πN part comes from

$$[F_{47}{}^1(\bar{B}_4B_7 - \bar{B}_7B_4) + F_{56}{}^1(\bar{B}_5B_6 - \bar{B}_6B_5)]P_1$$
$$+ [F_{46}{}^2(\bar{B}_4B_6 - \bar{B}_6B_4) + F_{57}{}^2(\bar{B}_5B_7 - \bar{B}_7B_5)]P_2$$
$$+ [F_{45}{}^3(\bar{B}_4B_5 - \bar{B}_5B_4) + F_{67}{}^3(\bar{B}_6B_7 - \bar{B}_7B_6)]P_3 \tag{5.4}$$

Substituting $B_4 \to p/\sqrt{2}$, $B_5 \to ip/\sqrt{2}$, $B_6 \to n/\sqrt{2}$, $B_7 \to in/\sqrt{2}$ and the values of the $F_{jk}{}^i$ from Table 2.1, (5.4) reduces to

$$\tfrac{1}{2}[\sqrt{2}\,\bar{p}n\pi^+ + \sqrt{2}\,\bar{n}p\pi^- + (\bar{p}p - \bar{n}n)\pi^0] \tag{5.5}$$

which is $\frac{1}{2}\bar{N}\boldsymbol{\tau}N\cdot\boldsymbol{\pi}$ with $\pi^{\pm} = (\pi_1 \pm i\pi_2)/\sqrt{2}$, $\pi_3 = \pi^0$. The **D** term gives

$$[D_{46}{}^1(\bar{B}_4B_6 + \bar{B}_6B_4) + D_{57}{}^1(\bar{B}_5B_7 + \bar{B}_7B_5)]P_1$$
$$+ [D_{47}{}^2(\bar{B}_4B_7 + \bar{B}_7B_4) + D_{56}{}^2(\bar{B}_5B_6 + \bar{B}_6B_5)]P_2$$
$$+ [D_{44}{}^3\bar{B}_4B_4 + D_{55}{}^3\bar{B}_5B_5 + D_{66}{}^3\bar{B}_6B_6 + D_{77}{}^3\bar{B}_7B_7]P_3 \tag{5.6}$$

which when worked out coincides with (5.5). Thus the πN part of (5.3) is simply

$$2g[\alpha\tfrac{1}{2}\bar{N}\boldsymbol{\tau}N\cdot\boldsymbol{\pi} + \tfrac{1}{2}(1 - \alpha)\bar{N}\boldsymbol{\tau}N\cdot\boldsymbol{\pi}] = g\bar{N}\boldsymbol{\tau}N\cdot\boldsymbol{\pi} \tag{5.7}$$

independent of α.

The other couplings among the various isospin multiplets can be worked out in a similar way. The resulting *PBB* coupling constants are given in Table 5.1, where the *D*, *F*, and total contributions are indicated separately. (The units are chosen so that $g_{\pi NN} \equiv g = 1$.)

In Fig. 5.1 we have plotted $g_{PBB}{}^2/g^2$ as a function of α, in order to reveal more clearly the relative values of the various couplings.

The value of α has to be found from other considerations: comparison with experiment, dynamical models, or more restrictive symmetry requirements. The "empirical" values of the various coupling constants are almost always found with the aid of simple theoretical models, hopefully applied with discretion, to reactions in kinematical domains where the simplifying assumptions might be true. These models are subject to quantitative doubt, since they almost always boil down to "hindsight" perturbation theory. Nevertheless, the cumulative qualitative success of dispersion theory models of particle collisions is sufficient

TABLE 5.1

Isospin Couplings of the Pseudoscalar Octet Mesons to the Octet Baryons as a Function of the Mixing Parameter α.

Coupling Type	*D* Contribution	*F* Contribution	Total
πNN	α	$1-\alpha$	1
$\pi \Xi\Xi$	$-\alpha$	$1-\alpha$	$1-2\alpha$
$\pi \Lambda\Sigma$	$2\alpha/\sqrt{3}$	0	$2\alpha/\sqrt{3}$
$\pi \Sigma\Sigma$	0	$2(1-\alpha)$	$2(1-\alpha)$
$KN\Lambda$	$-\alpha/\sqrt{3}$	$-\sqrt{3}(1-\alpha)$	$-(3-2\alpha)/\sqrt{3}$
$K\Xi\Lambda$	$-\alpha/\sqrt{3}$	$\sqrt{3}(1-\alpha)$	$(3-4\alpha)/\sqrt{3}$
$KN\Sigma$	α	$-(1-\alpha)$	$-(1-2\alpha)$
$K\Xi\Sigma$	$-\alpha$	$-(1-\alpha)$	-1
ηNN	$-\alpha/\sqrt{3}$	$\sqrt{3}(1-\alpha)$	$(3-4\alpha)/\sqrt{3}$
$\eta \Xi\Xi$	$-\alpha/\sqrt{3}$	$-\sqrt{3}(1-\alpha)$	$-(3-2\alpha)/\sqrt{3}$
$\eta \Lambda\Lambda$	$-2\alpha/\sqrt{3}$	0	$-2\alpha/\sqrt{3}$
$\eta \Sigma\Sigma$	$2\alpha/\sqrt{3}$	0	$2\alpha/\sqrt{3}$

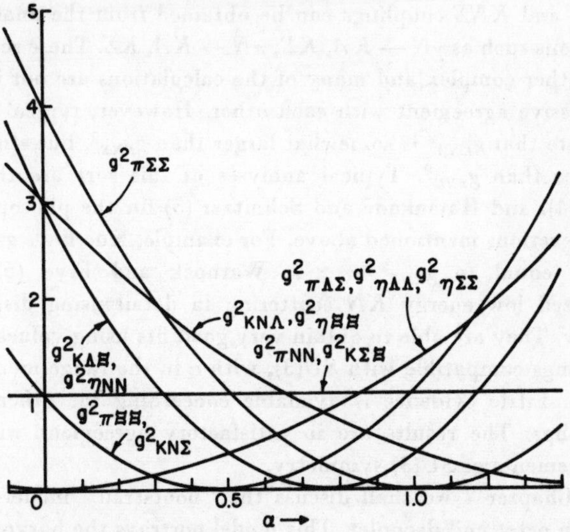

Fig. 5.1. The isospin Yukawa couplings of the octet pseudoscalar mesons to the baryon octet depend on the mixing parameter α, the latter measuring the ratio of D to F couplings in Eq. (5.3). The values of the couplings are shown as a function of α. The mixing parameter is not determined by pure $SU(3)$ symmetry considerations.

enough to deserve consideration. A further difficulty in comparison of (possibly model-dependent) coupling constants with results such as displayed in Table 5.1 lies in the fact that we have not taken into account the possibly large symmetry breaking effects. For all these reasons one can, at best, only expect qualitative success.

The analysis of the binding of Λ and Σ hyperons in hypernuclei indicates that the $\pi\Lambda\Sigma$ coupling is comparable to the πNN coupling but that the $\pi\Sigma\Sigma$ coupling is rather weak (1, 2). From Fig. 5.1 one sees that this already puts the acceptable value of α above about 0.6, and more likely about 0.75. A value in this region is further favored by the relatively small η production cross section in πN collisions (3). Some information about the

$KN\Lambda$ and $KN\Sigma$ couplings can be obtained from the analysis of reactions such as $\gamma N \to K\Lambda$, $K\Sigma$; $\pi N \to K\Lambda$, $K\Sigma$. These reactions are rather complex and many of the calculations are not in very impressive agreement with each other. However, typical results indicate that $g_{KN\Lambda}^2$ is somewhat larger than $g_{KN\Sigma}^2$, but still quite smaller than $g_{\pi NN}^2$. Typical analyses of this sort are those of Kuo (4), and Hatsukade and Schnitzer (5) for the photoproduction reactions mentioned above. For example, Kuo finds $g_{KN\Lambda}^2/4\pi$ about equal to $g_{KN\Sigma}^2/4\pi \cong 4$. Warnock and Frye (6) have analyzed low energy KN scattering in detail using dispersion theory. They are able to obtain very good fits using values of the couplings compatible with $SU(3)$, with α in the range mentioned above. Little evidence is available concerning the other PBB couplings. The results are in satisfactory agreement with the requirements of $SU(3)$ symmetry.

In Chapter 7 we shall discuss the "bootstrap" model of the baryon octet and decuplet. This model portrays the baryon octet as primarily a bound state in the PB channel, held together by attractive forces due to decuplet exchange. Similarly, the decuplet is supposed to be a composite of P and B, held together mostly by B exchange. The dynamical equations of this model give rise to a self-consistency condition (7, 8) which determines α to be about 0.7. In this model, the occurrence of the $P_{3/2}$ decuplet rather than the 27-dimensional representation also restricts α to a rather narrow range. [In a more complete analysis, including the effect of vector meson exchange and actual masses, the representation 27 is suppressed (10).]

Next consider the coupling of an octet of vector mesons to the baryons. For purposes of normalization and reference to easily accessible experimental information, we write down the isospin invariant couplings of the ρ meson to the nucleon. As in the electromagnetic case, there is a vector ("electric") coupling

$$\mathcal{H}_{\rho NN}{}^{V} = f_{\rho NN}\bar{N}\gamma_{\mu}\tfrac{1}{2}\boldsymbol{\tau}N\cdot\boldsymbol{\rho}^{\mu} \tag{5.8}$$

and an effective tensor ("magnetic") coupling:

$$\mathcal{H}_{\rho NN}{}^{T} = \frac{g_{\rho NN}}{4M} \overline{N}\sigma_{\mu\nu}\boldsymbol{\tau}N \cdot (\partial^{\mu}\boldsymbol{\rho}^{\nu} - \partial^{\nu}\boldsymbol{\rho}^{\mu}) \tag{5.9}$$

[Notation: The γ-matrices and metric are characterized as follows: $\gamma_0{}^{\dagger} = \gamma_0$; $\gamma_i{}^{\dagger} = -\gamma_i$, $i = 1, 2, 3$; $\gamma_5 = \gamma_0\gamma^1\gamma^2\gamma^3$, $\gamma_5{}^{\dagger} = -\gamma_5$; $\sigma_{\mu\nu} = i[\gamma_\mu,\gamma_\nu]/2$, $g_{00} = -g_{ii} = 1$, $i = 1, 2, 3$.]. In (5.8) the coupling constant $f_{\rho NN}$ has been accompanied by $\frac{1}{2}\boldsymbol{\tau}$ rather than $\boldsymbol{\tau}$ so that the equality $f_{\rho NN} = f_{\rho\pi\pi}$, the latter defined by

$$\mathcal{H}_{\rho\pi\pi} = f_{\rho\pi\pi}\boldsymbol{\rho}_{\mu} \cdot \boldsymbol{\pi} \times \partial^{\mu}\boldsymbol{\pi} \tag{5.10}$$

gives a natural description of the ρ being coupled to a conserved isospin current (11). In Eq. (5.9) the normalization of $g_{\rho NN}$ has been chosen so that in the analogous electromagnetic case g would be κe, where κ is the anomalous magnetic moment in units of $e/2M$ and $e^2/4\pi = 1/137$.

The coupling constants $f_{\rho NN}$ and $g_{\rho NN}$ can be related to the residues of the annihilation amplitudes $N\overline{N} \to \pi\pi$, Γ_1 and Γ_2 used by Frazer and Fulco (12) (in the ρ-dominant approximation) by computing the perturbation graph of Fig. 5.2 from Eqs. (5.8)–(5.10). The result is (13)

$$\begin{aligned} f_{\rho\pi\pi}f_{\rho NN}/4\pi &= -3\gamma_1 \\ f_{\rho\pi\pi}g_{\rho NN}/4\pi &= -3M\gamma_2 \end{aligned} \tag{5.11}$$

where $\text{Im}\,\Gamma_i(t) \equiv \pi\gamma_i\,\delta(t - m_\rho{}^2)$ in the pole approximation. Ball and Wong (14) estimate (on the basis of their study of the nucleon isovector form factor) that $\gamma_1 \cong -1.0$ and $M\gamma_2/\gamma_1 \cong 1.83$. The former gives a resultant $f_{\rho NN}f_{\rho\pi\pi}/4\pi$ in fairly good agreement with the "universal" value, if one takes $f_{\rho\pi\pi}$ from the ρ width, given by

$$\Gamma_{\rho\to 2\pi} = \frac{2}{3}\left(\frac{f_{\rho\pi\pi}{}^2}{4\pi}\right)\frac{k_\pi{}^3}{m_\rho{}^2} = \frac{1}{12}\left(\frac{f_{\rho\pi\pi}{}^2}{4\pi}\right) m_\rho \left(1 - \frac{4\mu^2}{m_\rho{}^2}\right)^{3/2} \tag{5.12}$$

where k_π is the center-of-mass pion momentum. Studies of low-energy πN scattering (15) suggest similar values of $f_{\rho NN}$ and $g_{\rho NN}$, and an explicit evaluation of the residues using a particular

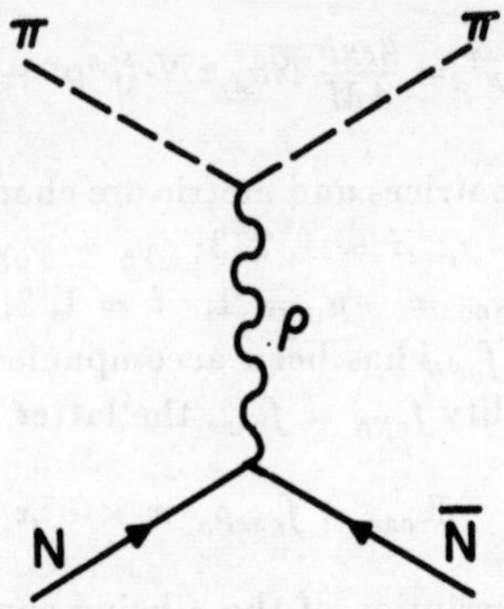

Fig. 5.2. Nucleon annihilation into two pions through a ρ-intermediate state is shown. The associated perturbation calculation yields the connection among the constants given in Eq. (5.11).

model of the annihilation reaction (16) gives about the same result.

The $SU(3)$ invariant VBB couplings can now be constructed by analogy with the PBB interaction. For the vector (electric) coupling we have

$$\mathcal{H}_{VBB}{}^V = f_{\rho NN}\bar{B}\gamma_\mu[\alpha_E\mathbf{D} + (1 - \alpha_E)\mathbf{F}]B \cdot \mathbf{V}^\mu \tag{5.13}$$

where V transforms as P in Eq. (3.63), and for the tensor (magnetic) coupling

$$\mathcal{H}_{VBB}{}^T = \frac{g_{\rho NN}}{2M}\,\bar{B}\sigma_{\mu\nu}[\alpha_M\mathbf{D} + (1 - \alpha_M)\mathbf{F}]B \cdot (\partial^\mu\mathbf{V}^\nu - \partial^\nu\mathbf{V}^\mu) \tag{5.14}$$

(We might remark that if unequal baryon masses are permitted then a third Lorentz-invariant coupling can be formed: see ref. 4.)

Concrete information about VBB coupling constants is very scarce. There is a substantial current prejudice in favor of predominantly F-type couplings ($\alpha_E = 1$) for the γ_μ term and a largely D coupling, with $\alpha_M = \alpha \cong .6 - .7$, for the magnetic coupling. The situation is further complicated by the ϕ–ω mixing problem, discussed in Chapter 6.

We note in passing that there is no corresponding freedom in the Sakata model PBB couplings. Denoting the Sakata triplet (p,n,Λ) by ψ, we have the obviously unique coupling of the octet P to the triplet:

$$\mathcal{H} = g\bar{\psi}\gamma_5\boldsymbol{\lambda}\psi\cdot\mathbf{P} \qquad \text{(Sakata model)} \tag{5.15}$$

where g is again the πNN coupling constant. Writing (5.15) out in full gives

$$\mathcal{H} = g\left[\bar{N}\gamma_5\boldsymbol{\tau}N\cdot\boldsymbol{\pi} + \frac{1}{\sqrt{3}}\bar{N}\gamma_5N\eta - \frac{2}{\sqrt{3}}\bar{\Lambda}\gamma_5\Lambda\eta + \sqrt{2}(\bar{N}\gamma_5K\Lambda + \text{H.c.})\right] \tag{5.16}$$

Similar constructions hold for the electric and magnetic couplings of a vector meson octet with a Sakata triplet.

A commonly used expression for $SU(3)$ invariant PBB couplings involves the trace of products of the 3×3 matrices introduced in Section 3.4. For example, the expressions

$$\text{Tr}\,(\bar{\mathcal{B}}\mathcal{B}\mathcal{P} \pm \bar{\mathcal{B}}\mathcal{P}\mathcal{B}) \tag{5.17}$$

are invariant under simultaneous unitary transformation of $\mathcal{B}$ and $\mathcal{P}$ by the matrix $U = \exp\,(i\boldsymbol{\alpha}\cdot\boldsymbol{\lambda}/2)$. Expanding the matrices in terms of the λ_i and the B_i, P_i as in Section 3.4 we use the trace condition and definitions [Eqs. (2.22)–(2.24)] as follows:

$$\begin{aligned} \text{Tr}\,[\bar{\mathcal{B}}\mathcal{B}\mathcal{P} + \bar{\mathcal{B}}\mathcal{P}\mathcal{B}] &= 2^{-3/2}\,\text{Tr}\,[\bar{B}_k\lambda_k B_i P_j(\lambda_i\lambda_j + \lambda_j\lambda_i)] \\ &= 2^{-3/2}\bar{B}_k B_i P_j\,\text{Tr}\,[\lambda_k(\tfrac{4}{3}\delta_{ij} + 2d_{ijl}\lambda_l] \\ &= 2^{-1/2}\bar{B}_k B_i P_j\, d_{ijl}\,\text{Tr}\,\lambda_k\lambda_l \\ &= \sqrt{2}\,\bar{B}\mathbf{D}B\cdot\mathbf{P} \end{aligned} \tag{5.18}$$

For the other combination we obtain

$$\begin{aligned} \text{Tr}\,[\bar{\mathcal{B}}\mathcal{B}\mathcal{P} - \bar{\mathcal{B}}\mathcal{P}\mathcal{B}] &= -\sqrt{2}\,if_{kji}\bar{B}_k B_j P_i \\ &= \sqrt{2}\,\bar{B}\mathbf{F}B\cdot\mathbf{P} \end{aligned} \tag{5.19}$$

Therefore, we can write the PBB interaction in one of the two equivalent forms (γ_5 implicit)

$$\begin{aligned}\mathcal{H} &= 2g\bar{B}(\alpha\mathbf{D} + (1-\alpha)\mathbf{F})B\cdot\mathbf{P} \\ &= \sqrt{2}g[\alpha \operatorname{Tr}(\bar{\mathcal{B}}\mathcal{B}\mathcal{P} + \bar{\mathcal{B}}\mathcal{P}\mathcal{B}) + (1-\alpha)\operatorname{Tr}(\bar{\mathcal{B}}\mathcal{B}\mathcal{P} - \bar{\mathcal{B}}\mathcal{P}\mathcal{B})\end{aligned} \tag{5.20}$$

Under the particular R transformation $\mathcal{P} \to \mathcal{P}^T$, $\mathcal{B} \to \mathcal{B}^T$, $\bar{\mathcal{B}} \to \bar{\mathcal{B}}^T$ the two types of coupling behave as follows:

$$\begin{aligned}\operatorname{Tr}\bar{\mathcal{B}}(\mathcal{B}\mathcal{P} \pm \mathcal{P}\mathcal{B}) &\to \operatorname{Tr}\bar{\mathcal{B}}^T(\mathcal{B}^T\mathcal{P}^T \pm \mathcal{P}^T\mathcal{B}^T) \\ &= \operatorname{Tr}[\pm(\mathcal{B}\mathcal{P}\bar{\mathcal{B}})^T + (\mathcal{P}\mathcal{B}\bar{\mathcal{B}})^T] \\ &= \pm \operatorname{Tr}[\bar{\mathcal{B}}(\mathcal{B}\mathcal{P} \pm \mathcal{P}\mathcal{B})]\end{aligned} \tag{5.21}$$

since the trace of a matrix is unchanged by transposition. As remarked previously there is no reason to believe in R invariance of the strong interactions. Indeed, the double occurrence of the regular representation is one of the especially interesting features of the eightfold way.

The coupling of a unitary singlet meson S with the baryon octet B is clearly

$$\bar{B}BS \tag{5.22}$$

leaving the Lorentz structure unspecified.

Next consider the interaction between an octet of vector mesons V and two identical pseudoscalar meson octets P. In the Hermitian basis the octet fields are "real": $\mathbf{P}^\dagger = \mathbf{P}$ and $\mathbf{V}^\dagger = \mathbf{V}$. Thus the four-vector quantity

$$P^b \overleftrightarrow{\partial_\mu} P^c \equiv P^b \partial_\mu P^c - \partial_\mu P^b \cdot P^c \tag{5.23}$$

is Hermitian (reordering as usual) and antisymmetric in the particle labels b, c. The coupling is thus of the form (recalling that $\partial_\mu V^\mu = 0$)

$$g_{bc}{}^a V_a{}^\mu P^b \overleftrightarrow{\partial_\mu} P^c \tag{5.24}$$

where the $g_{bc}{}^a$ are real constants that have to be chosen to make (5.24) invariant under $SU(3)$ transformations. We have learned that there are only two such sets of coefficients, f_{abc} and d_{abc}. The symmetric coupling can be eliminated by invoking a generalized Bose symmetry for the P.S. mesons, which states that $\mathcal{H}$ is invariant under the permutation $P^b \leftrightarrow P^c$. Thus $g_{bc}{}^a = -g_{cb}{}^a$ and

$$\mathcal{H}_{PPV} = g_{PPV} f_{abc} V_\mu{}^a P^b \overleftrightarrow{\partial^\mu} P^c \tag{5.25}$$

A byproduct of this argument is that a unitary singlet vector meson cannot couple to two P octets. A similar argument leads to the form of the V^2P coupling (here $\varepsilon_{\alpha\beta\gamma\delta}$ is the completely antisymmetric tensor $\varepsilon_{0123} = 1$)

$$\mathcal{H}_{VVP} = g_{VVP} d_{abc} \varepsilon^{\alpha\beta\gamma\delta} P^a \partial_\alpha V_\beta{}^b \partial_\gamma V_\delta{}^c \tag{5.26}$$

Lipkin has emphasized the interesting point that $SU(3)$ invariant trilinear meson interactions do not forbid any reactions not already forbidden for other reasons (17). This circumstance arises from the occurrence of both symmetrical (d) and antisymmetrical (f) types of coupling coefficients in $SU(3)$. Comparison of Eqs. (5.10) with Eq. (5.25) indicates that $g_{PPV} = \frac{1}{2} f_{\rho\pi\pi}$. An equivalent expression for (5.25) involving the trace of the meson matrices $\mathscr{P}$ and $\mathcal{V}$ is

$$\mathcal{H}_{PPV} = \frac{-ig_{PPV}}{\sqrt{2}} \operatorname{Tr} \mathscr{P}(\partial_\mu \mathscr{P} \cdot \mathcal{V}^\mu - \mathcal{V}^\mu \partial_\mu \mathscr{P}) \tag{5.27}$$

Similarly, the trace form of the VVP coupling is

$$\mathcal{H}_{VVP} = \frac{g_{VVP}}{\sqrt{2}} \operatorname{Tr} \mathscr{P}(\partial_\alpha \mathcal{V}_\beta \partial_\gamma \mathcal{V}_\delta + \partial_\gamma \mathcal{V}_\delta \partial_\alpha \mathcal{V}_\beta) \varepsilon^{\alpha\beta\gamma\delta} \tag{5.28}$$

It is very useful to express the PPV interaction, Eq. (5.25) or (5.27), in terms of isospin couplings. One finds, after a little manipulation, the expression

$$\begin{aligned}\mathcal{H}_{PPV} = g_{PPV}\{&\boldsymbol{\rho}_\mu \cdot (\boldsymbol{\pi} \times \overleftrightarrow{\partial^\mu} \boldsymbol{\pi} + iK^\dagger \boldsymbol{\tau} \overleftrightarrow{\partial^\mu} K) + (iM_\mu{}^\dagger \boldsymbol{\tau} K \cdot \overleftrightarrow{\partial^\mu} \boldsymbol{\pi} + \text{H.c.}) \\ &+ \sqrt{3}(iM_\mu{}^\dagger K \overleftrightarrow{\partial_\mu} \eta + \text{H.c.}) + \sqrt{3}\, i\phi_\mu K^\dagger \overleftrightarrow{\partial^\mu} K\}\end{aligned} \tag{5.29}$$

Here we have denoted the $K^*(888)$ doublet by M to prevent overcrowding. The doublet M is composed of col (M^+, M^0), while $M^\dagger$

stands for (M^-,M^0). As alluded to before and discussed in the next chapter, the symbol ϕ appearing in (5.29) is to be interpreted as a mixture of the physical ϕ–ω states. Similarly, working out Eq. (5.26) or (5.28) yields

$$\begin{aligned}\mathcal{H}_{VVP} = g_{VVP}\varepsilon^{\alpha\beta\gamma\delta}\Big\{&\frac{2}{\sqrt{3}}\boldsymbol{\pi}\cdot\boldsymbol{\rho}_{\alpha,\beta}\phi_{\gamma,\delta} + \boldsymbol{\pi}\cdot M_{\alpha,\beta}{}^{\dagger}\boldsymbol{\tau}M_{\gamma,\delta} \\ &- \frac{1}{\sqrt{3}}(K^{\dagger}M_{\alpha,\beta} + M_{\alpha,\beta}{}^{\dagger}K)\phi_{\gamma,\delta} + \frac{1}{\sqrt{3}}\eta\boldsymbol{\rho}_{\alpha,\beta}\cdot\boldsymbol{\rho}_{\gamma,\delta} \\ &- \frac{1}{\sqrt{3}}M_{\alpha,\beta}{}^{\dagger}M_{\gamma,\delta}\eta - \frac{1}{\sqrt{3}}\phi_{\alpha,\beta}\phi_{\gamma,\delta}\eta\end{aligned} \qquad (5.30)$$

In writing (5.30) we have introduced the shorthand notation of expressing the derivative $\partial_\beta V_\alpha$ as $V_{\alpha,\beta}$. The complexity of the *VVP* coupling is less than it seems from the great number of indices. The coupling is really of the form that describes the $\pi^0\gamma\gamma$ vertex, which can also be written as $\pi^0\mathbf{E}\cdot\mathbf{H}$ or in the "covariant" form $\pi^0\varepsilon^{\alpha\beta\gamma\delta}\partial_\alpha A_\beta\partial_\gamma A_\delta$. ($A_\mu$ is the electromagnetic four-potential.)

Another method for constructing invariant vertices is to employ the $SU(3)$ Clebsch-Gordan coefficients. DeSwart has constructed the *PBB* couplings in this manner; Martin and Wali (8) have derived the coupling of a $J = 3/2$ decuplet to the baryon and meson octets, expressed in terms of the isospin couplings. (In the latter case there is no mixing parameter, since the identity representation occurs only once in the direct product $\mathbf{10} \times \mathbf{8} \times \mathbf{8}$.)

In the preceding we have not been concerned about whether the various couplings are "fundamental" or phenomenological. If no such field operators exist, then one should convert the effective vertices to momentum space, changing the coupling constants into form factors.

There is one interesting idea that deserves special comment at this point. We show that if the ρ is coupled to the (conserved) isospin current, $SU(3)$ invariance requires that the vector octet be coupled to the F-spin current (conserved in this limit), i.e.,

$\alpha_E = 0$ in (5.13) and $f_{\rho NN} = f_{\rho\pi\pi}$. From Table 5.1 we see that the ρBB coupling part of Eq. (5.13) is

$$\mathcal{H}_{\rho BB} = f_{\rho NN}\boldsymbol{\rho}^{\mu}\cdot\Big\{\overline{N}\gamma_{\mu}\tfrac{1}{2}\boldsymbol{\tau}N + (1-2\alpha_E)\overline{\Xi}\gamma_{\mu}\tfrac{1}{2}\boldsymbol{\tau}\Xi + \frac{2\alpha_E}{\sqrt{3}}(\bar{\Lambda}\gamma_{\mu}\boldsymbol{\Sigma} + \text{H.c.}) + (1-\alpha_E)(-i\overline{\boldsymbol{\Sigma}}\gamma_{\mu}\times\boldsymbol{\Sigma})\Big\} \quad (5.31)$$

Clearly, $\alpha_E = 0$ is required* in order that the ρBB coupling be of the form $f_{\rho NN}\boldsymbol{\rho}^{\mu}\cdot\mathscr{J}_{\mu}{}^{T}$

$$\partial^{\mu}\mathscr{J}_{\mu}{}^{T} = 0 \qquad \text{and} \qquad \mathbf{T} = \int d^3x\,\mathscr{J}_0(x) \quad (5.32)$$

where the densities $\mathscr{J}_0(x)$ are constructed as in Section 1.3.

If we add the contributions of the VPP coupling (with $g_{PPV} = \frac{1}{2}f_{\rho\pi\pi} = \frac{1}{2}f_{\rho NN}$) we obtain a major portion of the isospin current

$$\mathscr{J}_{\mu}{}^{T} = \overline{N}\gamma_{\mu}\tfrac{1}{2}\boldsymbol{\tau}N + \overline{\Xi}\gamma_{\mu}\tfrac{1}{2}\boldsymbol{\tau}\Xi + \overline{\boldsymbol{\Sigma}}\gamma_{\mu}\mathbf{t}\boldsymbol{\Sigma} + \tfrac{1}{2}\boldsymbol{\pi}\times\overleftrightarrow{\partial}_{\mu}\boldsymbol{\pi} + iK^{\dagger}\tfrac{1}{2}\boldsymbol{\tau}\partial_{\mu}K + \cdots \quad (5.33)$$

Moreover, the K^* doublet is coupled to the strangeness changing current $\mathscr{J}_{\mu}{}^{\Delta s}$ and the ϕ to the hypercharge current $\mathscr{J}_{\mu}{}^{Y}$ with definite strength:

$$\mathcal{H}_{VBB} = f_{\rho NN}\Big\{\boldsymbol{\rho}^{\mu}\cdot\mathscr{J}_{\mu}{}^{T} + \sqrt{3}(M^{\dagger\mu}\mathscr{J}_{\mu}{}^{\Delta s} + \text{H.c.}) + \frac{\sqrt{3}}{2}\phi^{\mu}\mathscr{J}_{\mu}{}^{Y}\Big\} \quad (5.34)$$

where the strangeness changing current transforms as a 2-component spinor under $SU(2)$ transformations, and the hypercharge current is

$$\mathscr{J}_{\mu}{}^{Y} = [\overline{N}\gamma_{\mu}N - \overline{\Xi}\gamma_{\mu}\Xi] + iK^{\dagger}\overleftrightarrow{\partial}_{\mu}K + \cdots \quad (5.35)$$

The above considerations are closely connected with Sakurai's generalization (11) of the Yang-Mills theory (18) in which there are fundamental vector mesons (ρ,ϕ,ω) coupled to the currents of

* From this it follows that the electric coupling of the vector mesons is given by the "F-spin" current (cf. Eq. 5.13). The D and F currents are respectively even and odd under R-conjugation.

the quantities conserved in strong interactions (isospin, hypercharge, and baryon number). In addition, the strange vector meson (K^* or M) is coupled to the "partially conserved" strangeness changing current. (For a discussion of the generalization to many compact Lie groups, see Gell-Mann and Glashow (19).) If the physical ω were a pure member of an octet then the ω would be coupled to the baryon current $\bar{B}\gamma_\mu B$ in the form

$$g_{\omega BB}\omega^\mu \bar{B}\gamma_\mu B \tag{5.36}$$

However the actual situation is more complicated than this, due to ϕ–ω mixing. In the absence of a symmetry greater than $SU(3)$, $g_{\omega BB}$ has no relation to $f_{\rho NN}$. Some (presently conflicting) estimates based on vector meson exchange models of nucleon–nucleon forces are now available.

The present time is not propitious for a detailed evaluation of various methods of determining effective coupling constants. We shall instead consider only one especially direct method, that of measuring the decay widths of resonances.

5.2 Branching Ratios in Strong Decay Processes

In the limit of perfect unitary symmetry the branching ratios for the decay of a resonance are given simply by Clebsch-Gordan coefficients. We can illustrate by reviewing the implications of isospin conservation for the decay of the 3–3 isobar N^*. The N^* occurs in four charge states with the usual wave functions

$$\begin{aligned} &N^{*++} \qquad \psi_{++} = \pi^+ p \\ &N^{*+} \qquad \psi_{+} = \sqrt{\tfrac{2}{3}}\pi^0 p + \sqrt{\tfrac{1}{3}}\pi^+ n \\ &N^{*0} \qquad \psi_{0} = \sqrt{\tfrac{2}{3}}\pi^0 n + \sqrt{\tfrac{1}{3}}\pi^- p \\ &N^{*-} \qquad \psi_{-} = \pi^- n \end{aligned} \tag{5.37}$$

In terms of the total width $\Gamma = \Gamma(\pi^+ p)$, we expect

$$\begin{aligned} \Gamma(N^{*+} \to \pi^0 p) &= \tfrac{2}{3}\Gamma \\ \Gamma(N^{*+} \to \pi^+ n) &= \tfrac{1}{3}\Gamma \end{aligned} \tag{5.38}$$

Because the masses of the different charge states of N^* are not exactly the same, the relations (5.38) will not be strictly valid. At the present level of understanding, the corrections are of two types: first, the mass differences affect the kinematical and phase space factors in a way that is easy to account for; second, the matrix elements differ from the ones predicted by "perfect symmetry" by an amount which is easily calculable only if the transformation property of the symmetry-breaking term is known. In practice, this extra term has to be weak if any simple estimate is to be made of its effect. For example, in the N^* decay we expect that the electric charge is responsible for deviations from charge independence. The effect is small and the extra interaction is linear in the third component of isotopic spin so that perturbation theory can be used. A systematic general way to handle such perturbations has been developed (20–22). Most applications to date simply make the obvious kinematical corrections.

As a first illustration we use the vertex [Eq. (5.25) or (5.29)] to correlate the ρ meson width (about 100 MeV) with that of the ϕ meson, assuming both to belong to an octet of vector mesons. As the masses are quite different (750 MeV for ρ, 1020 MeV for ϕ) the kinematical factors are very important. The only nonzero f_{abc} $(c = 8)$ coefficients are $f_{458} = f_{678} = \sqrt{3}/2$. Thus the ϕ couples only to the K mesons in the limit of unitary symmetry, as is seen explicitly in Eq. (5.29). The decay rates into K^+K^- and $\bar{K}^0K^0$ are equal; the total rate is quickly found to be

$$\Gamma_{\phi\to K\bar{K}} = \frac{4}{3}\frac{(\sqrt{3}g_{PPV})^2}{4\pi}\frac{p_K{}^3}{m_\phi{}^2} \tag{5.40}$$

The only significant allowed ρ decay mode is $\rho \to 2\pi$. The ρ width is

$$\Gamma_{\rho\to 2\pi} = \frac{2}{3}\frac{(2g_{PPV})^2}{4\pi}\frac{p_\pi{}^3}{m_\rho{}^2} \tag{5.41}$$

The ratio of the width of the ϕ to that of the ρ is thus

$$\frac{\Gamma_{\phi\to K\bar{K}}}{\Gamma_{\rho\to 2\pi}} = \frac{3}{2}\frac{p_K{}^3/m_\phi{}^2}{p_\pi{}^3/m_\rho{}^2} \simeq \frac{3.4\text{ MeV}}{100\text{ MeV}} \tag{5.42}$$

Later we shall wish to refine this value to account for the ϕ–ω mixing which reduces the octet component of the physical ϕ. For a further discussion of ϕ decay see the note by Sakurai (23). It is interesting to record here the measured value $\Gamma_\phi = 3.1 \pm 1.0$ MeV (24). Of the other PPV couplings, the $K^* \to K\eta$ mode is kinematically forbidden. The decay mode $K^* \to K\pi$ has width given by

$$\frac{\Gamma_{K^* \to K\pi}}{\Gamma_{\rho \to 2\pi}} = \frac{3}{4} \frac{p_{K\pi}{}^3/m_{K^*}{}^2}{p_{\pi\pi}{}^3/m_\rho{}^2} \tag{5.43}$$

where $p_{K\pi}$ ($p_{\pi\pi}$) is the center-of-mass momentum of the K or π (π or π) in the rest system of the K^* (ρ). Numerical evaluation gives $\Gamma_{K^*}/\Gamma_\rho \approx 0.30$ as compared to the experimental value 0.47.

Next we consider the branching ratios for the decay of the various members of the $P_{3/2}$ decuplet into the various isospin states. Here we observe that most of the two particle channels making up the $SU(3)$ wave functions are closed. The thresholds vary greatly and large symmetry breaking effects are to be expected. For example, the $T = 3/2$ quartet in **10** is composed of equal components of $N\pi$ and ΣK in the limit of perfect $SU(3)$ symmetry. How is one to reconcile the successful dispersion theory description of low energy pion–nucleon scattering (which ignores the ΣK channel altogether) with the spectacular mass formulas, which are seemingly predicated on the smallness of the symmetry violation? Here we only mention that the mass perturbations involve quantities distinct from the state vectors. Thus the actual $T = 3/2$, πN state may be nearly of the form $[\psi_{27}(1, 3/2) - \psi_{10}(1,3/2)]/\sqrt{2}$ but the perturbation which lifts the degeneracy nevertheless transform as **8**.

In the limit of $SU(3)$ symmetry the widths for the decays of N^*, $Y_1{}^*$, $\Xi_{1/2}{}^*$, and Ω would all be equal (all components of a V-spin multiplet have the same width). Or, if the particles were stable in the symmetric limit, the corresponding coupling constants would be equal. The wave functions of these particles can be read from Table 3.4. We observe that the Ω couples to only one pair, $\Xi\bar{K}$. Of the constituents of the Ξ^*, only the $\Xi\pi$

channel is open. Similarly, the decay of N^* into ΣK is energetically forbidden. However, the Y_1^* can decay into both $\Sigma\pi$ and $\Lambda\pi$. The symmetric branching ratio is

$$\frac{\Gamma(Y_1^* \to \Sigma\pi)}{\Gamma(Y_1^* \to \Lambda\pi)} = \frac{2}{3} \tag{5.44}$$

as compared with the experimental value (25) $\lesssim .04$! Of course the kinematical corrections have not yet been supplied. A favorite fudge factor is given by (7, 26)

$$\Gamma_l = \gamma_l \frac{p^{2l+1}}{(1 + a^2p^2)^l} \tag{5.45}$$

where l is the orbital momentum, $1/a$ an effective radius, and γ_l the reduced width of the resonance. The correction involving the parameter a has to be viewed with distrust in a relativistic theory; presumably it depends on dynamical details not always discovered by inspection. Fortunately, the threshold factor p^{2l+1} gives the major energy variation of Γ_l. It is then supposed that the symmetry considerations apply to γ_l, although the validity of this assumption is not yet known.

Taking $1/a \cong 1$ BeV (Glashow and Rosenfeld (26) used $1/a =$ 350 MeV) Cutkosky finds (7) $\Gamma(Y_1^* \to \Sigma\pi)/(Y_1^* \to \Lambda\pi) = .16$, still uncomfortably larger than the experimental value. On the basis of his investigation of the dynamics of the $P_{3/2}$ decuplet, Cutkosky suggested that there should be some admixture of **27** into the $P_{3/2}$ resonances. Let us see if "contamination" of the **10** by the **27** gives an easy interpretation of the suppression of the $\Sigma\pi$ decay mode of Y_1^*. We write (to lowest order)

$$\psi_{Y_1^*} = N[\psi_{10}(0,1) - \sqrt{\tfrac{5}{6}}\, r\psi_{27}(0,1)] \tag{5.46}$$

From the wave functions (Table 3.4) we notice: *1*) the **27** state has no $\Sigma\pi$ component, *2*) for $r > 0$ the $\Lambda\pi$ component is enhanced, while the heaviest two particle states ΞK and $\Sigma\eta$ are suppressed. (For $r = 1$ the latter states are completely absent.) The ratio for decay of a pure **10** state [e.g., Eq. (5.44) modified by (5.45)] is then multiplied by the factor $(1 + r)^{-2}$. An r of order unity then suppresses the relative $\Sigma\pi$ decay to a value compatible with experiment.

Suppose, for simplicity, that the Y_1^* actually corresponds to the mixture (5.46) with $r = 1$. Then the wave function (5.46) reduces to

$$\psi_{Y_1^*} = \frac{1}{\sqrt{11}}[\sqrt{6}(\Lambda\pi)_1 + (\Sigma\pi)_1 - 2(N\bar{K})_1] \qquad (5.47)$$

and the width of Y_1^* is [ignoring the factor $(1 + a^2p^2)$ in (5.45), which is not very important here]

$$\Gamma(Y_1^*) = [(p_{\Sigma\pi}{}^3 + 6p_{\Lambda\pi}{}^3)/11p_{N\pi}{}^3]\Gamma(N^*) \cong .4\Gamma(N^*) \qquad (5.48)$$

Taking $\Gamma(N^*)$ to be 125 MeV yields 50 MeV for the width of Y_1^*. This value compares favorably with the experimental value of 53 MeV (25).

Next consider the width of $\Xi_{1/2}^*$. Since the $(\Xi\pi)_{1/2}$ component of **27** is very small we consider a pure **10** state, corrected for kinematical factors in the usual way. This gives

$$\Gamma(\Xi_{1/2}^*) = \tfrac{1}{4}(p_{\Xi\pi}{}^3/p_{N\pi}{}^3)\Gamma(N^*) = .07\Gamma(N^*) \qquad (5.49)$$

The predicted value (9 MeV) compares well with the experimental one (7 MeV).

We wish to emphasize that the theory of broken $SU(3)$ is still in a very primitive state, and that the above calculations may not have more than qualitative validity. Nevertheless, it is satisfying that a few sensible corrections of the type just described seem adequate to bring theory in line with experiment.

A valid question to raise at this point is whether some components of the **27** $P_{3/2}$ states have observable effects. This might seem likely, especially in view of our discussion of the Y_1^* branching ratio. Calculations by Golowich (10) and Wali and Warnock (27) show that the **27** representation is less important than might be expected.

An interesting situation obtains in the decay of a baryon octet resonance state into octets, e.g., a resonance $B^* \to B + P$, because there are two independent decay amplitudes. [Recall that the identity representation occurs twice in the decomposition $8 \times 8 \times 8$ which enters into the decay matrix element (ψ_{B^*}, ψ_{BP}).] Consider the $T = 1/2$, $Y = 1$ member of the octet. From Table 3.4 we find

$$\begin{aligned} \psi_{8_1} &= \frac{1}{2\sqrt{5}}[3(N\pi) - 3(\Sigma K) - (N\eta) - (\Lambda K)] \\ \psi_{8_2} &= \frac{1}{2}[(N\pi) + (\Sigma K) + (N\eta) - (\Lambda K)] \end{aligned} \tag{5.50}$$

where $(N\pi)$ denotes a normalized $T = 1/2$ isospin wave function, etc.

The observed state ψ_{B^*} will decay into a linear combination of ψ_{8_1} and ψ_{8_2}, specified by the mixing *angle* θ:

$$\psi_{B^*} = \cos\theta\psi_{8_1} + \sin\theta\psi_{8_2} \tag{5.51}$$

which gives the probability of the $T = 1/2$ state of $(N\pi)$, (ΣK), $(N\eta)$, and ΛK:

$$\begin{aligned} &(N\pi) && (\Sigma K) \\ &\left(\frac{3\cos\theta}{2\sqrt{5}} + \tfrac{1}{2}\sin\theta\right)^2, && \left(\tfrac{1}{2}\sin\theta - \frac{3}{2\sqrt{5}}\cos\theta\right)^2, \\ &(N\eta) && (\Lambda K) \\ &\left(\tfrac{1}{2}\sin\theta - \frac{1}{2\sqrt{5}}\cos\theta\right)^2, && \left(\tfrac{1}{2}\sin\theta + \frac{1}{2\sqrt{5}}\cos\theta\right)^2 \end{aligned} \tag{5.52}$$

The time reversal symmetry of strong interactions has been used in writing the probability amplitudes of ψ_{8_1}, ψ_{8_2} as relatively real.

Figure 5.3 shows the variation of the probability for a given particle pair (in the $T = 1/2$ state) as a function of the mixing angle. It will be observed that $P_{N\pi}(\theta) = P_{\Sigma K}(-\theta)$, $P_{\Lambda K}(\theta) = P_{N\eta}(-\theta)$. The dominance of πN interactions in the $Y = 1$, $T = 1/2$ channel suggests that θ is positive. Of course, when given an octet one can find θ by comparing the experimental branching ratios of a given (Y, T) state with Fig. 5.3. This has been done by

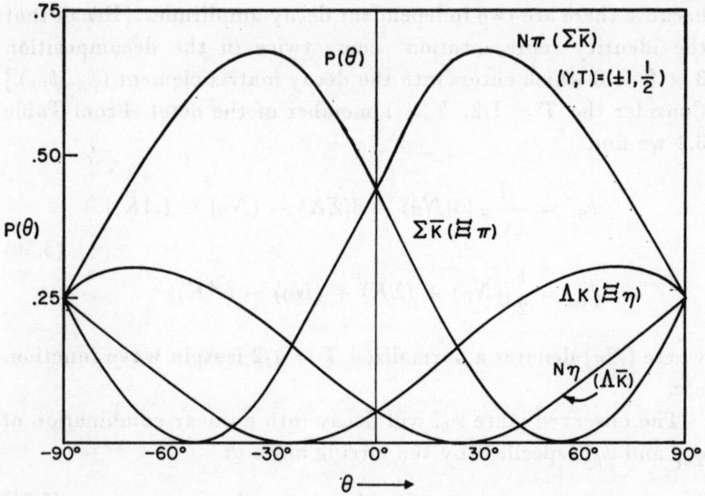

Fig. 5.3. The general octet wave function built from the pseudoscalar meson and baryon octets has an arbitrary parameter determining the relative probability of various two particle isospin components (see Eq. (5.51)). The probabilities $P(\theta)$ of finding $T = 1/2$, $Y = \pm 1$ components are shown.

Glashow and Rosenfeld (26) for a $D_{3/2}$ octet (including the $T = 1/2$, "2nd" πN resonance at 1512 MeV) and existing members of a presumed $F_{5/2}$ octet (including the "3rd" πN resonance at 1688 MeV). As the experimental situation with regard to these "octets" is rather fluid, we shall not give a detailed discussion. (For example, the 1520 MeV, $D_{3/2}$ $Y_0{}^*$ is now believed to be a unitary singlet, rather than the $T = 0$ member of an octet.) Further, all members of the presumed $F_{5/2}$ octet have not yet been discovered. We mention, however, that the value of $\theta \approx 35°$ gives a satisfactory fit to all the octets. One direct piece of evidence is the very small (or completely absent) decay mode of the 1688 MeV state into the ηN channel (3, 29).

One further important remark is that the most plausible dynamical models of the higher baryon resonances lead to essentially the same ratio of $\mathbf{8}_1$ and $\mathbf{8}_2$. If we regard the baryon octet

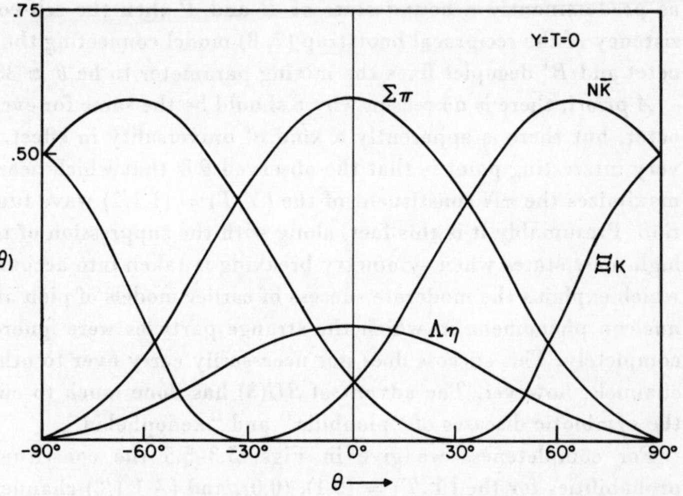

Fig. 5.4. The probability of finding the $T = Y = 0$ two particle components in the octet wave function is given as a function of the mixing angle θ.

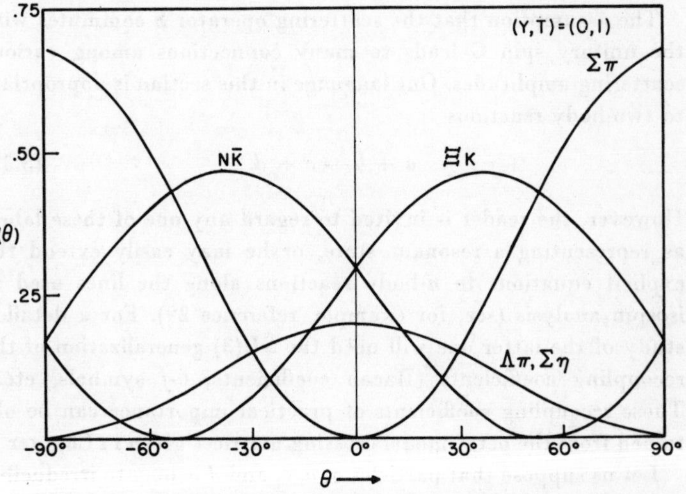

Fig. 5.5. The probability of finding the $T = 1$, $Y = 0$ two particle components in the octet wave function is given as a function of the mixing angle θ.

as predominantly a bound state of B and P then the self-consistency of the reciprocal bootstrap (7, 8) model connecting the B octet and B^* decuplet fixes the mixing parameter to be $\theta \approx 33°$.

A priori, there is no reason why θ should be the same for every octet, but there is apparently a kind of universality in effect. A very interesting point is that the observed θ is that which nearly maximizes the πN constituent of the $(Y,T) = (1,1/2)$ wave function. Presumably it is this fact, along with the suppression of the high mass states when symmetry breaking is taken into account, which explains the moderate success of earlier models of pion and nucleon phenomena in which the strange particles were ignored completely. This success does not necessarily carry over to other channels, however. The advent of $SU(3)$ has done much to cure the symbiotic diseases of "piophilia" and "xenophobia".

For completeness we give in Figs. 5.3–5.5 the constituent probabilities for the $(Y,T) = (0,1)$, $(0,0)$, and $(-1,1/2)$ channels.

5.3 $SU(3)$ Invariance and Scattering Amplitudes

The assumption that the scattering operator S commutes with the unitary spin $\mathbf{G}$ leads to many connections among various scattering amplitudes. Our language in this section is appropriate to two-body reactions

$$a + b \rightarrow c + d. \tag{5.53}$$

However, the reader is invited to regard any one of these labels as representing a resonant state, or he may easily extend the explicit equations to n-body reactions along the lines used in isospin analysis (see, for example, reference 29). For a detailed study of the latter one will need the $SU(3)$ generalization of the recoupling coefficients (Racah coefficients, 6-j symbols, etc.). Those recoupling coefficients of practical importance can be obtained from the octet-model crossing matrices given in Chapter 7.

Let us suppose that particles a, b, c, and d belong to irreducible representations of $SU(3)$. Using the $SU(3)$ Clebsch-Gordan coefficients discussed in Chapter 4 we can expand the states $|ab\rangle$

and $|cd\rangle$ in terms of various irreducible representations contained in the products of $a \times b$ and $c \times d$, as in Eq. (4.9).

$$|ab\rangle = \sum_{\mu\nu\gamma} \begin{pmatrix} \mu_a & \mu_b & \mu_\gamma \\ \nu_a & \nu_b & \nu \end{pmatrix} \psi \begin{pmatrix} \mu_a & \mu_b & \mu_\gamma \\ & & \nu \end{pmatrix} \quad (5.54)$$

A similar equation holds for the final state $|cd\rangle$. We thus obtain

$$\langle cd|\, S\, |ab\rangle = \sum_{\mu\nu\gamma} \sum_{\mu'\nu'\gamma'} \begin{pmatrix} \mu_a & \mu_b & \mu_\gamma \\ \nu_a & \nu_b & \nu \end{pmatrix} \begin{pmatrix} \mu_c & \mu_d & \mu'_{\gamma'} \\ \nu_c & \nu_d & \nu' \end{pmatrix} \langle cd(\mu'_{\gamma'}\nu')|\, S\, |ab(\mu_\gamma\nu)\rangle \quad (5.55)$$

where in writing the $\langle cd(\mu'_{\gamma'}\nu')|\, S\, |ab(\mu_\gamma\nu)\rangle$ we have suppressed the constant quantities μ_a, μ_b, μ_c, and μ_d. Invariance of S under the subgroup $SU(2)_T \times U(1)_Y$ (the actual symmetry group of the strong interactions) guarantees that the only nonzero contributions to (5.55) occur for $\nu' = \nu$. Next we show that if the representations $\mu_{\gamma'}$ [specifically $D^{(\mu_{\gamma'})}(p',q')$] and $\mu_\gamma(D^{(\mu_\gamma)}(p,q))$ are inequivalent then the matrix element $\langle cd\mu'_{\gamma'}\nu|\, S\, |ab\mu\nu\rangle$ vanishes. By assumption of $SU(3)$ invariance the two Casimir operators [Eq. (3.46)] commute with S:

$$[C_2,S] = [C_3,S] = 0 \quad (5.56)$$

Taking matrix elements of these relations shows that

$$\begin{aligned} (C_2(p',q') - C_2(p,q))\langle cd(\mu'_{\gamma'}\nu)|\, S\, |ab(\mu_\gamma\nu)\rangle &= 0 \\ (C_3(p',q') - C_3(p,q))\langle cd(\mu'_{\gamma'}\nu)|\, S\, |ab(\mu_\gamma\nu)\rangle &= 0 \end{aligned} \quad (5.57)$$

Thus the S matrix vanishes unless $p' = p$ and $q' = q$. In the usual way $\langle cd|\, S\, |ab\rangle$ is independent of the T_3 component contained in ν. This follows from the fact that S commutes with $T_\pm$. Moreover, this matrix element is independent of ν because of the occurrence of generators that change the eigenvalues T, Y. Thus Eq. (5.46) reduces to

$$\langle cd|\, S\, |ab\rangle = \sum_{\mu\nu\gamma\gamma'} \begin{pmatrix} \mu_a & \mu_b & \mu_\gamma \\ \nu_a & \nu_b & \nu \end{pmatrix} \begin{pmatrix} \mu_c & \mu_d & \mu_{\gamma'} \\ \nu_c & \nu_d & \nu \end{pmatrix} \langle cd(\mu\gamma')|\, S\, |ab(\mu\gamma)\rangle \quad (5.58)$$

The content of the above can be recognized as a restatement of the Wigner-Eckart theorem discussed in Chapter 4.

One new feature that emerges here is the multiple occurrence of (equivalent) irreducible representations. For example, in the scattering of P and B octets ($\mathbf{8} \times \mathbf{8} = \mathbf{1} + \mathbf{8}_1 + \mathbf{8}_2 + \mathbf{10} + \mathbf{10}^* + \mathbf{27}$) we need seven amplitudes to describe all possible scatterings $P_a + B_b \to P_c + B_d$:

$$S(\mathbf{1}), S(\mathbf{8}_1), S(\mathbf{8}_2), S(\mathbf{8}_1 \to \mathbf{8}_2), S(\mathbf{10}), S(\mathbf{10}^*), S(\mathbf{27}). \qquad (5.59)$$

The amplitude $S(8_1 \to 8_2)$ is not distinct from that for $8_2 \to 8_1$ because of the time-reversal invariance of strong interactions.

One can invert the procedure by starting from $SU(3)$ wave functions and expanding the corresponding S-matrix elements in terms of particle (isospin-hypercharge) states, using the isoscalar factors.

For example, from Eq. (5.50) we see that the $T = 1/2$, $Y = 1$ octet scattering amplitudes are

$$\begin{aligned}
\langle 8_1 | \, S \, | 8_1 \rangle &= \tfrac{1}{20}[9S(\pi N) + 9S(\Sigma K) + S(N\eta) + S(\Lambda K)] \\
\langle 8_2 | \, S \, | 8_2 \rangle &= \tfrac{1}{4}[S(N\pi) + S(\Sigma K) + S(N\eta) + S(\Lambda K)] \qquad (5.60) \\
\langle 8_2 | \, S \, | 8_1 \rangle &= \frac{1}{4\sqrt{5}}[3S(N\pi) - 3S(\Sigma K) - S(N\eta) + S(\Lambda K)]
\end{aligned}$$

As discussed in the preceding section, a resonant or bound octet state is, in general, a mixture of $\mathbf{8}_1$ and $\mathbf{8}_2$. Corresponding to the linear combination (5.51) (with θ fixed by dynamics or possibly some still greater symmetry) a pole in the S matrix $\langle \psi_B | \, S \, | \psi_B \rangle$ is expected near the resonance energy in the appropriate partial wave amplitude on the second sheet in the energy available. The other independent state, $\psi_{B'} = -\sin\theta\psi_{8_1} + \cos\theta\psi_{8_2}$, exhibits no special behavior there.

The assumption of $SU(3)$ symmetry as applied to the full reaction amplitude has not yet had as impressive success as certain other predictions. At least part of the reason is that every partial wave amplitude requires a different correction factor due to kinematical considerations. (Only when a resonant state can be isolated is it easy to make comparisons of the type of Section 5.2.) One rough means of accounting for this circumstance has been proposed by Meshkov, Snow, and Yodh (30), who compare various reactions of the type $P + B \rightarrow B^* + P$ at the same kinetic energy in the center-of-mass frame. Another method commonly used in the construction of dynamical models of various reactions is to use physical masses, but $SU(3)$ coupling constants for the computation of forces. This approach makes use of the apparent fact that the $SU(3)$ values of reduced couplings seem to be less spoiled than the magnitude of the amplitudes. Moreover, in a bootstrap model one can recompute the coupling constants and (hopefully) arrive at a self-consistent dynamics.

We conclude this section by describing how reactions can be related by use of the U- or V-spin subgroups. This method requires only the $SU(2)$ Clebsch-Gordan coefficients and is very simple and rapid in execution. Our discussion follows that of Lipkin (31). To illustrate this technique consider the reactions:

$$\begin{aligned} \pi^- + P &\rightarrow K^+ + Y_1{}^{*-} \\ \pi^- + P &\rightarrow \pi^+ + N^{*-} \\ K^- + P &\rightarrow K^+ + \Xi^{*-} \\ K^- + P &\rightarrow \pi^+ + Y_1{}^{*-} \end{aligned} \tag{5.61}$$

The $P_{3/2}$ resonances $(N^{*-}, Y_1{}^{*-}, \Xi^-)$ belong to the same U-spin quartet (they all have the same charge). The pairs (π^-, K^-) and (K^+, π^+) also belong to U-spin doublets and the proton is the $U_3 = 1/2$ member of the U-spin doublet. Thus the total U-spin of the left-hand side of (5.61) is 0 or 1, while it is 1 or 2 on the right-hand side. Thus to the extent that U-spin is conserved, only one amplitude ($U = 1$) describes the reactions (5.61). The first two reactions have $U_3 = +1$ and the last two have $U_3 = 0$. The amplitudes are given by the $U = 1$ reaction amplitude (called a_1) multiplied by the projection of the initial and final states on the $U = 1$ state. Thus the amplitudes are in the ratio $-\frac{1}{2}a_1 : \frac{\sqrt{3}}{2}a_1 : -\frac{1}{2}a_1 : \frac{1}{2}a_1$.

Reactions involving the emission or absorption of photons provide an especially powerful utilization of the U-spin method. This is because the charge operator is a U-spin scalar. Hence the initial and final stages, $|i\rangle$ and $|f\rangle$, of any product of current operators $j_\mu(x)$ have the same value of U and U_3:

$$\langle f|\, j_\alpha(x_1)\cdots j_\nu(x_n)\,|i\rangle \qquad U_f = U_i;\quad U_{3f} = U_{3i} \tag{5.62}$$

The charge is a component of the octet vector $(G_3 + G_8/\sqrt{3})$ and hence is not invariant under $SU(3)$. Thus we shall place the discussion of electromagnetic process in the following chapter on "broken $SU(3)$."

References

1. R. H. Dalitz, *Ann. Revs. Nucl. Sci.*, **13**, 339 (1963).
2. J. J. de Swart and C. K. Iddings, *Phys. Rev.*, **130**, 319 (1963).
3. P. Carruthers, *Phys. Rev. Letters*, **12**, 259 (1964); G. Altarelli, F. Buccella, and R. Gatto, *Nuovo Cimento*, **35**, 331 (1965).
4. T. K. Kuo, *Phys. Rev.*, **129**, 2264 (1963); **130**, 1537 (1963).
5. S. Hatsukade and H. J. Schnitzer, *Phys. Rev.*, **128**, 468 (1962); **132**, 1301 (1963).
6. R. L. Warnock and G. Frye, *Phys. Rev.*, **138**, 947 (1965).
7. R. E. Cutkosky, *Ann. Phys. (N.Y.)*, **23**, 405 (1963).
8. A. W. Martin and K. C. Wali, *Nuovo Cimento*, **31**, 1324 (1964).
9. A. W. Martin and K. C. Wali, *Phys. Rev.*, **130**, 2455 (1963).
10. E. Golowich, *Phys. Rev.*, **134**, B1297 (1965).
11. J. J. Sakurai, *Ann. Phys. (N.Y.)*, **11**, 1 (1960).
12. W. R. Frazer, and J. R. Fulco, *Phys. Rev.*, **117**, 1603, 1609 (1960).
13. P. Carruthers, *Lectures in Theoretical Physics*, Vol. VIIb, Univ. of Colorado Press, Boulder, Colo., 1965, p. 82.
14. J. S. Ball, and D. Y. Wong, *Phys. Rev.*, **133**, B179 (1964).
15. A. Donnachie, J. Hamilton, and A. T. Lea, *Phys. Rev.*, **135**, B515 (1964).
16. M. Der Sarkissian, *Nuovo Cimento*, **34**, 1010 (1964).
17. H. J. Lipkin, *Phys. Lett.*, **7**, 221 (1963).
18. C. N. Yang and R. Mills, *Phys. Rev.*, **96**, 191 (1954).
19. M. Gell-Mann, and S. L. Glashow, *Ann. Phys. (N.Y.)*, **15**, 437 (1961).
20. C. Dullemond, A. J. MacFarlane, and E. C. G. Sudarshan, *Phys. Rev. Letters*, **10**, 423 (1963).
21. V. Gupta and V. Singh, *Phys. Rev.*, **135**, B1442 (1964); **136**, B782 (1964).
22. C. Beechi, E. Eberle, and G. Morpurgo, *Phys. Rev.*, **136**, B808 (1964).
23. J. J. Sakurai, *Phys. Rev. Letters*, **9**, 472 (1962).

24. N. Gelfand et al., *Phys. Rev. Letters*, **11**, 438 (1963).
25. A. H. Rosenfeld, A. Barbaro-Galtieri, W. H. Barkas, P. L. Bastien, J. Kirz, and M. Roos, *Rev. Mod. Phys.*, **37**, 633 (1965).
26. S. L. Glashow and A. H. Rosenfeld, *Phys. Rev. Letters*, **10**, 192 (1963).
27. K. C. Wali and R. Warnock, *Phys. Rev.*, **135**, B1358 (1964).
28. F. Bulos et al., *Phys. Rev. Letters*, **13**, 486 (1964).
29. P. Carruthers, *Phys. Rev.*, **122**, 1949 (1961).
30. S. Meshkov, G. A. Snow, and G. B. Yodh, *Phys. Rev. Letters*, **12**, 148 (1964).
31. H. J. Lipkin, *Lie Groups for Pedestrians*, Interscience, New York, 1965.

Chapter 6

Broken $SU(3)$

6.1 Introduction

As we have mentioned before, one of the remarkable aspects of unitary symmetry is its survival in the face of the large mass differences among particles belonging to the unitary multiplets. At present, it is not clear whether this lack of perfect symmetry is due to the explicit occurrence of forces which are not $SU(3)$ invariant (e.g., as the Zeeman splitting of atomic energy levels due to the rotationally non-invariant magnetic field), or rather to the self-consistency requirements of (now obscure) dynamical mechanisms possibly underlying the observed particles. In the absence of a fundamental understanding of this situation, we shall be fairly brief in our description of symmetry breaking. Fortunately, the data suggest that $SU(3)$ is broken in a very simple way. More surprising is the success of rather naive perturbation theory calculations. Despite the dubious dynamical approximations involved in such a treatment of the strong interactions, it is difficult not to regard the results as further *a posteriori* support for the validity of the "broken eightfold way."

In Chapter 1 we discussed the violation of isospin by electromagnetism (neglecting gravity and the weak interactions). In that case the strong interactions were supposed to have the symmetry $SU(2)_T \times U(1)_Y$ except for the small electromagnetic corrections. In a Lagrangian formalism we would write

$$\mathfrak{L} = \mathfrak{L}_{\text{strong}} + \mathfrak{L}_{e-m} \tag{6.1}$$

where $\mathfrak{L}_{\text{strong}}$ is invariant under $SU(2)_T \times U(1)_Y$ but $\mathfrak{L}_{e-m}$, containing the charge Q, is not invariant but nevertheless has a simple transformation property in the invariance group of $\mathfrak{L}_{\text{strong}}$. ($\mathfrak{L}_{e-m}$ transforms as the sum of a scalar and the third component of a vector. In particular, the fields entering into $\mathfrak{L}_{e-m}$ have simple transformation properties under the group.)

The reader is by now no doubt aware that $\mathfrak{L}_{\text{strong}}$ is approximately invariant under $SU(3)$. Therefore one might consider the division

$$\mathfrak{L}_{\text{strong}} = \mathfrak{L}_S + \mathfrak{L}_{MS} \tag{6.2}$$

where $\mathfrak{L}_S$ is the "very strong" part ($SU(3)$ invariant) and the "medium strong" part $\mathfrak{L}_{MS}$ conserves isospin and hypercharge. Thus $\mathfrak{L}_{MS}$ commutes with Y, $\mathbf{T}^2$, and T_3. The structure of $\mathfrak{L}_{MS}$ has to be taken from experiment.

To see what is involved we consider some specific models. Suppose we consider deviations from isospin conservation as reflected in the energy levels of nuclei. Imagine that the sole cause of these deviations comes from the neutron-proton mass difference. (This is unrealistic because of the $\pi^0 - \pi^+$ mass difference.) Then if the forces holding the nucleons together are charge independent the perturbation to the kinetic energy term is nonrelativistically, approximately $\sum (P_j^2/2M)(\Delta M_j/M)$ where $\Delta M_j = M - M_j$, with M the average mass and $M_j = \frac{1}{2}(M_p - M_n) + T_3^j(M_p - M_n)$ where T_3^j is the third component of the isospin for the jth nucleon. Thus each particle contributes a perturbation proportional to T_3^j of order of magnitude $E_{\text{kin}} \times (\Delta M/M)$ so that the splitting is easily and legitimately estimated by perturbation theory.

In the Sakata or quark model a similar treatment, which recognizes the mass difference between the isospin doublet and singlet, is quite natural. The mass term in Lagrangian theory is (cf. Eq. 3.60)

$$m_d(\bar{q}_1 q_1 + \bar{q}_2 q_2) + m_s \bar{q}_3 q_3 \tag{6.3}$$

Introducing the average mass $m_0 = \frac{2}{3}m_d + \frac{1}{3}m_s$ we can write (6.3) in the form

$$m_0 \bar{q}q - \frac{1}{\sqrt{3}}(m_d - m_s)\bar{q}\lambda_8 q \tag{6.4}$$

The role of λ_8 in distinguishing the iso-doublet and iso-singlet has been noted previously. In this model, the symmetry breaking term transforms as the eighth component of the unitary spin, G_8. Moreover, in the eightfold way G_8 has the physical significance of the hypercharge.

There is little evidence bearing on the validity of the specific form (6.4). However, such detailed information is not necessary for many purposes. In fact we can proceed in several stages of increasingly restrictive assumptions on the nature of $\mathfrak{L}_{MS}$. The main virtue of the form (6.4) is in suggesting the hypothesis that $\mathfrak{L}_{MS}$ transforms as G_8 (rather than, say, some function of G_8). This hypothesis is in striking analogy to the fact that the electromagnetic term $\mathfrak{L}_{e-m}$ transforms as the component of **G**, $G_3 + (1/\sqrt{3})G_8$.

Following an introductory section on mass splitting neglecting electromagnetism, we proceed on the following path of increasing specialization. First, we investigate the consequences of the hypothesis that the total Lagrangian breaks up into three pieces of decreasing magnitude with the indicated symmetry:

$$\begin{array}{lccccccc} & \mathfrak{L} & = & \mathfrak{L}_S & + & \mathfrak{L}_{MS} & + & \mathfrak{L}_{e-m} \\ \text{symmetry} & & & SU(3) & & SU(2)_T \times U(1)_Y & & SU(2)_U \times U(1)_Q \end{array} \tag{6.5}$$

Here we follow the approach of Feldman and Matthews (1). This method exhibits clearly which results depend on the "conservative" assumptions of (6.5) in distinction to the more specific ones that $\mathfrak{L}_{MS}$ transforms as G_8 and $\mathfrak{L}_{e-m}$ as $G_3 + (1/\sqrt{3})G_8$.

As we do not wish to solve the dynamical problem posed by (6.5), we convert (6.5) to an effective mass operator. The construction of effective Hamiltonians by means of eliminating certain dynamical variables is a standard procedure. We leave the details to the reader (see the paper by Marshak et al. (2) for one method). The mass operator corresponding to a specific type of particle is of the form

$$M = M_0 + M_T + M_U \tag{6.6}$$

where M_0 is $SU(3)$ invariant, M_T is an isospin scalar, and M_U is a U-spin scalar [cf. (6.5)]. Experimentally one notes that M_T is about an order of magnitude smaller than M_0; in turn, M_U is about an order of magnitude smaller than M_T. For mesons, we expect an expression similar to (6.6) involving the squares of the masses.

6.2 Mass Formulas (Neglecting Electromagnetism)

Let us assume explicitly that the medium strong mass operator M_T transforms like the hypercharge Y ($\propto G_8$). If we take the expectation value of $M_0 + M_T$ in the state ν, belonging to the *irreducible* representation μ, a mass formula relating various isospin multiplets can be obtained. (If the particles belong to a *reducible* representation of $SU(3)$ then mass inequalities can be obtained (3).) The mass is given by

$$M(\mu,\nu) = a(\mu) + \langle \mu,\nu | \, M_T \, | \mu,\nu \rangle \tag{6.7}$$

where $a(\mu)$ is a constant within the irreducible representation. We can, if we choose, use the Wigner-Eckart theorem [Eq. (4.25)] to express the matrix element in (6.7) in terms of a number of arbitrary constants. That number is equal to the number of times μ occurs in the decomposition $\mathbf{8} \times \mu$. Recall that the multiple occurrence of representations sometimes makes the $SU(3)$ Wigner-Eckart theorem more complicated than the $SU(2)$ version. Thus when $\mu = \mathbf{8}$ (an especially important case) two arbitrary constants occur in (6.7) in addition to $a(\mu)$. Hence we cannot assert that the matrix element of M_T is, in general, proportional to G_8. However, we can do just as well and also avoid looking up $SU(3)$ Clebsch-Gordan coefficients if we examine the behavior of L_{MS} under the subgroup of transformations $SU(2)_U \times U(1)_Q$.

By assumption, M_T transforms like Y. Recall that the operator Y is related to the diagonal generator $\mathbf{H}$ by $Y = 2\sqrt{3}\mathbf{r}'(1)\cdot\mathbf{H}$ [Eq. (2.55)]. By resolving $\mathbf{r}'(1)$ into orthogonal vectors $\mathbf{r}(3)$ and $\mathbf{r}'(3)$ we observe that Y is composed of U_3 and Q. From the definitions of Section 2.3 we find $\mathbf{r}'(1) = (\sqrt{3}/2)\mathbf{r}(3) - \frac{1}{2}\mathbf{r}'(3)$, from which we derive the relation

$$Y = U_3 + \tfrac{1}{2}Q \tag{6.8}$$

Eq. (6.8) will be recognized as a "rotated" version of the relation $Q = T_3 + \frac{1}{2}Y$.

Thus under $SU(2)_U \times U(1)_Q$ the operator M_T transforms as the sum of a U-spin vector and a U-spin scalar. Applying the $SU(2)$ Wigner-Eckart theorem to this subgroup leads to the result that *within a U-spin multiplet the mass is given by the equal-spacing rule*

$$M(U,U_3) = A + BU_3,$$

$$\text{or} \qquad M(U,U_3) - M(U, U_3 - 1) = \text{constant.} \tag{6.9}$$

As is well known, this expression is very well satisfied with a spacing of about 150 MeV for the baryon decuplet. Here only two constants enter in (6.7) since **10** × **8** contains **10** only once. Moreover, the weight diagram is nondegenerate so that the U-spin eigenfunctions have definite isospin as well. From (6.9) we get the result

$$m(N^*) - m(Y^*) = m(Y^*) - m(\Xi^*) = m(\Xi^*) - m(\Omega) \tag{6.10}$$

For the baryon octet, the non-empty relation following from (6.9) is

$$m(n) - m(\Sigma_U{}^0) = m(\Sigma_U{}^0) - m(\Xi^0) \tag{6.11}$$

where $\Sigma_U{}^0 = -\frac{1}{2}\Sigma^0 + (\sqrt{3}/2)\Lambda^0$ is the $U_3 = 0$ member of the U-spin triplet $(n, \Sigma_U{}^0, \Xi^0)$. Since $m(\Sigma_U{}^0) = \frac{1}{4}m(\Sigma) + \frac{3}{4}m(\Lambda)$, (6.11) can be rewritten in the form (4)

$$\tfrac{1}{2}[m(N) + m(\Xi)] = \tfrac{1}{4}[m(\Sigma) + 3m(\Lambda)] \tag{6.12}$$

This formula, which closely resembles an old one in the global symmetry scheme (5) $(\Lambda \leftrightarrow \Sigma)$, is also well satisfied. Using average multiplet masses the left-hand side is 1128 MeV as compared to 1134 MeV on the right-hand side.

The pseudoscalar mesons also form an octet; however, (6.12) is not at all valid. One can note that the perturbation is scarcely small in this case since the deviations of the actual masses from the average mass exceed the latter in some cases. Clearly, one cannot rely on perturbation theory in such a situation. However, the following speculation enormously improves the agreement. In relativistic field theories of mesons the mass m always enters as m^2. Therefore we might try the relation

$$m^2(K) = \tfrac{1}{4}[m^2(\pi) + 3m^2(\eta)] \tag{6.13}$$

(by charge conjugation invariance, K and $\bar{K}$ have the same mass). The most lenient validity condition on the derivation of (6.13), i.e., $\delta m^2 \ll m^2$, is flagrantly violated. Nevertheless, (6.13) is satisfied to within 5%. At present, there is no basic understanding of this question.

Some confusion arises if we consider the vector mesons; the ω (750 MeV) and ϕ (1020 MeV) both have the same quantum numbers ($J = 1^-$, $G = -1$, $T = Y = 0$). Indeed, neither mass fits the formula

$$m^2(K^*) = \tfrac{1}{4}[m^2(\rho) + 3m^2(x)] \tag{6.14}$$

which requires $m_x = 930$ MeV. It has been emphasized, especially by Sakurai (6), that there is likely to be a substantial mixing of such states, so that the observed ω and ϕ may be considered to be mixtures of a unitary single ω^0 and the isosinglet member of the unitary octet, ϕ^0. In this case, the violation of unitary symmetry is aggravated by the unstable dynamics of nearly degenerate states. Applying ordinary degenerate perturbation theory leads to the following picture.

We write the physical ϕ and ω states as linear superpositions

$$\begin{aligned} \phi &= \cos\lambda\phi^0 + \sin\lambda\omega^0 \\ \omega &= -\sin\lambda\phi^0 + \cos\lambda\omega^0 \end{aligned} \tag{6.15}$$

The (mass)^2 matrix is written in the two-dimensional space of ϕ^0 and ω^0:

$$M^2 = \begin{pmatrix} m^2(\phi^0) & m^2(\phi\omega) \\ m^2(\phi\omega) & m^2(\omega^0) \end{pmatrix} \tag{6.16}$$

and λ is determined by requiring col ($\cos\lambda$, $\sin\lambda$) to be an eigenvector of (6.16). The eigenvalues of (6.16) are

$$\left\{ \begin{matrix} m^2(\phi) \\ m^2(\omega) \end{matrix} \right\} = \tfrac{1}{2}[m^2(\phi^0) + m^2(\omega^0)] \pm \tfrac{1}{2}\{[m^2(\phi^0) - m^2(\omega^0)]^2 + 4m^4(\phi\omega)\}^{1/2} \tag{6.17}$$

while λ is determined from

$$\tan 2\lambda = \frac{2m^2(\phi\omega)}{m^2(\omega^0) - m^2(\phi^0)} \tag{6.18}$$

Taking the product of the eigenvalues we obtain an equation to eliminate $m^2(\phi\omega)$

$$m^2(\phi\omega) = [m^2(\phi^0)m^2(\omega^0) - m^2(\omega)m^2(\phi)]^{1/2} \tag{6.19}$$

To determine λ, we take the ϕ and ω masses from experiment and calculate ϕ^0 to be 930 MeV from the mass formula (6.14). $m(\omega^0)$ is determined from the sum rule

$$m^2(\phi) + m^2(\omega) = m^2(\phi^0) + m^2(\omega^0) \tag{6.20}$$

to be 885 MeV. The resulting mixing angle is $\lambda = 39°$. The mass values are shown in Fig. 6.1. For this calculation we have used

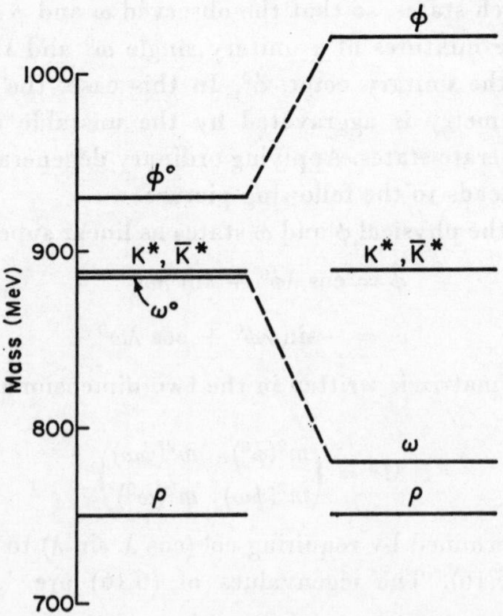

Fig. 6.1. The effect of $\phi - \omega$ mixing on the masses of the unitary singlet ω^0 and the $T = Y = 0$ member of the octet (ϕ^0) are indicated. For reference the masses of the remaining members of the vector meson octet are shown.

$m(\phi) = 1020$ MeV, $m(K^*) = 888$ MeV, $m(\omega) = 780$ MeV, and $m(\rho) = 750$ MeV.

According to this simple model, the physical ϕ spends $(\cos 39°)^2 = 60\%$ of its time as ϕ^0 and 40% as the singlet ω^0. (For the ω, interchange ϕ^0 and ω^0.) Of course (6.15) is only a rough approximation since many particle configurations are expected to be important constituents of the ϕ and ω mesons. However, it is interesting to follow up the implications of (6.15). To do this we suppose that, apart from simple kinematical corrections, the only violations of $SU(3)$ are due to ϕ–ω mixing.

With these assumptions let us reconsider the vertices analyzed in Chapter 5. First consider the decay $\phi \to K\bar{K}$. Since ω^0 is presumably an $SU(3)$ singlet, it cannot decay into two octet particles. Thus the rate previously calculated [Eq. (5.42)] should be decreased by the factor $(\cos \lambda)^2 = .6$. We thus get $\Gamma(\phi \to K\bar{K}) =$ 2 MeV. The mode $\phi \to \rho + \pi$ seems to be infrequent (7) ($< 10\%$ of $\phi \to K\bar{K}$). Of course the physical ω is too light to decay into $K\bar{K}$.

Consider next the isoscalar nucleon electromagnetic form factor, whose momentum transfer dependence is generally believed to be dominated by the ω and ϕ mesons (8). Since the photon couples through Q, which is a component of a vector operator, the $SU(3)$ singlet component ω^0 does not couple to the photon. This leads to a reduction factor $\cos \lambda$ and $-\sin \lambda$, respectively, for ϕ and ω, both given in terms of the $\phi^0\gamma$ coupling.

Consider the ϕBB and ωBB coupling, where B is the baryon octet. The singlet ω^0 couples to BB independently of the V octet coupling.

Further discussion of various applications may be found in the paper by Dashen and Sharp (9).

The phenomenon of ϕ–ω mixing is very interesting and provides a fertile source of speculations. We shall not describe these here, despite their great interest. Only one further point of view with regard to ϕ–ω mixing will be mentioned. The preceding discussion presumes that the effect is due to the breakdown of $SU(3)$. However, we could start from the point of view that the symmetry is greater than that of $SU(3)$, since we have nine nearly-degenerate vector mesons. The following simple model (10) illustrates such a circumstance. From the quarks q and $\bar{q}$ we can construct nine $J = 1^-$ bound states. *If* the quark components q_i are degenerate and the forces are independent of the $SU(3)$ index i for this partial wave, the nine states with wave functions

$$\begin{aligned} &(\lambda_i)_{jk}\bar{q}^j q^k \qquad (\mathbf{8}) \\ &\bar{q}\, q \qquad (\mathbf{1}) \end{aligned} \tag{6.21}$$

are degenerate (neglecting exchange forces). The $T = 0$ member of the octet (ϕ^0) is given by Eq. (3.61), with an extra (arbitrary) minus sign for convenience

$$\phi^0 = -\frac{1}{\sqrt{6}}(\bar{q}_1 q_1 + \bar{q}_2 q_2 - 2\bar{q}_3 q_3) \tag{6.22}$$

while the normalized $SU(3)$ singlet $\bar{q}q$ is

$$\omega^0 = \frac{1}{\sqrt{3}}(\bar{q}_1 q_1 + \bar{q}_2 q_2 + \bar{q}_3 q_3). \tag{6.23}$$

If we now let the mass m_3 of the $SU(2)$ singlet q_3 be different from that ($m_1 = m_2$) of the doublet (q_1,q_2), ϕ^0 and ω^0 no longer are physical eigenstates. Instead, the $T = Y = 0$ eigenstates are

$$\begin{aligned} \phi &= \bar{q}_3 q_3 \\ \omega &= \frac{1}{\sqrt{2}}(\bar{q}_1 q_1 + \bar{q}_2 q_2) \end{aligned} \tag{6.24}$$

[For the signs in the ω eigenfunction, refer to Eq. (1.31)] Expressing the physical states in terms of ϕ^0 and ω^0 gives

$$\begin{aligned} \phi &= \sqrt{\tfrac{2}{3}}\phi^0 + \sqrt{\tfrac{1}{3}}\omega^0 \\ \omega &= -\sqrt{\tfrac{1}{3}}\phi^0 + \sqrt{\tfrac{2}{3}}\omega^0 \end{aligned} \tag{6.25}$$

The mixing angle λ is now 35°, in good agreement with the "experimental" value given before.

Although this model should perhaps not be taken seriously, it exhibits some features of general interest. The symmetry of the model is $U(3)$, with basis $\bar{q}_i q_j$, reducible to $\mathbf{8} + \mathbf{1}$. No mass formula results unless assumptions are made about the nature of the forces (here independent of the unitary spin). However, in the general case mass inequalities can be derived (3). The present model is so specific that more explicit mass relations can be given. Since the ρ triplet is composed of the same components as ω (q_1,q_2) we have

$$m(\rho) = m(\omega) \tag{6.26}$$

Furthermore, since the usual mass formula holds for ϕ^0, which is $\frac{2}{3}\phi$ and $\frac{1}{3}\omega$, we obtain the relation

$$2m^2(\phi) + m^2(\omega) + m^2(\rho) = 4m^2(K^*) \tag{6.27}$$

Although these relations are in fair agreement with experiment, the reader is advised to regard with distrust all mass formulas based on simplified models.

To conclude this section we give the Okubo mass formula (11) for an arbitrary, irreducible representation of $SU(3)$. It is supposed that the mass operator for baryons [or (mass)^2 for mesons] transforms as the sum of an $SU(3)$ scalar and the $T_3{}^3$ ($Y = T = 0$) member of the octet. From Eq. (4.61) we know that the tensor operator $T_3{}^3$ has within an irreducible representation the effective form

$$T_3{}^3 = aA_3{}^3 + b[A_\lambda{}^3 A_3{}^\lambda - \tfrac{1}{3}(A,A)] \tag{6.28}$$

where a and b are representation-dependent constants. We next express (6.28) in terms of physical quantities. *A priori*, these are expected to be T and Y because (6.28) is invariant under $SU(2)_T \times U(1)_Y$. Further we know that $(A,A) = 2\mathbf{G}^2$ is a constant within an irreducible representation. The correlation (3.57) can be used to express the $A_\nu{}^\mu$ in terms of the G_i. We have $A_3{}^3 = -Y$. For $A_\lambda{}^3 A_3{}^\lambda$ we find

$$\begin{aligned} A_\lambda{}^3 A_3{}^\lambda &= (G_4 + iG_5)(G_4 - iG_5) + (G_6 + iG_7)(G_6 - iG_7) + \tfrac{4}{3}G_8{}^2 \\ &= G_4{}^2 + G_5{}^2 + G_6{}^2 + G_7{}^2 + G_8{}^2 + \tfrac{1}{3}G_8{}^2 \\ &\quad + i[G_5,G_4] + i[G_7,G_6] \\ &= \mathbf{G}^2 - \mathbf{T}^2 + \tfrac{1}{4}Y^2 + \tfrac{3}{2}Y \end{aligned} \tag{6.29}$$

recalling that $\mathbf{T}^2 = \Sigma_{i=1}^3 G_i^2$ and that G_8 is $(\sqrt{3}/2)Y$. Thus we find

$$T_3{}^3 = A + BY + C[\mathbf{T}^2 - \tfrac{1}{4}Y^2] \tag{6.30}$$

as an alternate form of (6.28). The mass formula is accordingly

$$M(\text{or } M^2) = A + BY + C[T(T+1) - \tfrac{1}{4}Y^2] \tag{6.31}$$

For mesons the term linear in Y is absent by charge conjugation invariance. For triangular representations, $T = 1 + \frac{1}{2}Y$ and (6.31) reduces to a linear relation

$$M(\text{triangular representations}) = A' + B'Y \tag{6.32}$$

also derivable from U-spin considerations. [Combine (6.9) with (6.8); for triangular representations there is no degeneracy, and the U-spin eigenfunctions are also T-spin eigenfunctions.)

We note here the "rotated" forms of (6.30):

$$T_1{}^1 = A' + B'Q + C'[U(U+1) - \tfrac{1}{4}Q^2] \tag{6.33a}$$

$$T_2{}^2 = A'' + B''Z + C''[V(V+1) - \tfrac{1}{4}Z^2] \tag{6.33b}$$

Equation (6.33a) is useful in the study of electromagnetic effects in systems of strongly interacting particles (12) (the charge operator Q transforms like $T_1{}^1$).

For further information on the conversion of tensor operators to useful forms the reader will wish to consult papers by Diu (13), Ginibre (14), Rosen (15), and Goldberg and Lehrer-Ilamed (16).

6.3 Mass Formulas (Including Electromagnetism)

We now discuss what can be learned from (6.6) including the electromagnetic term M_U and *not* making an explicit assumption on the form of M_T. For orientation consider the parallelogram formed by four neighboring points in a weight diagram (Fig. 6.2), supposed to be nondegenerate. If M_U were absent then isospin conservation would imply the vanishing of the equality

$$m(1) - m(2) = m(4) - m(3) \tag{6.34}$$

On the other hand, if M_T were absent the equality

$$m(1) - m(4) = m(2) - m(3) \tag{6.35}$$

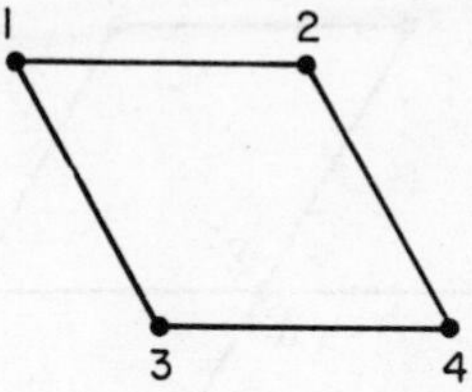

Fig. 6.2. The parallelogram of occupied sites (nondegenerate) illustrates the mass relation of Eqs. (6.34) and (6.35).

would also vanish. Now (6.34) and (6.35) are algebraically the same, and so it seems plausible that they be valid in the presence of *both* terms M_U and M_T [but the values of $m(1) - m(2)$, etc., are no longer zero]. That this is true follows on writing out (6.34) in detail

$$M_T(1) + M_U(1) - M_T(2) - M_U(2) = M_T(4) + M_U(4) - M_T(3) - M_U(3) \quad (6.36)$$

where $M_T(1) = \langle 1| M_T |1\rangle$, etc., and the states $|i\rangle$ belong to an irreducible representation of $SU(3)$. The states $|1\rangle$ and $|2\rangle$ are transformed into each other by $T_\pm$, which commute with M_T. Hence $M_T(1) = M_T(2)$, and similarly $M_T(3) = M_T(4)$. In the same way we see that $M_U(1) = M_U(4)$ and $M_U(2) = M_U(3)$, establishing the desired equality.

This "parallelogram law" can be generalized to include the case of degeneracy in the weight diagram. Before turning to this, we apply (6.34) to the baryon decuplet, obtaining

$$\begin{aligned} m(N^{*-}) - m(N^{*0}) &= m(Y_1^{*-}) - m(Y_1^{*0}) \\ m(N^{*0}) - m(N^{*+}) &= m(Y_1^{*0}) - m(Y_1^{*+}) \qquad (6.37) \\ m(Y_1^{*-}) - m(Y_1^{*0}) &= m(\Xi^{*-}) - m(\Xi^{*0}) \end{aligned}$$

The great width of these $P_{3/2}$ resonances relative to the electromagnetic splittings makes the relations (6.37) difficult to test.

The baryon octet provides a good example of how to handle a case of degeneracy. The sites are labeled as in Fig. 6.3. The center

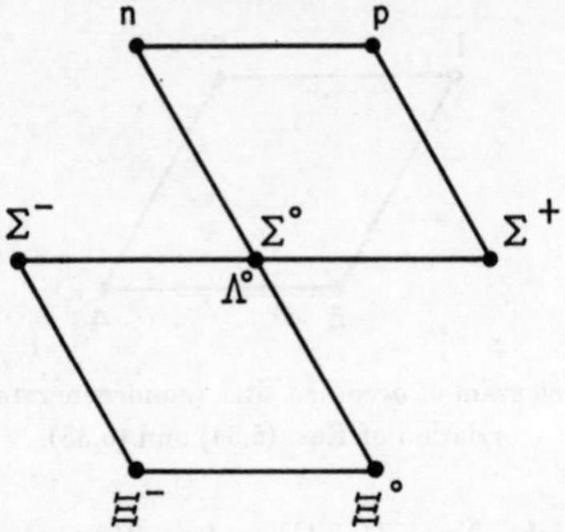

Fig. 6.3. Parallelograms in the baryon octet weight diagram useful in deriving mass relations are shown.

is degenerate and so the U-spin eigenfunctions differ from the isospin eigenfunctions. (The $U = 1$ and 0 eigenfunctions are $\Sigma_U{}^0 = -\frac{1}{2}\Sigma^0 + (\sqrt{3}/2)\Lambda^0$, $\Lambda_U{}^0 = (\sqrt{3}/2)\Sigma^0 + \frac{1}{2}\Lambda^0$.) The mass operators have matrix elements related by

$$\begin{aligned} m_T(n) &= m_T(p) & m_T(\Sigma^+) &= m_T(\Sigma^0) \\ m_U(n) &= m_U(\Sigma_U{}^0) & m_U(p) &= m_U(\Sigma^+) \\ m_T(\Sigma^-) &= m_T(\Sigma^0) & m_T(\Xi^-) &= m_T(\Xi^0) \\ m_U(\Sigma^-) &= m_U(\Xi^-) & m_U(\Xi^0) &= m_U(\Sigma_U{}^0) \end{aligned} \tag{6.38}$$

We thus find

$$\begin{aligned} m(n) - m(p) &= m_U(n) - m_U(p) \\ &= m_U(\Sigma_U{}^0) - m_U(\Sigma^+) \\ &= \tfrac{1}{4}m_U(\Sigma^0) + \tfrac{3}{4}m_U(\Lambda^0) - \frac{\sqrt{3}}{2}\, m_U(\Sigma\Lambda) - m_U(\Sigma^+) \\ &= m_U(\Sigma^0) - m_U(\Sigma^+) + \tfrac{3}{4}[m_U(\Lambda^0) - m_U(\Sigma^0)] \\ &\quad - \frac{\sqrt{3}}{2}\, m_U(\Sigma\Lambda) \end{aligned} \tag{6.39}$$

Since $m_T(\Sigma^0) = m_T(\Sigma^+)$ we find

$$m(n) - m(p) + m(\Sigma^+) - m(\Sigma^0) = \tfrac{3}{4}[m_U(\Lambda^0) - m_U(\Sigma^0)] - \frac{\sqrt{3}}{2}\, m(\Sigma\Lambda) \quad (6.40)$$

The "transition mass" $m(\Sigma\Lambda)$ is defined by

$$m(\Sigma\Lambda) = \langle\Sigma^0|\, M \,|\Lambda\rangle = \langle\Sigma^0|\, M_U \,|\Lambda^0\rangle = m_U(\Sigma\Lambda) \quad (6.41)$$

The right side of (6.40) can be further simplified by noting the relation

$$\tfrac{3}{4}[m_U(\Lambda) - m_U(\Sigma^0)] = -\frac{\sqrt{3}}{2}\, m(\Sigma\Lambda) \quad (6.42)$$

This follows immediately from the equality

$$\langle\Sigma_U{}^0|\, M_U \,|\Lambda_U{}^0\rangle = 0 \quad (6.43)$$

Thus Eq. (6.40) now reads

$$m(n) - m(p) + m(\Sigma^+) - m(\Sigma^0) = -\sqrt{3}\, m(\Sigma\Lambda) \quad (6.44)$$

The quantity $m(\Sigma\Lambda)$ depends entirely on the isospin-violating electromagnetism. Equation (6.44) gives a measure of the isospin impurity in the Σ^0–Λ^0 system, discussed below.

First, we notice that a similar analysis carried out for the other parallelogram of Fig. 6.3 yields the relation

$$m(\Xi^-) - m(\Xi^0) + m(\Sigma^0) - m(\Sigma^-) = \sqrt{3}\, m(\Sigma\Lambda) \quad (6.45)$$

Addition of (6.44) gives the relation first derived by Coleman and Glashow (17)

$$m(\Xi^-) - m(\Xi^0) = m(\Sigma^-) - m(\Sigma^+) + m(p) - m(n) \quad (6.46)$$

The right side of (6.46) is 7.0 ± 0.5 MeV, while the left side has been measured to be 6.1 ± 1.6 MeV, 6.8 ± 1.6 MeV, and 5 ± 3 MeV. (The experimental sources are given in reference 18.) This very satisfactory result is especially important because it provides support of $SU(3)$ independent of any special assumptions about the transformation properties of M_T and M_U.

For octet mesons the extra symmetry associated with charge conjugation reduces the equality corresponding to (6.46) to an empty identity. However, there is an analogue of the transition mass formula (6.44). For the pseudoscalar meson octet it is

$$\sqrt{3}\, m^2(\pi^0\eta) = m^2(K^+) - m^2(K^0) + m^2(\pi^0) - m^2(\pi^+) \quad (6.47)$$

Let us now restrict our attention to the case in which M_T transforms as Y, as in Section 6.2, but without restricting M_U. To first order, in the medium strong interactions, we again have the formula

$$M = A + BU_3 \quad (6.48)$$

within a U-spin multiplet. The argument of Section 6.2 works here because M_U (as well as M_0) is constant in a U-spin multiplet.

Therefore Eq. (6.10) is true (now including electromagnetism) for the negative particles:

$$m(N^{*-}) - m(Y_1^{*-}) = m(Y_1^{*-}) - m(\Xi^{*-}) = m(\Xi^{*-}) - m(\Omega^-) \quad (6.49)$$

while (6.11) is still valid in the form originally given. In terms of particle states, (6.11) becomes

$$2[m(n) + m(\Xi^0)] = m(\Sigma^0) + 3m(\Lambda) - 2\sqrt{3}\, m(\Sigma\Lambda) \quad (6.50)$$

$m(\Sigma\Lambda)$ can now be eliminated using either or both of Eqs. (6.44) and (6.45). We choose the latter alternative, obtaining the formula

$$m(n) + m(p) + m(\Xi^0) + m(\Xi^-) = 3m(\Lambda) + m(\Sigma^+) + m(\Sigma^-) - m(\Sigma^0) \quad (6.51)$$

The corresponding results for the pseudoscalar meson octet are

$$4m^2(K^0) = 3m^2(\eta) + m^2(\pi^0) - 2\sqrt{3}\, m^2(\pi^0\eta) \quad (6.52)$$

$$2[m^2(K^+) + m^2(K^0)] = 3m^2(\eta) + 2m^2(\pi^+) - m^2(\pi^0) \quad (6.53)$$

If there were no electricity these formulas would collapse to the forms given in Section 6.2.

The implications of the predicted value of $m(\Sigma^0\Lambda)$ have been studied by Dalitz and von Hippel (18). The existence of $m(\Sigma\Lambda)$ implies that the physical particles are not pure $SU(2)_T$ eigenstates. The resulting mixing problem is very similar to that in the ϕ–ω discussion. We write

$$\begin{aligned}\Lambda_{\text{phys}} &= \cos\lambda\cdot\Lambda + \sin\lambda\cdot\Sigma^0 \\ \Sigma_{\text{phys}} &= -\sin\lambda\cdot\Lambda + \cos\lambda\cdot\Sigma^0\end{aligned} \tag{6.54}$$

The mass operator has the matrix form

$$M = \begin{pmatrix} m_0(\Lambda) & m(\Sigma\Lambda) \\ m(\Sigma\Lambda) & m_0(\Sigma)\end{pmatrix} \tag{6.55}$$

The eigenvalues of (6.55) give the actual mass $m(\Lambda)$ and $m(\Sigma)$

$$m\begin{pmatrix}\Sigma \\ \Lambda\end{pmatrix} = \tfrac{1}{2}\{m_0(\Lambda) + m_0(\Sigma) \pm [[m_0(\Sigma) - m_0(\Lambda)]^2 + 4m^2(\Sigma\Lambda)]^{1/2}\} \tag{6.56}$$

Since the effect is very small [$m(\Sigma\Lambda) = 1.5 \pm 0.4$ MeV] the actual masses

$$\begin{aligned}m(\Sigma) &\cong m_0(\Sigma) + \frac{2m^2(\Sigma\Lambda)}{m_0(\Sigma) - m_0(\Lambda)} \\ m(\Lambda) &\cong m_0(\Lambda) - \frac{2m^2(\Sigma\Lambda)}{m_0(\Sigma) - m_0(\Lambda)}\end{aligned} \tag{6.57}$$

differ by a negligible amount from the unmixed ones.

The mixing angle λ is given by

$$\tan 2\lambda = \frac{2m(\Sigma\Lambda)}{m_0(\Lambda) - m_0(\Sigma)} \tag{6.58}$$

and to good approximation this reduces to

$$\lambda \cong \frac{1}{\sqrt{3}}\left[\frac{m(p) - m(n) + m(\Sigma^0) - m(\Sigma^+)}{m(\Lambda) - m(\Sigma)}\right] \tag{6.59}$$

numerically one finds $\lambda = -0.019 \pm 0.006$ radians, small but larger than the order-of-magnitude parameter $e^2/\pi\hbar c$ characterizing second order electromagnetic corrections.

Of the several applications discussed by Dalitz and von Hippel, we review the induced $\Lambda\Lambda\pi^0$ coupling and its influence on the Λ binding energy in hypernuclei. Here we must note that the physical π^0 state contains some η component because of $m^2(\pi^0\eta)$ given by Eq. (6.52). According to reference 17 the numerical value of $m^2(\pi^0\eta)$ is -2960 ± 365 (MeV)^2. The physical π^0 is then given by

$$\pi_{\text{phys}}{}^0 = \pi^0 \cos\mu + \eta \sin\mu \tag{6.60}$$

where $\tan 2\mu = 2m^2(\pi^0\eta)[m^2(\pi^0) - m^2(\eta)]^{-1}$ reduces to $\mu \cong 0.0105 \pm 0.0013$. Evaluation of the physical $\Lambda\Lambda\pi^0$ vertex $\langle\Lambda_{\text{phys}}|\ \pi_{\text{phys}}{}^0\ |\Lambda_{\text{phys}}\rangle$ then gives the coupling constant

$$g_{\Lambda\Lambda\pi} = 2\sin\lambda\cos\lambda\cos\mu\, g_{\Sigma\Lambda\pi} + \sin\mu\cos^2\lambda\, g_{\Lambda\Lambda\eta} + \sin^2\lambda\sin\mu\, g_{\Sigma\Sigma\eta} \tag{6.61}$$

Since λ and μ are quite small, we can set the cosines equal to unity and approximate the sines by their arguments. Thus the $g_{\Sigma\Sigma\eta}$ term in (6.61) can be dropped. According to $SU(3)$, $g_{\Lambda\Lambda\eta} = -g_{\Sigma\Lambda\pi}$ and so (6.61) is approximately

$$\begin{aligned} g_{\Lambda\Lambda\pi} &\cong \left[\frac{2m(\Sigma\Lambda)}{m(\Lambda) - m(\Sigma)} + \frac{m^2(\pi^0\eta)}{m^2(\eta) - m^2(\pi^0)}\right] g_{\Sigma\Lambda\pi} \\ g_{\Lambda\Lambda\pi} &\cong (-0.0485 \pm 0.012) g_{\Sigma\Lambda\pi} \end{aligned} \tag{6.62}$$

The mirror hypernuclei ${}_\Lambda\text{He}^4$ and ${}_\Lambda\text{H}^4$ have Λ binding energies 2.33 ± 0.10 MeV and 2.03 ± 0.09 MeV, respectively. These numbers are close enough to support the idea of charge symmetry in the lambda–nucleon interaction but reveal a small discrepancy $B = 0.30 \pm 0.14$ MeV apparently outside experimental error.

Although $g_{\Lambda\Lambda\pi}{}^2$ in (6.62) seems to be minute, the effect may be of disproportionate size because the existence of the $\Lambda\Lambda\pi$ vertex permits the long range $[\sim 1/m(\pi)]$ one-pion-exchange force between Λ and N. On the other hand, the longest range charge independent force involves the exchange of two pions and so has range $1/2m(\pi)$. Numerical estimates (with $g_{\Sigma\Lambda\pi} \cong g_{NN\pi}$) give $\Delta B_\Lambda = 0.21 \pm 0.05$ MeV arising from the one-pion-exchange potential. Evaluation of other charge-dependent effects bolster the conclusion that the $SU(3)$ prediction (6.62) is essential in bringing theory in line with experiment.

6.4 Magnetic Moments

In the previous section the influence of electromagnetic forces on the masses of the strongly interacting particles was assessed. We now examine the implications of $SU(3)$ for magnetic moments, photoproduction reactions, and photon decay vertices. Recall that in the eightfold way the electric charge Q is $G_3 + (1/\sqrt{3})G_8$, or $T_1^{\ 1}$, a component of a traceless tensor operator $T_\nu^{\ \mu}$. Some results may be derived without assuming the trace condition. Since the current operator $j_\mu(x)$ commutes with U, the matrix elements $\langle a|\, j_\alpha(x_1)\ldots j_\nu(x_n)\,|a\rangle$ are the same for all members a of a U-spin multiplet. An especially important case is the magnetic moment. The magnetic moment of a quantum system is generally defined to be the maximal projection of the operator

$$\mathbf{M} = \tfrac{1}{2}\int \mathbf{r} \times \mathbf{j}(\mathbf{r})\, d^3x \tag{6.63}$$

Since the M_i commute with the U_j we can derive relations like

$$\begin{aligned} &\mu(p) = \mu(\Sigma^+) \qquad \mu(\Xi^-) = \mu(\Sigma^-) \\ &\mu(n) = \mu(\Xi^0) = \mu(\Sigma_U^{\ 0}) = \tfrac{1}{4}\mu(\Sigma^0) + \tfrac{3}{4}\mu(\Lambda^0) - \frac{\sqrt{3}}{2}\,\mu(\Sigma\Lambda) \end{aligned} \tag{6.64}$$

where $\mu(\Sigma\Lambda)$ is the transition magnetic moment, which can be estimated from the decay $\Sigma^0 \to \Lambda + \gamma$.

From isospin conservation alone we know (Section 1.4)

$$\mu(\Sigma^0) = \tfrac{1}{2}[\mu(\Sigma^+) + \mu(\Sigma^-)] \tag{6.65}$$

Further relations emerge if we restrict $\mathbf{M}$ to be a traceless operator. We can then write for the magnetic moment of the baryon octet, using Eq. (6.32)

$$\mu = aQ + b[(\tfrac{1}{2}Q + 1)^2 - U(U + 1)] \tag{6.66}$$

This formula exhibits the two independent constants expected in the matrix element $\langle B|\ \mu_{op}\ |B\rangle$ (since $\mathbf{8} \times \mathbf{8} \times \mathbf{8}$ contains $\mathbf{1}$ twice).

We apply (6.66) to $\Sigma_U{}^0$ and $\Lambda_U{}^0$.

$$\begin{aligned} \mu(\Sigma_U{}^0) &= \tfrac{1}{4}\mu(\Sigma^0) + \tfrac{3}{4}\mu(\Lambda^0) - \frac{\sqrt{3}}{2}\,\mu(\Sigma\Lambda) = -b \\ \mu(\Lambda_U{}^0) &= \tfrac{3}{4}\mu(\Sigma^0) + \tfrac{1}{4}\mu(\Lambda^0) + \frac{\sqrt{3}}{2}\,\mu(\Sigma\Lambda) = b \end{aligned} \tag{6.67}$$

Adding, we obtain

$$\mu(\Sigma^0) + \mu(\Lambda^0) = 0 \tag{6.68}$$

one new relation. For the neutron we have $\mu(n) = \mu(\Sigma_U{}^0) = -b$. Using Eq. (6.65) and

$$\begin{aligned} \mu(\Sigma^+) &= a + \tfrac{3}{2}b \\ \mu(\Sigma^-) &= -a - \tfrac{1}{2}b \end{aligned} \tag{6.69}$$

we find

$$\mu(\Sigma^0) = \tfrac{1}{2}b = -\tfrac{1}{2}\mu(n) \tag{6.70}$$

The transition moment is given by [use (6.67), (6.68), and (6.70)]

$$\mu(\Sigma\Lambda) = \frac{\sqrt{3}}{2}\,b = -\frac{\sqrt{3}}{2}\,\mu(n) \tag{6.71}$$

Using the U-spin equalities (6.64) we can convert (6.65) to the form

$$\mu(\Sigma^-) + \mu(p) + \mu(n) = 0 \tag{6.72}$$

All these relations hold in the $SU(3)$ symmetric limit for the electromagnetic form factors of the baryons. The effect of symmetry breaking on the magnetic moments and form factors has not been studied, to the author's knowledge.

The most recent measurement (19) of the Λ magnetic moment gave the result $\mu(\Lambda) = (-0.77 \pm 0.27)\ e\hbar/2Mc$, in reasonable agreement with the $SU(3)$ value $\mu(\Lambda) = \tfrac{1}{2}\mu(n) = -0.95\ e\hbar/2Mc$. (Here $e\hbar/2Mc$ is the nuclear magneton.)

Consider the magnetic moments of the baryon decuplet. The moments are equal along the U-spin direction

$$\begin{aligned} \mu(N^{*-}) &= \mu(Y_1{}^{*-}) = \mu(\Xi^{*-}) = \mu(\Omega^-) \\ \mu(N^{*0}) &= \mu(Y_1{}^{*0}) = \mu(\Xi^{*0}) \\ \mu(N^{*+}) &= \mu(Y_1{}^{*+}) \end{aligned} \tag{6.73}$$

Actually, since $\mathbf{10}^* \times \mathbf{8} \times \mathbf{10}$ contains 1 only once, we expect that all moments can be expressed in terms of a single constant. For $\mathbf{10}$, $\mathbf{G}^2 = 6$, $\frac{1}{2}Q + U = 1$, and Eq. (6.32) reduces to $\mu = \text{const.}\ Q$, or

$$\mu(B^*) = Q\mu(N^{*+}) \tag{6.74}$$

We can also consider the transition magnetic moment $\mu_T = \langle B^*|\, \mu \,|B\rangle$. This matrix element can be derived from photoproduction data; for example, the 3–3 resonance in pion photoproduction is excited mainly through a magnetic dipole transition. Again only one independent constant occurs, since the matrix element involves $\mathbf{10}^* \times \mathbf{8} \times \mathbf{8}$. To analyze this problem we use U-spin invariance. The transitions permitted by charge and hypercharge conservation are

$$\begin{aligned} &P \to N^{*+} && n \to N^{*0} \\ &\Sigma^- \to Y_1{}^{*-} && \Lambda, \Sigma^0 \to Y_1{}^{*0} \\ &\Sigma^+ \to Y_1{}^{*+} && \Xi^0 \to \Xi^{*0} \\ & && \Xi^- \to \Xi^{*-} \end{aligned} \tag{6.75}$$

The baryons are grouped into the U-spin multiplets $(p, -\Sigma^+)$, $(n, \Sigma_U{}^0 = -\frac{1}{2}\Sigma^0 + (\sqrt{3}/2)\Lambda^0, -\Xi^0)$, $\Lambda_U{}^0 = (\sqrt{3}/2)\Sigma^0 + \frac{1}{2}\Lambda^0$ and (Σ^-, Ξ^-). The decuplet U-spin states do not have any problems of tricky minus signs or degeneracy. Note that since Σ^- and Ξ^- have $U = 1/2$, while $Y_1{}^{*-}$ and Ξ^{*-} have $U = 3/2$, we obtain the prediction

$$\langle Y_1{}^{*-}|\, \mu \,|\Sigma^-\rangle = \langle \Xi^{*-}|\, \mu \,|\Xi^-\rangle = 0 \tag{6.76}$$

Next we use the U-spin raising and lowering operators

$$\langle N^{*+}|\,\mu\,|p\rangle = -\langle Y_1^{*+}|\,U_-\mu U_+\,|\Sigma^+\rangle = -\langle Y_1^{*+}|\,\mu\,|\Sigma^+\rangle \tag{6.77}$$

since $U_-U_+ = \mathbf{U}^2 - U_3(U_3+1)$. Similarly, one finds the equality

$$\langle N^{*0}|\,\mu\,|n\rangle = \langle Y_1^{*0}|\,\mu\,|\Sigma_U{}^0\rangle$$
$$= -\tfrac{1}{2}\langle Y_1^{*0}|\,\mu\,|\Sigma^0\rangle + \frac{\sqrt{3}}{2}\langle Y_1^{*0}|\,\mu\,|\Lambda\rangle \tag{6.78}$$

This result can be shortened by noting that $\langle Y_1^{*0}|\,\mu\,|\Lambda_U{}^0\rangle = 0$, or

$$\langle Y_1^{*0}|\,\mu\,|\Lambda\rangle = -\sqrt{3}\langle Y_1^{*0}|\,\mu\,|\Sigma^0\rangle \tag{6.79}$$

Using this result, (6.78) can be re-expressed in the form

$$\langle N^{*0}|\,\mu\,|n\rangle = \frac{2}{\sqrt{3}}\langle Y_1^{*0}|\,\mu\,|\Lambda^0\rangle = -2\langle Y_1^{*0}|\,\mu\,|\Sigma^0\rangle \tag{6.80}$$

Further motion along the N^{*0}, U-spin triplet yields

$$\langle N^{*0}|\,\mu\,|n\rangle = \langle Y_1^{*0}|\,\mu\,|\Sigma_U{}^0\rangle = -\langle \Xi^{*0}|\,\mu\,|\Xi^0\rangle \tag{6.81}$$

One further relation which allows one to express all six nonzero matrix elements in terms of one number follows on applying the "reflection" operator $R = \exp(i\pi T_2)$. Notice that in the matrix element $\langle N^{*+}|\,\mu\,|p\rangle$, $\Delta T = 1$ so that only the isovector part of the magnetic moment operator contributes. Further $R_T\,|p\rangle = -|n\rangle$ and $R_T\,|N^{*+}\rangle = |N^{*0}\rangle$ since $\langle\mu|\exp(i\pi T_2)\,|\nu\rangle = (-1)^{T+\mu}\delta_{\mu,-\nu}$ (cf. Section 1.3). The isovector moment μ_v transforms as $R_T\mu_v R_T{}^{-1} = -\mu_v$ and so

$$\langle N^{*+}|\,\mu\,|p\rangle = \langle N^{*0}|\,\mu\,|n\rangle \tag{6.82}$$

These results are summarized in the equations

$$\langle N^{*+}|\,\mu\,|p\rangle = \langle N^{*0}|\,\mu\,|n\rangle = -\langle \Xi^{0*}|\,\mu\,|\Xi^0\rangle$$
$$= -\langle Y_1^{*+}|\,\mu\,|\Sigma^+\rangle = \frac{2}{\sqrt{3}}\langle Y_1^{*0}|\,\mu\,|\Lambda^0\rangle \tag{6.83}$$
$$= -2\langle Y_1^{*0}|\,\mu\,|\Lambda^0\rangle$$

Identical relations hold for the decay amplitudes $B^* \rightarrow B + \gamma$.

For spinless mesons there are no magnetic moments. The charge-form factors of the pseudoscalar octet are all proportional to each other since the term in $T_1{}^1$ linear in Q vanishes by charge conjugation invariance. We can write

$$F_Q(q^2) = QF_{\pi^+}(q^2) \tag{6.84}$$

where $F_{\pi^+}(q^2)$ is the π^+ form factor $[F_{\pi^+}(0) = 1]$ and q^2 the invariant momentum transfer squared.

Little concrete evidence exists which bears on the validity of most of these relations.

We have mentioned before that it is more difficult to correct for symmetry breaking in 4-particle amplitudes than for 3-particle vertices, unless resonances occur among pairs of the particles. For this reason we give only a few examples of the use of U-spin to analyze production amplitudes.

For Compton scattering one has obvious relations such as

$$\begin{aligned} \langle \gamma p | \, S \, | \gamma p \rangle &= \langle \gamma \Sigma^+ | \, S \, | \gamma \Sigma^+ \rangle \\ \langle \gamma n | \, S \, | \gamma n \rangle &= \langle \gamma \Xi^0 | \, S \, | \gamma \Xi^0 \rangle \end{aligned} \tag{6.85}$$

etc. In lowest order in the electromagnetic interaction the process $\gamma + a \to b$ has matrix element

$$\langle b | \int \mathbf{j} \cdot \mathbf{A} d^3x \, | a \rangle \tag{6.86}$$

where $[j_\mu, U] = 0$. Thus states $|a\rangle$ and $|b\rangle$ must have the same value of U. Examples of this sort have been given by Lipkin (20).

The presentation of this section has been based on the work of references 1, 2, 12, 17, and 20–24. For further results the reader is referred to these papers.

References

1. G. Feldman and P. T. Matthews, *Ann. Phys. (N.Y.)*, **31**, 469 (1965).
2. J. H. Wojtaszek, R. E. Marshak, and Riazuddin, *Phys. Rev.*, **136**, B1053 (1964).
3. S. Coleman, S. Glashow, and D. Kleitman, *Phys. Rev.*, **135**, B779 (1964).
4. M. Gell-Mann, *Phys. Rev.*, **125**, 1067 (1962).
5. M. Gell-Mann, *Phys. Rev.*, **106**, 1296 (1957).

6. J. J. Sakurai, *Phys. Rev. Letters*, **9**, 472 (1962); Phys. Rev., **132**, 434 (1963).
7. P. L. Connolly et al., *Phys. Rev. Letters*, **10**, 371 (1963).
8. R. R. Wilson and J. S. Levinger, *Ann. Rev. Nuc. Sci.*, **14**, 135 (1964).
9. R. F. Dashen and D. H. Sharp, *Phys. Rev.*, **133**, B1585 (1964).
10. F. Gursey, T. D. Lee, and M. Nauenberg, *Phys. Rev.*, **135**, B467 (1964).
11. S. Okubo, *Prog. Theor. Phys. (Kyoto)*, **27**, 949 (1962).
12. S. P. Rosen, *Phys. Rev. Letters*, **11**, 100 (1963).
13. B. Diu, *Nuovo Cimento*, **28**, 466 (1963).
14. J. Ginibre, *J. Math. Phys.*, **4**, 720 (1963).
15. S. P. Rosen, *J. Math. Phys.*, **5**, 289 (1963).
16. H. Goldberg and Y. Lehrer-Ilamed, *J. Math. Phys.*, **4**, 501 (1963).
17. S. Coleman and S. L. Glashow, *Phys. Rev. Letters*, **6**, 423 (1961).
18. R. H. Dalitz and F. von Hippel, *Phys. Letters*, **10**, 155 (1964).
19. D. A. Hill, K. K. Li, E. W. Jenkins, T. F. Kycia, and H. Ruderman, *Phys. Rev. Letters*, **15**, 85 (1965).
20. H. J. Lipkin, *Lie Groups for Pedestrians*, Interscience, New York, 1965.
21. A. J. Macfarlane and E. C. G. Sudarshan, *Nuovo Cimento*, **31**, 1176 (1964).
22. S. Okubo, *Phys. Letters*, **4**, 14 (1963).
23. R. J. Oakes, *Phys. Rev.*, **132**, 2349 (1963).
24. N. Cabibbo and R. Gatto, *Nuovo Cimento*, **21**, 872 (1961).

Chapter 7

Crossing Symmetry in Strong Interactions

7.1 Crossing Matrices for Arbitrary Isospin

"Crossing symmetry" or, as it is sometimes known, the "substitution rule," is one of the most far-reaching consequences of quantum field theory (1–3). In this chapter we discuss the relations among reaction amplitudes which follow from the invariance of strong interactions under transformations of the internal symmetry groups $SU(2)$ (isospin) and $SU(3)$. The development follows reference 4 closely.

Since the spin structure of the amplitudes is not of concern here, we consider only the case of spinless bosons. To be definite, we begin with isospin amplitudes and consider "two-body" reactions of the type

$$a + b \rightarrow c + d \qquad (s \text{ channel}) \qquad (7.1)$$

among particles of isospins a, b, c, and d having third components α, β, γ, and δ, respectively. The four-momentum of particle a is denoted by p_a, etc. When no confusion can arise the labels a, b, c, and d are supposed to include the specification of the component labels. By convention, we shall call (7.1) the s-channel reaction, using Mandelstam's kinematical invariants (5). The amplitude for (7.1) is physical only when $s = (p_a + p_b)^2 \geqslant \max\,[(m_a + m_b)^2, (m_c + m_d)^2]$. The antiparticles of particles a, b, c, and d, denoted by $\bar{a}$, $\bar{b}$, $\bar{c}$, and $\bar{d}$, have isospins a, b, c, and d and third components $-\alpha$, $-\beta$, $-\gamma$, and $-\delta$.

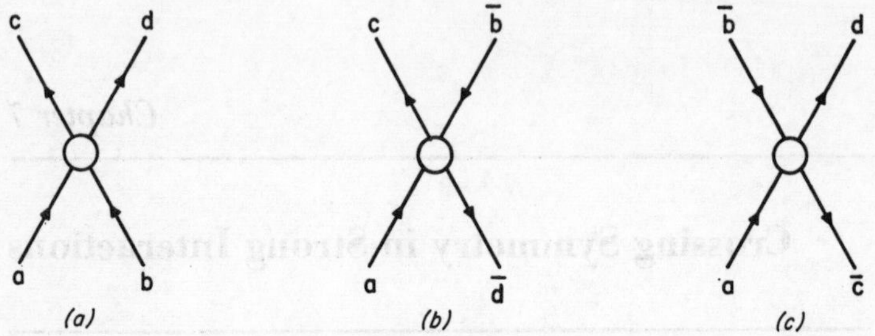

Fig. 7.1. The three processes $a + b \to c + d$, $a + \bar{d} \to c + \bar{b}$, and $a + \bar{c} \to \bar{b} + d$ are related by crossing symmetry.

In addition to (7.1), two varieties of crossed reactions must be considered

$$a + \bar{d} \to c + \bar{b} \qquad (u \text{ channel}) \tag{7.2}$$

$$a + \bar{c} \to \bar{b} + d \qquad (t \text{ channel}) \tag{7.3}$$

The three reactions under consideration are sketched in Fig. 7.1. The reactions (7.2) and (7.3) are physical in the domains of the "crossed channels" $u \equiv (p_a + \bar{p}_d)^2 \geqslant \max[(m_a + m_d)^2, (m_c + m_b)^2]$ and $t \equiv (p_a + \bar{p}_c)^2 \geqslant \max[(m_a + m_c)^2, (m_b + m_d)^2]$, respectively. The center-of-mass energy variables in the s, u, and t channels are $\sqrt{s}$, $\sqrt{u}$, and $\sqrt{t}$, respectively. Of course the scattering angle θ has to satisfy ($|\cos\theta| \leqslant 1$) for the reaction to be physical. The amplitudes for reactions (7.1)–(7.3) are denoted by

$$(cd|\ M_s\ |ab) : a + b \to c + d \tag{7.4}$$

$$(c\bar{b}|\ M_u\ |a\bar{d}) : a + \bar{d} \to c + \bar{b} \tag{7.5}$$

$$(\bar{b}d|\ M_t\ |a\bar{c}) : a + \bar{c} \to \bar{b} + d \tag{7.6}$$

"Crossing symmetry" asserts that if the four momenta p_a, p_b, p_c, and p_d (more precisely the invariants s, t, and u formed from them) are continued to the physical domain of a crossed channel, the continued amplitude actually describes the crossed reaction in question. Explicitly, we have the connection

$$(cd|\ M_s\ |ab)_c = \xi_{su}(c\bar{b}|\ M_u\ |a\bar{d}) \tag{7.7}$$

$$(cd|\ M_s\ |ab)_c = \xi_{st}(\bar{b}d|\ M_t\ |a\bar{c}) \tag{7.8}$$

where the subscript c denotes "continued" and the phases ξ_{su} and ξ_{st}, which depend on the isospin quantum numbers, will be determined subsequently. We shall not describe the actual method of performing the analytic continuation and shall generally omit the label "c" in (7.7) and (7.8) which specifies that the continuation has been performed. The results (7.7) and (7.8) will be demonstrated in Section 7.2. Particular methods of performing the continuation are given in references 1 and 6.

We now employ isospin conservation to express the amplitudes (7.4)–(7.6) in terms of the isospin amplitudes for the various channels. As explained in Chapter 1 we shall always use the Condon-Shortley phase convention (7) to define the relative phase of states within an isotopic multiplet. Using the notation of Rose (8) for the $SU(2)$ Clebsch-Gordan coefficient gives

$$(cd|\ M_s\ |ab) = \sum_{s'} M_s(s')C(abs';\alpha,\beta)C(cds';\gamma,\delta) \tag{7.9}$$

$$(c\bar{b}|\ M_u\ |a\bar{d}) = \sum_{u'} M_u(u')C(adu';\alpha,-\delta)C(cbu';\gamma,-\beta) \tag{7.10}$$

$$(\bar{b}d|\ M_t\ |a\bar{c}) = \sum_{t'} M_t(t')C(act';\alpha,-\gamma)C(bdt';-\beta,\delta) \tag{7.11}$$

In these expressions, the amplitude $M_v(v')$ denotes the amplitude for scattering in a state of isospin v' in channel v.

Comparison of the crossing assumption (7.7) and (7.8) with Eq. (7.9) shows that the continued isospin amplitudes can be expressed in terms of crossed-channel amplitudes by the use of standard recoupling techniques. Employing the usual symmetry properties of the Clebsch-Gordan coefficients one can rearrange standard formulas (8) involving the recoupling (Racah) coefficients to desired form. We find

$$C(abs';\alpha\beta)C(cds';\gamma\delta)$$
$$= \sum_{u'} (2s' + 1)(-1)^{\gamma-\alpha+a-c} W(abcd;s'u') \cdot C(adu';\alpha - \delta) \cdot C(cbu';\gamma - \beta) \quad (7.12)$$

$$C(abs';\alpha\beta)C(cds';\gamma\delta)$$
$$= \sum_{t'} (2s' + 1)(-1)^{\delta-\alpha+a+d} W(as't'd;bc) \cdot C(bdt';-\beta\delta) \cdot C(act';\alpha - \gamma) \quad (7.13)$$

where W is the Racah coefficient as defined in reference 8.

The crossing matrices are defined by

$$M_u(u') = \sum_{s'} X_{u's'} M_s(s') \quad (7.14)$$

$$M_t(t') = \sum_{s'} X_{t's'} M_s(s') \quad (7.15)$$

We shall refer to X_{us} and X_{ts} as the u-channel and t-channel crossing matrices, respectively. From Eqs. (7.9)–(7.13) one finds immediately

$$X_{us} = \xi_{su}{}^{-1}(-1)^{\gamma-\alpha+a-c}(2s + 1) W(abdc;su) \quad (7.16)$$

$$X_{ts} = \xi_{st}{}^{-1}(-1)^{\delta-\alpha+a+d}(2s + 1) W(astd;bc) \quad (7.17)$$

The physical interpretation of these relations is easily understood from Fig. 7.2. Suppose that in the s channel particles a and b unite to form an intermediate state of isospin T_s (Fig. 7.2a). In the t or u channels the kinematics is such that the "particle" T_s is an exchanged "particle." To obtain the magnitudes of the various isospin amplitudes in the t or u channels we have to project the s-channel states onto the appropriate states. That is, given particles a and b with isospin T_s and projection $T_3 = \alpha + \beta$ (similarly, c and d combine to give isospin T_s and projection $T_3 = \gamma + \delta = \alpha + \beta$), what is the amplitude for a and $\bar{d}$ to have isospin T_u and projection $\alpha - \delta$, while c and $\bar{b}$ have isospin

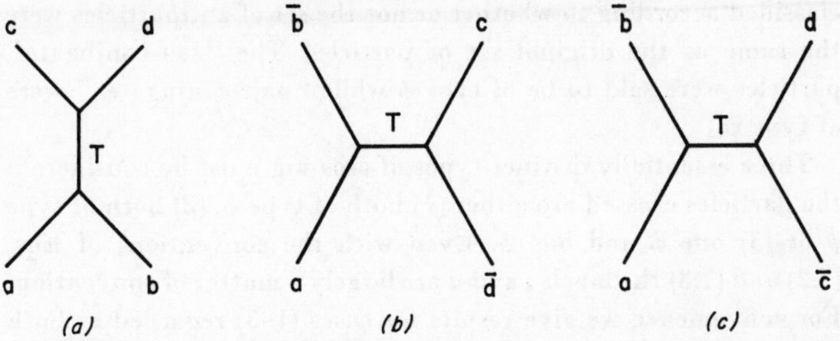

Fig. 7.2. Suppose particles a and b coalesce to form a state of isospin T. In the crossed channels it appears that a particle of isospin T has been exchanged. The amplitude for isospin T' in the crossed channel is then given by the appropriate crossing matrix.

T_u and projection $\gamma - \delta$? The answer is given by the recoupling expressions (7.12) and (7.13).

In employing our results it is sometimes necessary to rearrange the particle labels. Besides the usual symmetry properties of $SU(2)$ Clebsch-Gordan coefficients, we need a property which follows from time-reversal invariance. It is well known that there is a special phase convention in terms of which the S matrix is symmetric (9). But since we are defining all amplitudes in terms of the Condon-Shortley convention we have to insert the appropriate phase factor to correct for this fact. The result is easily found:

$$(cd|\, M\, |ab) = (-1)^{a+b-c-d}(ab|\, M\, |cd) \tag{7.18}$$

In Section 1.3 field operators were constructed for isospin multiplets in accordance with the Condon-Shortley phase convention. In order to discuss the crossing conditions in a systematic way, we find it very useful to use the "reduction formalism" of Lehmann, Symanzik, and Zimmerman (10) which relates S-matrix elements to Fourier transforms of matrix elements of various field operators. The field operators describing the isospin multiplets are those of Section 1.3. Recall that particles were there classified according to whether or not the set of antiparticles were the same as the original set of particles. The "self-conjugate" particles were said to be of type ϕ while "pair-conjugates" were of type ψ.

Three essentially distinct types of crossing must be considered; the particles crossed are either (*1*) both of type ϕ, (*2*) both of type ψ or (*3*) one ϕ and one ψ. Even with the conventions of Eqs. (7.2) and (7.3) the labels t and u are largely a matter of convention. For convenience we give results for cases (1–3) regarded as both u- and t-channel crossing. Thus consider the following pairs of reactions.

$$\mathrm{I}_u \begin{cases} a + \phi_b \to c + \phi_d & (7.19\text{a}) \\ a + \bar{\phi}_d \to c + \bar{\phi}_b & (7.19\text{b}) \end{cases}$$

$$\mathrm{I}_t \begin{cases} a + \phi_b \to \phi_c + d & (7.20\text{a}) \\ a + \bar{\phi}_c \to \bar{\phi}_b + d & (7.20\text{b}) \end{cases}$$

$$\mathrm{II}_u \begin{cases} a + \psi_b \to c + \psi_d & (7.21\text{a}) \\ a + \bar{\psi}_d \to c + \bar{\psi}_b & (7.21\text{b}) \end{cases}$$

$$\mathrm{II}_t \begin{cases} a + \psi_b \to \psi_c + d & (7.22\text{a}) \\ a + \bar{\psi}_c \to \bar{\psi}_b + d & (7.22\text{b}) \end{cases}$$

$$\mathrm{III}_u \begin{cases} a + \phi_b \to c + \psi_d & (7.23\text{a}) \\ a + \bar{\psi}_d \to c + \bar{\phi}_b & (7.23\text{b}) \end{cases}$$

$$\mathrm{III}_t \begin{cases} a + \phi_b \to \psi_c + d & (7.24\text{a}) \\ a + \bar{\psi}_c \to \bar{\phi}_b + d & (7.24\text{b}) \end{cases}$$

In order to discuss the crossing condition for (7.19) it is useful to use Eq. (1.57) to invert Eq. (1.55):

$$a_\mu(k) = i \int d^3x\, f_k{}^*(x) \overleftrightarrow{\partial_0} \phi^{(\mu)}(x) \tag{7.25}$$

$$a_\mu{}^*(k) = \eta_{-\mu}{}^T i \int d^3x \phi^{(-\mu)}(x) \overleftrightarrow{\partial_0} f_k(x) \tag{7.26}$$

One can then use the reduction formalism to contract the particles b and d in reaction (7.19a). (We follow the conventions of

Barton (11).) If particle b has momentum k and T_3 component β, while particle d has momentum k' and T_3 component δ, the S matrix for reaction (7.19a) is

$$S = \langle c;k'd\delta \text{ out} \mid a;kb\beta \text{ in}\rangle \tag{7.27}$$

Ignoring the unit operator which occurs for elastic scattering one finds

$$S = i^2\eta_{-\beta}{}^b \int dxdy\, f_k(x)f_{k'}{}^*(y)K_x{}^bK_y{}^d\langle c|\ T\phi_d{}^{(\delta)}(y)\phi_b{}^{(-\beta)}(x)\ |a\rangle \tag{7.28}$$

where T is the time ordering operator and $K_x{}^b = \Box_x + m_b{}^2$. We may also consider reaction (7.19b), where b has momentum q and T_3 component β', and d has momentum q' and T_3 component δ'. The S matrix for this crossed process is

$$\begin{aligned} S^x &= \langle c;q'b\beta' \text{ out} \mid a;qd\delta' \text{ in}\rangle \\ &= i^2\eta_{-\delta'}{}^d \int dxdy\, f_q(x)f_{q'}{}^*(y)K_x{}^dK_y{}^b\langle c|\ T\phi_b{}^{(\beta')}(y)\phi_d{}^{(-\delta')}(x)\ |a\rangle \end{aligned} \tag{7.29}$$

Disregarding the $(2\omega)^{1/2}$ factors that have to be extracted to obtain the Lorentz-invariant amplitude we see that the integrand of (7.29) coincides with that of (7.28) if we set $q = -k'$, $q' = -k$, $\beta' = -\beta$, and $\delta' = -\delta$. Thus

$$\eta_{-\beta}{}^bS(c,k'd\delta;a,kb\beta) = \eta_\delta{}^dS^x(c,-kb-\beta;\, a,-k'd-\delta) \tag{7.30}$$

Comparison of Eq. (7.30) with Eq. (7.7) indicates that for reactions of type (7.19) the crossing phase is

$$\xi_{su}{}^{\mathrm{I}} = \eta_{-\beta}{}^b\eta_\delta{}^d = (-1)^{\gamma-\alpha-b-d} \tag{7.31}$$

Similar calculations lead to the following phases:

$$\xi_{st}{}^{\mathrm{I}} = \eta_{-\beta}{}^b\eta_\gamma{}^c = (-1)^{\delta-\alpha-b-c} \tag{7.32}$$

$$\xi_{su}{}^{\mathrm{II}} = \zeta_\beta{}^b\zeta_\delta{}^d = (-1)^{\gamma-\alpha+b-d} \tag{7.33}$$

$$\xi_{st}{}^{\mathrm{II}} = \zeta_\beta{}^b\zeta_\gamma{}^c = (-1)^{\delta-\alpha+b-c} \tag{7.34}$$

$$\xi_{su}{}^{\mathrm{III}} = \eta_{-\beta}{}^b\zeta_\delta{}^d = (-1)^{\gamma-\alpha-b-d} \tag{7.35}$$

$$\xi_{st}{}^{\mathrm{III}} = \eta_{-\beta}{}^b\zeta_\gamma{}^c = (-1)^{\delta-\alpha-b-c} \tag{7.36}$$

The corresponding crossing matrices are therefore

$$X_{us}{}^{\text{I}} = X_{us}{}^{\text{III}} = (-1)^{a+b-c+d}(2s+1)W(abdc;su) \tag{7.37}$$

$$X_{ts}{}^{\text{I}} = X_{ts}{}^{\text{III}} = (-1)^{a+b+c+d}(2s+1)W(astd;bc) \tag{7.38}$$

$$X_{us}{}^{\text{II}} = (-1)^{a-b-c+d}(2s+1)W(abdc;su) \tag{7.39}$$

$$X_{ts}{}^{\text{II}} = (-1)^{a-b+c+d}(2s+1)W(astd;bc) \tag{7.40}$$

The $6j$ symbols, defined by

$$\begin{Bmatrix} a & b & e \\ c & d & f \end{Bmatrix} = (-1)^{a+b+c+d}W(abdc;ef) \tag{7.41}$$

possess simpler symmetry properties than the Racah coefficients. Occasionally it is useful to express the crossing matrices in terms of the former. In addition extensive tables of $6j$ symbols exist.

In applications, the relative phases exhibited in (7.37)–(7.40) are not always significant, but should be observed when several channels are being considered simultaneously in order to avoid sign errors.

Before giving practical examples we make a few miscellaneous remarks of interest for applications. First consider the important special case of elastic scattering ($a = c$, $b = d$). As is well known (3) crossing symmetry plays an essential role in determining the sign and magnitude of forces in the direct (s) channel due to crossed (t and u channel) processes. A bound on these forces follows from the fact that (8) the Racah coefficients $W(abcd;ef)$ form a unitary matrix if supplied with the normalizing factor $[(2e+1)(2f+1)]^{1/2}$. Hence

$$|X_{us}| = (2s+1)\,|W(abdc;su)| \leqslant \left(\frac{2s+1}{2u+1}\right)^{1/2} \tag{7.42}$$

$$\begin{aligned} |X_{ts}| &= (2s+1)\,|W(astd;bc)| \\ &= (2s+1)\,|W(abcd;st)| \leqslant \left(\frac{2s+1}{2t+1}\right)^{1/2} \end{aligned} \tag{7.43}$$

From these bounds one learns that a high isospin state can lead to a larger crossing matrix element for low isospin states in crossed channels than in the opposite situation (high $\leftrightarrow$ low).

This does not, of course, imply that the exchange of low isospin states is unimportant since the resulting "forces" depend on other variables such as mass, spin, and angular momentum. (For example, the usual theory of the 3–3 resonance (N^*) in πN scattering relies on the attractive force in the $T = J = 3/2$, p-wave due to nucleon ($T = J = 1/2$) exchange. The relevant isospin crossing matrix elements are 2/3 for the amplitude in the N^* channel due to nucleon exchange and 4/3 in the nucleon channel ($T = J = 1/2$, p-wave) due to N^* exchange. In this example Eqs. (7.43) read $2/3 \leqslant (1/2)^{1/2}$ $(0.67 \leqslant 0.71)$ for $X_{3/2\ 1/2}$ and $4/3 \leqslant 2^{1/2}$ $(1.33 \leqslant 1.41)$ for $X_{1/2\ 3/2}$. For this case the upper bounds are closely approached by the actual values.)

A second important property of crossing matrices for elastic scattering is that the square is unity:

$$\sum_{s'} X_{ss'} X_{s's''} = \delta_{ss''} \tag{7.44}$$

We shall prove an important generalization below.

This relation is a very good check on calculations and can often be used to complete a crossing matrix if only part of it is known. The physical content of (7.44) is, of course, that two crossings return one to the same situation. The proof follows from the orthogonality theorem for Racah coefficients (8). Consider the u-channel crossing matrix:

$$\begin{aligned} \sum_{s'} X_{ss'} X_{s's''} &= \sum_{s'} (2s' + 1)(2s'' + 1) W(abdc;s's) W(abdc;s''s') \\ &= \sum_{s'} (2s' + 1)(2s'' + 1) W(abdc;s's) W(adbc;s's'') \end{aligned} \tag{7.45}$$

the second equality following from a standard symmetry relation. Now if $b = d$, i.e., if the crossed particles have the same isospin, the orthogonality theorem applies and $X^2 = 1$. The same result holds for X_{ts} if $b = c$, i.e., if the crossed particles have the same isospin.

If all four particles have the same isospin then the t- and u-channel crossing matrix elements are identical except for sign. In

TABLE 7.1

Isospin Crossing Matrices and Their Inverses.

Process	X_{us}	$(X^{-1})_{su}$	(X_{ts})	$(X^{-1})_{st}$
$NK \to NK$ $N\bar{K} \to N\bar{K}$ $N\bar{N} \to \bar{K}K$	$\begin{pmatrix} -1/2 & 3/2 \\ 1/2 & 1/2 \end{pmatrix}$	X_{su}	$\begin{pmatrix} -1/2 & -3/2 \\ -1/2 & 1/2 \end{pmatrix}$	X_{ts}
$N\pi \to N\pi$ $N\bar{\pi} \to N\bar{\pi}$ $N\bar{N} \to \bar{\pi}\pi$	$\begin{pmatrix} -1/3 & 4/3 \\ 2/3 & 1/3 \end{pmatrix}$	X_{su}	$\begin{pmatrix} \sqrt{6}/3 & 2\sqrt{6}/3 \\ 2/3 & -2/3 \end{pmatrix}$	$\begin{pmatrix} \sqrt{6}/6 & 1 \\ \sqrt{6}/6 & -1/2 \end{pmatrix}$
$N\pi \to N^*\pi$ $N\bar{\pi} \to N^*\bar{\pi}$ $N\bar{N}^* \to \bar{\pi}\pi$	$\begin{pmatrix} 2/3 & -\sqrt{10}/3 \\ -\sqrt{10}/6 & -2/3 \end{pmatrix}$	X_{su}	$\begin{pmatrix} 1/3 & \sqrt{10}/3 \\ \sqrt{3}/3 & -\sqrt{30}/15 \end{pmatrix}$	$\begin{pmatrix} 1/2 & 5\sqrt{3}/6 \\ \sqrt{10}/4 & -\sqrt{30}/12 \end{pmatrix}$
$N^*\pi \to N^*\pi$ $N^*\bar{\pi} \to N^*\bar{\pi}$ $N^*\bar{N}^* \to \bar{\pi}\pi$	$\begin{pmatrix} 1/6 & -2/3 & 3/2 \\ -1/3 & 11/15 & 3/5 \\ 1/2 & 2/5 & 1/10 \end{pmatrix}$	X_{su}	$\begin{pmatrix} -\sqrt{3}/3 & -2\sqrt{3}/3 & -\sqrt{3} \\ -\sqrt{10}/6 & -2\sqrt{10}/15 & 3\sqrt{10}/10 \\ -\sqrt{6}/6 & 4\sqrt{6}/15 & -\sqrt{6}/10 \end{pmatrix}$	$\begin{pmatrix} -\sqrt{3}/6 & -\sqrt{10}/4 & -5\sqrt{6}/12 \\ -\sqrt{3}/6 & -\sqrt{10}/10 & \sqrt{6}/3 \\ -\sqrt{3}/6 & 3\sqrt{10}/20 & -\sqrt{6}/12 \end{pmatrix}$
$\Sigma\pi \to \Sigma\pi$ $\Sigma\bar{\pi} \to \Sigma\bar{\pi}$ $\Sigma\bar{\Sigma} \to \bar{\pi}\pi$	$\begin{pmatrix} 1/3 & -1 & 5/3 \\ -1/3 & 1/2 & 5/6 \\ 1/3 & 1/2 & 1/6 \end{pmatrix}$	X_{su}	$\begin{pmatrix} 1/3 & 1 & 5/3 \\ 1/3 & 1/2 & -5/6 \\ 1/3 & -1/2 & 1/6 \end{pmatrix}$	X_{ts}
$N^*K \to N^*K$ $N^*\bar{K} \to N^*\bar{K}$ $N^*\bar{N}^* \to \bar{K}K$	$\begin{pmatrix} -1/4 & 5/4 \\ 3/4 & 1/4 \end{pmatrix}$	X_{su}	$\begin{pmatrix} -3\sqrt{2}/4 & -5\sqrt{2}/4 \\ -\sqrt{10}/4 & \sqrt{10}/4 \end{pmatrix}$	$\begin{pmatrix} -\sqrt{2}/4 & -\sqrt{10}/4 \\ -\sqrt{2}/4 & 3\sqrt{10}/20 \end{pmatrix}$

all cases the factor is $(-1)^{s+t}$. A familiar example is provided by the crossing matrix for $\pi\pi$ scattering. (See the $\Sigma\pi \rightarrow \Sigma\pi$ reaction in Table 7.1.) Moreover, for large values of isospin the crossing matrices can be approximated by Legendre polynomials (6). This follows by using well-known approximate formulas for Racah coefficients with large arguments (8, 12). This latter application has not yet assumed any practical importance.

In Table 7.1 we have listed crossing matrices for many cases likely to arise in practice. To be definite we have labeled isospin states by the names of appropriate real particles. Although the reactions are listed as baryon–meson reactions, so that particles a and c are always of the type ψ, other reactions involving the same isospins can be described by our results with simple modifications. In practice the inverses of the crossing matrices defined by Eqs. (7.14) and (7.15) are of importance and so are listed. In using these results, it is important to adhere to the phase and labeling conventions described previously.

To employ these results recall that the physical interpretation of the crossing matrices is as follows. Suppose we have scattering in the s channel in isospin state s'. In the u channel this "crossed scattering" can be looked upon as the "exchange" of a state with isospin s' which gives rise to certain forces in the various allowed isospin values u. To find these coefficients one reads down the column s'; the force in state u' is then proportional to the entry in the u'th row. Our tables include examples of the type $(ab \rightarrow cd)$: $(\frac{1}{2}\,\frac{1}{2} \rightarrow \frac{1}{2}\,\frac{1}{2})$; $(\frac{1}{2}\,1 \rightarrow \frac{1}{2}\,1)$; $(\frac{1}{2}\,1 \rightarrow \frac{3}{2}\,1)$; $(\frac{3}{2}\,1 \rightarrow \frac{3}{2}\,1)$; $(11 \rightarrow 11)$; $(\frac{3}{2}\,\frac{1}{2} \rightarrow \frac{3}{2}\,\frac{1}{2})$. Explicit crossing matrices for reactions involving particles of still higher isospins can be found in reference 4.

The fact that crossing matrices are essentially the recoupling coefficients was realized as early as 1954 by Dyson (13). The present exposition (4) is a generalization of the work of Mandelstam et al. (14). The first general expression for arbitrary isospin was apparently given by Barut and Unal (15). Isospin crossing matrices for many-particle processes have been considered by Kotanski and Zalewski (16).

7.2 $SU(3)$ Crossing Matrices

In order to derive crossing matrices for reactions of the type (7.1) involving particles interacting through $SU(3)$-invariant forces, we need the standard phase factor of Eq. (2.91) relating a representation N and its complex conjugate N*. Rather than use this general form we shall specialize to the eightfold way. The representations of the latter have the especially simple phase factor $(-1)^Q$ with integral Q and so requires less vigilance with signs than the general case. [The more general case has been analyzed by Nieto (17), who also works out in detail the crossing matrices for **3** + **8** → **3** + **8**, required for the study of Sakaton (or quark)-meson octet scattering.] The crossing matrix for **8** + **8** → **8** + **8** was first worked out by Cutkosky (19) using projection operator techniques. Neville (20) approached the same problem using tensorial methods. Here we use the generalization of the method of the preceding section which emphasizes the connection between crossing matrices and the group recoupling coefficients. This is the method used by de Swart (21) and Nieto (17). [See also the work by Krammer (18).]

Rewriting Eq. (5.58) for the Lorentz-invariant transition matrix M rather than the full S matrix gives for the s-, u-, and t-channel amplitudes [the three channels are defined in Eqs. (7.1)–(7.3)].

$$(cd|\ M_s\ |ab) = \sum_{\mu\nu\gamma\gamma'} \begin{pmatrix} \mu_c & \mu_d & \mu_{\gamma'} \\ \nu_c & \nu_d & \nu \end{pmatrix} \begin{pmatrix} \mu_a & \mu_b & \mu_\gamma \\ \nu_a & \nu_b & \nu \end{pmatrix} M_s(\mu,\gamma'\gamma) \tag{7.46}$$

$$(c\bar{b}|\ M_u\ |a\bar{d}) = \sum_{\mu\nu\gamma\gamma'} \begin{pmatrix} \mu_c & \mu_b{}^* & \mu_{\gamma'} \\ \nu_c & \bar{\nu}_b & \nu \end{pmatrix} \begin{pmatrix} \mu_a & \mu_d{}^* & \mu_\gamma \\ \nu_a & \bar{\nu}_d & \nu \end{pmatrix} M_u(\mu,\gamma'\gamma) \tag{7.47}$$

$$(\bar{b}d|\ M_t\ |a\bar{c}) = \sum_{\mu\nu\gamma\gamma'} \begin{pmatrix} \mu_b{}^* & \mu_d & \mu_{\gamma'} \\ \bar{\nu}_b & \nu_d & \nu \end{pmatrix} \begin{pmatrix} \mu_a & \mu_c{}^* & \mu_\gamma \\ \nu_a & \bar{\nu}_c & \nu \end{pmatrix} M_t(\mu,\gamma'\gamma) \tag{7.48}$$

Here the notation is as follows. The particle symbol a (similarly for b, c, and d) includes specification of the representation μ_a and component $\nu_a = (T_a, T_{az}, Y_a)$. Similarly, $\bar{a}$ belongs to the representation $\mu_a{}^*$ and component $\bar{\nu}_a = (T_a, -T_{az}, -Y_a)$. The indices

$\gamma(\gamma')$ distinguish among equivalent representations in the initial (final) states.

The crossing phases ξ_{su} and ξ_{st} of Eqs. (1.7) and (1.8) are (in the octet model) simply

$$\xi_{su} = (-1)^{Q_b \pm Q_d} \tag{7.49}$$

$$\xi_{st} = (-1)^{Q_b \pm Q_c} \tag{7.50}$$

Combining Eqs. (1.7) and (1.8) with (7.46)–(7.48) we can use the orthogonality relations for the Clebsch-Gordan coefficients to obtain the crossing matrices X_{us} and X_{ts}, defined by

$$M_u(\mu,\delta'\delta) = \sum_{\mu'\gamma'\gamma} (\mu\delta'\delta|\, X_{us}\,|\mu'\gamma'\gamma) M_s(\mu',\gamma'\gamma) \tag{7.51}$$

$$M_t(\mu,\delta'\delta) = \sum_{\mu'\gamma'\gamma} (\mu\delta'\delta|\, X_{ts}\,|\mu'\gamma'\gamma) M_s(\mu',\gamma'\gamma) \tag{7.52}$$

The elements of the crossing matrices are given by:

$$\begin{aligned}(\mu\delta'\delta|\, X_{us}\,|\mu'\gamma'\gamma) &= \sum_{\nu_a\bar{\nu}_b\nu_c\bar{\nu}_d\nu'} (-1)^{Q_b \pm Q_d} \begin{pmatrix} \mu_c & \mu_b^* & \mu_{\delta'} \\ \nu_c & \bar{\nu}_b & \nu \end{pmatrix} \begin{pmatrix} \mu_a & \mu_d^* & \mu_\delta \\ \nu_a & \bar{\nu}_d & \nu \end{pmatrix} \\ &\quad \times \begin{pmatrix} \mu_c & \mu_d & \mu'_{\gamma'} \\ \nu_c & \nu_d & \nu' \end{pmatrix} \begin{pmatrix} \mu_a & \mu_b & \mu'_\gamma \\ \nu_a & \nu_b & \nu' \end{pmatrix}\end{aligned} \tag{7.53}$$

$$\begin{aligned}(\mu\delta'\delta|\, X_{ts}\,|\mu'\gamma'\gamma) &= \sum_{\nu_a\bar{\nu}_c\bar{\nu}_b\nu_d\nu'} (-1)^{Q_b \pm Q_c} \begin{pmatrix} \mu_b^* & \mu_d & \mu_{\delta'} \\ \bar{\nu}_b & \nu_d & \nu \end{pmatrix} \begin{pmatrix} \mu_a & \mu_c^* & \mu_\delta \\ \nu_a & \bar{\nu}_c & \nu \end{pmatrix} \\ &\quad \times \begin{pmatrix} \mu_c & \mu_d & \mu'_{\gamma'} \\ \nu_c & \nu_d & \nu' \end{pmatrix} \begin{pmatrix} \mu_a & \mu_b & \mu'_\gamma \\ \nu_a & \nu_b & \nu' \end{pmatrix}\end{aligned} \tag{7.54}$$

The multiple summations occurring in these formulas are very inconvenient if brute force is used in their evaluation. One method which can be used to reduce the labor is to factor the $SU(3)$ Clebsch-Gordan coefficients into their constituent $SU(2)$ and isoscalar parts as in Eq. (4.8). Then some of the summations can be performed, with resulting $SU(2)$ Racah coefficients in the summation. (It is scarcely surprising that the $SU(3)$ crossing matrices can be expressed as a sum of $SU(2)$ crossing matrices.) We omit the details of this calculation (see reference 17). One finds the results

$$
\begin{aligned}
(\mu\delta'\delta|\, X_{us}\, |\mu'\gamma'\gamma)
&= \sum_{\substack{T_aY_aT_bY_b\\ T_cY_cT_dY_d}} (-1)^{Q_b-Q_d}\begin{pmatrix}\mu_c & \mu_b{}^* & \big|\, \mu_{\delta'}\\ T_cY_c & T_b-Y_b & \big|\, TY\end{pmatrix}\\
&\quad\times\begin{pmatrix}\mu_a & \mu_d{}^* & \big|\, \mu_\delta\\ T_aY_a & T_d-Y_d & \big|\, TY\end{pmatrix}\times\sum_{T'Y'} Z_{us}(T_aT_bT_cT_d;T'T)\\
&\quad\times\begin{pmatrix}\mu_c & \mu_d & \big|\, \mu'_{\gamma'}\\ T_cY_c & T_dY_d & \big|\, T'Y'\end{pmatrix}\begin{pmatrix}\mu_a & \mu_b & \big|\, \mu'_{\gamma}\\ T_aY_a & T_bY_b & \big|\, T'Y'\end{pmatrix}
\end{aligned}\tag{7.55}
$$

where Z_{us} is defined by

$$
\begin{aligned}
Z_{us}(T_aT_bT_cT_d;T'T) &= (-1)^{T_c-T_a}(2T'+1)W(T_aT_bT_cT_d;T'T)\\
&\equiv (-1)^{T_b+2T_c+T_d}(2T'+1)\begin{pmatrix}T_a & T_b & T'\\ T_c & T_d & T\end{pmatrix}
\end{aligned}\tag{7.56}
$$

and

$$
\begin{aligned}
(\mu\delta'\delta|\, X_{ts}\, |\mu'\gamma'\gamma)
&= \sum_{\substack{T_aY_aT_bY_b\\ T_cY_cT_dY_d}} (-1)^{Q_c-Q_b}\begin{pmatrix}\mu_b{}^* & \mu_d & \big|\, \mu_{\delta'}\\ T_b-Y_b & T_dY_d & \big|\, TY\end{pmatrix}\\
&\quad\times\begin{pmatrix}\mu_a & \mu_c{}^* & \big|\, \mu_\delta\\ T_aY_a & T_c-Y_c & \big|\, TY\end{pmatrix}\times\sum_{T'Y'} Z_{ts}(T_aT_bT_cT_d;T'T)\\
&\quad\times\begin{pmatrix}\mu_c & \mu_d & \big|\, \mu'_{\gamma'}\\ T_cY_c & T_dY_d & \big|\, T'Y'\end{pmatrix}\begin{pmatrix}\mu_a & \mu_b & \big|\, \mu'_{\gamma}\\ T_aY_a & T_bY_b & \big|\, T'Y'\end{pmatrix}
\end{aligned}\tag{7.57}
$$

with Z_{ts} given by

$$
\begin{aligned}
Z_{ts}(T_aT_bT_cT_d;T'T) &= (-1)^{T_a+T_d}(2T'+1)W(T_aT'TT_d;T_bT_c)\\
&= (-1)^{T+T'}(2T'+1)\begin{Bmatrix}T_a & T' & T_b\\ T_d & T & T_c\end{Bmatrix}
\end{aligned}\tag{7.58}
$$

The quantities Z_{us} and Z_{ts} are the same as the $SU(2)$ crossing matrices, up to a phase.

Since the crossing matrices (7.55) and (7.57) are independent of T and Y, the latter may be chosen so as to take advantage of special properties of the isoscalar factors to reduce the number of terms in the sums.

In the especially important case of scattering of octet particles X_{us} and X_{ts} are identical up to a phase factor, the latter given by

$$(\mu\delta'\delta|\ X_{ts}\ |\mu'\gamma'\gamma) = \xi_1(\mathbf{88}\mu_{\delta'})\xi_1(\mathbf{88}\mu'_{\gamma'})(\mu\delta'\delta|\ X_{us}\ |\mu'\gamma'\gamma) \quad (7.59)$$

where the ξ_1 factors are given in Table 4.1.

The $\mathbf{8} \times \mathbf{8}$ crossing matrices are given in Table 7.2. The upper sign refers to the X_{us} and the lower to X_{ts}. In each of these cases

TABLE 7.2

Octet Crossing Matrix ($\mathbf{8} \times \mathbf{8} \rightarrow \mathbf{8} \times \mathbf{8}$). The Upper (Lower) Signs Refer to the U-Channel (T-Channel) Crossing Matrices.

$\mu_{\delta'\delta}$ \ $\mu'_{\gamma'\gamma}$	**27**	**10**	**10***	$\mathbf{8}_{11}$	$\mathbf{8}_{12}$	$\mathbf{8}_{21}$	$\mathbf{8}_{22}$	**1**
27	7/40	$\pm 1/12$	$\pm 1/12$	1/5	0	0	$\pm 1/3$	1/8
10	$\pm 9/40$	1/4	1/4	$\pm 2/5$	$\pm 1/\sqrt{5}$	$1/\sqrt{5}$	0	$\mp 1/8$
10*	$\pm 9/40$	1/4	1/4	$\pm 2/5$	$\mp 1/\sqrt{5}$	$-1/\sqrt{5}$	0	$\mp 1/8$
$\mathbf{8}_{11}$	27/40	$\pm 1/2$	$\pm 1/2$	$-3/10$	0	0	$\mp 1/2$	1/8
$\mathbf{8}_{12}$	0	$\pm\sqrt{5}/4$	$\mp\sqrt{5}/4$	0	$-1/2$	$\pm 1/2$	0	0
$\mathbf{8}_{21}$	0	$\sqrt{5}/4$	$-\sqrt{5}/4$	0	$\pm 1/2$	$-1/2$	0	0
$\mathbf{8}_{22}$	$\pm 9/8$	0	0	$\mp 1/2$	0	0	1/2	$\mp 1/8$
1	27/8	$\mp 5/4$	$\mp 5/4$	1	0	0	∓ 1	1/8

$X^2 = 1$ and so $X = X^{-1}$. As in the previous section the column labels refer to the "exchanged state ' and the row labels to the "output force."

The result found for isospin crossing matrices, that $X^2 = 1$ when the crossed particles have the same isospin, has a simple generalization in $SU(3)$. If the crossed particles belong to representations that are complex conjugate to each other then $X^2 = 1$

TABLE 7.3

U-Channel Crossing Matrix Relating **8** + **10** → **8** + **10** to **8*** + **10** → **8*** + **10**.

	8	**10***	**27**	**35***	
8	1/5	−1/2	−9/20	7/4	
10	−2/5	3/4	−9/40	7/8	X_{us}
27	−2/15	−1/12	37/40	7/24	
35	2/5	1/4	9/40	1/8	

follows from the orthogonality relations for the Clebsch-Gordan coefficients. For example, if $\mu_d = \mu_b$ then $X_{us}{}^2 = 1$.

The crossing matrices (20, 21) for $a = c = \mathbf{8}$, $b = d = \mathbf{10}$ are given in Tables 7.3 and 7.4.

TABLE 7.4

T-Channel Crossing Matrix Relating **8** + **10** → **8** + **10** to **8** + **8*** → **10*** + **10**.

	1	$\mathbf{8}_1$	$\mathbf{8}_2$	**27**	
8	$\sqrt{5}/20$	$\sqrt{2}/5$	$\sqrt{10}/5$	$9\sqrt{7}/20$	
10	$\sqrt{5}/20$	$3\sqrt{2}/10$	$\sqrt{10}/10$	$-9\sqrt{7}/20$	X_{ts}
27	$\sqrt{5}/20$	$-3\sqrt{2}/10$	$\sqrt{10}/30$	$-\sqrt{7}/20$	
35	$\sqrt{5}/20$	$\sqrt{2}/10$	$-\sqrt{10}/10$	$9\sqrt{7}/140$	

7.3 Dynamical Relation of the Baryon Octet and Decuplet

It has been emphasized previously that group theory, unaided by dynamical considerations, is quite unable to predict which representations should occur in nature. Much progress has been made in understanding the dynamical relations among the strongly interacting elementary particles in recent years. This understanding, mostly of a qualitative or semiquantitative nature, is based on imposing $SU(3)$ symmetry on the dynamical framework (3) of the so-called dispersion relations. Since our understanding in this area changes rapidly with time, only one especially important example is given in this book. Further references and a detailed discussion of the baryon resonance spectrum may be found in reference 22.

We first review the Chew-Low theory (23) of the 3–3 resonance. The nucleon is regarded as fixed so that only p-wave mesons interact. States are labeled by $L_{2T,2J}$ where L is the orbital and J the total angular momentum. The four states P_{11}, P_{13}, P_{31}, and P_{33} are labeled by an index α which takes on the values 1, 2, 3, and 4 corresponding to the four P states in the order listed above. Each of these states is described by the amplitude $h_\alpha(\omega)$:

$$h_\alpha(\omega) = e^{i\delta_\alpha} \sin \delta_\alpha / p^3 v^2(p) \tag{7.60}$$

where δ_α is the phase shift in state α and $v(p)$ is the cutoff function, which makes the theory exist. The amplitudes h_α obey the equation

$$h_\alpha(\omega) = \frac{\lambda_\alpha}{\omega} + \frac{1}{\pi}\int_\mu^\infty \frac{d\omega' \operatorname{Im} h_\alpha(\omega')}{\omega' - \omega - i\varepsilon} + \sum_{\beta=1}^{4} A_{\alpha\beta} \int_\mu^\infty \frac{d\omega' \operatorname{Im} h_\beta(\omega')}{\omega' + \omega} \tag{7.61}$$

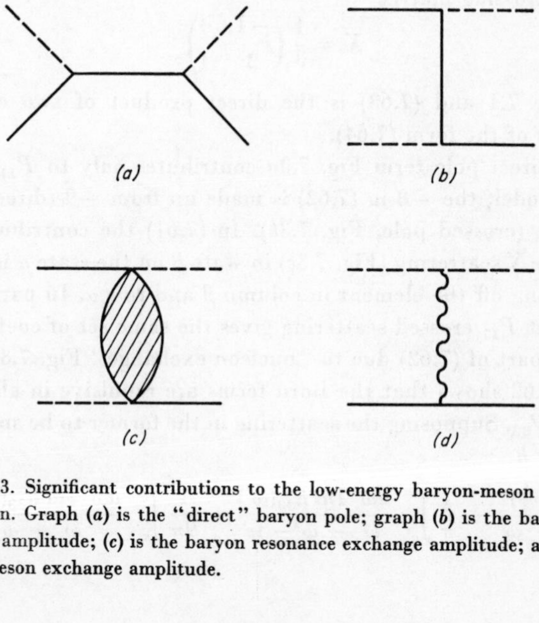

Fig. 7.3. Significant contributions to the low-energy baryon-meson scattering are shown. Graph (*a*) is the "direct" baryon pole; graph (*b*) is the baryon "exchange" amplitude; (*c*) is the baryon resonance exchange amplitude; and (*d*) the vector meson exchange amplitude.

Here ω is the pion energy $(p^2 + \mu^2)^{1/2}$ and μ the pion mass. λ_α is the coefficient of the sum of the renormalized Born approximation terms (Fig. 7.3*a*,*b*)

$$[\lambda_\alpha] = \frac{f^2}{3}\begin{pmatrix} -8 \\ -2 \\ -2 \\ +4 \end{pmatrix} \begin{matrix} P_{11} \\ P_{13} \\ P_{31} \\ P_{33} \end{matrix} \tag{7.62}$$

where $f^2 = .08$ is the unrationalized πN coupling constant and $A_{\alpha\beta}$ is the p-wave crossing matrix

$$A = \frac{1}{9}\begin{pmatrix} 1 & -4 & -4 & 16 \\ -2 & -1 & 8 & 4 \\ -2 & 8 & -1 & 4 \\ 4 & 2 & 2 & 1 \end{pmatrix} \tag{7.63}$$

The p-wave static theory crossing matrix is identical with the isospin crossing matrix

$$X = \frac{1}{3}\begin{pmatrix} -1 & 4 \\ 2 & 1 \end{pmatrix} \tag{7.64}$$

of Table 7.1 and (7.63) is the direct product of two crossing matrices of the form (7.64).

The direct pole term Fig. 7.3*a* contributes only to P_{11} in the static model; the -8 in (7.62) is made up from -9 (direct pole) plus $+1$ (crossed pole, Fig. 7.3*b*). In (7.61) the contribution of crossed πN scattering (Fig. 7.3*c*) in state β on the state α is found by reading off the element in column β and row α. In particular, note that P_{11} crossed scattering gives the same set of coefficients as that part of (7.62) due to "nucleon exchange" Fig. 7.3*b*.

Eq. 7.62 shows that the Born terms are repulsive in all states except P_{33}. Supposing the scattering in the former to be small, we have for h_{33}:

$$h_{33} = \frac{\frac{4}{3}f^2}{\omega} + \frac{1}{\pi}\int_\mu^\infty \frac{d\omega' \operatorname{Im} h_{33}(\omega')}{\omega' - \omega - i\varepsilon} + \frac{1}{9\pi}\int_\mu^\infty \frac{d\omega' \operatorname{Im} h_{33}(\omega')}{\omega' + \omega} \tag{7.65}$$

Let us neglect the last term in (7.65) temporarily on the basis of its small coefficient. Then assuming elastic unitarity, the truncated equation has the standard N/D solution (3) (normalizing so that $D_{33}(0) = 1$)

$$h_{33} = N_{33}/D_{33}; \qquad N_{33} = 4f^2/3\omega$$

$$D_{33} = 1 - \frac{\omega}{\pi}\int_{\mu}^{\infty} \frac{d\omega' k'^3 v^2(k') N_{33}(\omega')}{\omega'(\omega' - \omega - i\varepsilon)} \tag{7.66}$$

Fixing the cutoff so that Re $D_{33}(\omega_r) = 0$ and replacing the real part of the integral in (7.66) by a constant (effective range approximation) gives the Breit-Wigner form

$$e^{i\delta_{33}} \sin \delta_{33} = \frac{\frac{1}{2}\Gamma}{\omega_r - \omega - \frac{1}{2}i\Gamma}, \qquad \tfrac{1}{2}\Gamma = (\tfrac{4}{3})f^2 v^2(k) k^3 \left(\frac{\omega}{\omega_r}\right) \tag{7.67}$$

For a small width we see that h_{33} has a pole near ω_r with residue $-\gamma_{33} = -\frac{4}{3}f^2$. ($\gamma_{33}$ is also the reduced half-width.) More generally, we define γ_{33} by

$$\text{Res}\, h_{33}(\omega_r) \equiv -\gamma_{33} \tag{7.68}$$

From (7.67) we see that in the "sharp resonance approximation"

$$\text{Im}\, h_{33}(\omega) \approx \pi\gamma_{33}\delta(\omega - \omega_r) \tag{7.69}$$

Using the approximation (7.69) to perform the last integral in Eq. (7.65) gives a two-pole problem which is easily solved. Again assuming a linear D function, one finds $\gamma_{33} = \frac{3}{2}f^2$. [Note that in using (7.69) we did not assume $\gamma_{33} = \frac{4}{3}f^2$ but instead used (7.68) to find γ_{33} self-consistently. Alternatively, one can obtain the same answer by iteration.]

In the preceding discussion we showed how to build a 3–3 resonance from the attractive forces due to nucleon "exchange." One is thereby able to understand the existence of, and the numerical value of the *reduced* width of the 3–3 resonance. (The position is not predicted, however.)

In the preceding discussion we regarded the nucleon and f^2 as "given" and derived the existence and half-width of the N^*. Next we investigate the P_{11} channel, which contains the nucleon direct pole. Notice that N^* exchange gives a large attractive force in the P_{11} channel. h_{11} obeys (approximately)

$$h_{11} = -\frac{\gamma_{11}}{\omega} + \frac{\gamma_{11}}{9\omega} + \frac{16}{9}\frac{\gamma_{33}}{\omega + \omega_r} + \frac{1}{\pi}\int_{\mu}^{\infty}\frac{d\omega' \operatorname{Im} h_{11}(\omega')}{\omega' - \omega - i\varepsilon} \tag{7.70}$$

where $\gamma_{11} = 3f^2$ is the negative residue of the *direct* pole, Fig. 7.3*a*.

$$\operatorname{Res} h_{11}(0)\,|_{\text{direct pole}} \equiv -\gamma_{11} \tag{7.71}$$

Comparing (7.71) and (7.68) one notes that the reduced half width plays the role of a coupling constant. (The small numerical gain of distinguishing the "true" direct pole from the "exchange" pole, which really is a cut in the partial wave projection of the relativistic nucleon exchange amplitude of Fig. 7.3*b*, is a luxury perhaps undeserved by the crude static theory. We retain this distinction because the results attain thereby a certain simplicity.) Since $\gamma_{33} = \frac{1}{2}\gamma_{11}$ we see that the γ_{33} term in Eq. (7.70) is typically larger than the attractive force (pole term) in (7.65) that gave rise to the 3–3 resonance. Thus the first term in (7.70) might be a bound state pole, analogous to that which results from the second term of (7.65) if (7.69) is used to evaluate the integral. By arranging for D_{11} to have a zero at $\omega = 0$ instead of putting a pole in N_{11} one can obtain a relation between γ_{11} and γ_{33} (the latter now regarded as given). Neglecting $\frac{1}{9}(\gamma_{11}/\omega)$ and setting $D_{11}(-\omega_r) = 1$ gives

$$h_{11} = N_1/D_{11} \qquad N_{11} = \frac{16}{9}\frac{\gamma_{33}}{\omega + \omega_r} \tag{7.72}$$

By using a slightly different cutoff from that needed to obtain $\operatorname{Re} D_{33}(\omega_r) = 0$, as can be justified by appeal to the relativistic case, one can make $D_1(0) = 0$. Again approximating $D_{11}(\omega)$ by a straight line, $D_{11}(\omega) \cong -\omega/\omega_r$ gives from (7.71)

$$\gamma_{11} \cong \tfrac{16}{9}\,\gamma_{33} \tag{7.73}$$

which value is close to $\frac{1}{2}\gamma_{11} = \gamma_{33}$ obtained before. In fact complete agreement can be achieved if we include the $\frac{1}{9}(\gamma_{11}/\omega)$ piece of Eq. (7.70). To avoid confusing this term with the direct pole one can use the trick of displacing the exchange pole to $-\varepsilon$ by writing $\frac{1}{9}\gamma_{11}/(\omega + \varepsilon)$ and finally taking $\varepsilon \to 0$. One then finds ($D_{11} \cong -\omega/\omega_r$)

$$\gamma_{11} = 2\gamma_{33} \tag{7.74}$$

so that the *ratio* of the coupling constants is consistently determined.

Although the quantitative validity of this calculation is questionable, a most interesting physical idea has been made plausible: the nucleon can be regarded as a bound state of a pion and a nucleon, held together principally by N^* exchange, in precisely the same way that the N^* can be regarded as a composite particle made up from a pion and a nucleon, held together mainly by N exchange. Chew (24) has described this situation as the "reciprocal" bootstrap, in analogy to the ρ meson bootstrap (25) wherein the forces due to ρ meson exchange in π–π scattering give rise to the ρ. Although the N–N^* bootstrap is not so simple, the relation of N to N^* is clearly reciprocal. According to this point of view there is no way to tell which of N or N^* is the more fundamental. Likewise, γ_{11} and γ_{33} are on a completely equivalent footing. To be sure, the argument has a definitely circular character of the chicken-egg type and does not explain, as yet, why *either* particle exists. It will be noticed that only the ratio γ_{11}/γ_{33} emerges from the preceding calculation. Moreover, the ratio is independent of the various masses in the problem.

Improved calculations (with relativistic kinematics) of the N–N^* bootstrap have been made by Abers and Zemach (26) and Ball and Wong (27). These models include the ρ-meson exchange term (Fig. 7.3*d*) in addition to the N, N^* exchange forces already discussed. (We might remark here that even this force should be regarded as part of the bootstrap since the sign and magnitude of the $N\bar{N} \to \rho \to 2\pi$ amplitude depends essentially on N, N^* exchange forces. Thus we do not have to regard this contribution as something extraneous to the bootstrap, which has to be put in simply because it is there.) These authors conclude that the observed πN coupling constant, N^* width, and N, N^* masses are compatible with the bootstrap model to within the expected accuracy of such calculations ($\sim 20\%$).

One of the most impressive achievements of $SU(3)$ is the simple way in which the mutual existence of the baryon octet and $P_{3/2}$ decuplet can be understood dynamically (19, 28). We sketch here the salient features of this theory, emphasizing the group-theoretical aspects. In the degenerate mass approximation (M = baryon mass and μ = meson mass) one can classify the scattering amplitude according to the irreducible representations occurring in $\mathbf{8} \times \mathbf{8}$. However, since $\mathbf{8}$ occurs twice, there will, in general, be off-diagonal elements corresponding to transitions $\mathbf{8}_1 \rightarrow \mathbf{8}_2$ and $\mathbf{8}_2 \rightarrow \mathbf{8}_1$, corresponding to the F or D matrices occurring at the two vertices in Fig. 7.3*a*,*b*. $\mathbf{F}^2$ and $\mathbf{D}^2$ are respectively $3I$ and $\frac{5}{3}I$ in the octet states so that the projection operators for a meson in state i going to state j ($i, j = 1, 2, \ldots, 8$ run over the appropriate octet) the projection operators are

$$\begin{aligned} (\mathscr{P}_{8_2})_{ji} &= \tfrac{1}{3} F_j F_i \\ (\mathscr{P}_{8_1})_{ji} &= \tfrac{3}{5} D_j D_i \end{aligned} \tag{7.75}$$

The appropriately normalized operator Q for $8_1 \leftrightarrow 8_2$ is (19)

$$Q_{ji} = \frac{1}{\sqrt{5}} (F_j D_i + D_j F_i) \tag{7.76}$$

Thus the *direct* pole contributions to the $P_{1/2}$ matrix amplitude h are given by

$$\mathbf{h} = -\frac{f^2}{\omega} \begin{pmatrix} \frac{20}{3}\alpha^2 & 4\sqrt{5}\,\alpha(1-\alpha) \\ 4\sqrt{5}\,\alpha(1-\alpha) & 12(1-\alpha)^2 \end{pmatrix} \tag{7.77}$$

Only one eigenamplitude of (7.77) has the pole at $\omega = 0$ since the determinant of the Born matrix (7.77) is zero. This state is

$$\psi_8 = N\left[\alpha\psi_{8_1} + \frac{3}{\sqrt{5}}(1-\alpha)\psi_{8_2}\right] \tag{7.78}$$

where N is the normalization constant.

To find the contribution of baryon exchange to the various irreducible representations of the $SU(3)$ baryon–boson scattering states one needs to combine the $SU(3)$ crossing matrix with Eq. (7.77).

In the static model the crossing relation reads

$$h_{i\mu}(\omega) = \sum_{j\nu} C_{ij} X_{\mu\nu}^{(us)} h_{j\nu}(-\omega) \tag{7.79}$$

where i and j refer to the $J = l \mp \frac{1}{2}$ states and μ and ν to the irreducible representations. C_{ij} is the p-wave crossing matrix [identical to Eq. (7.64)] and $X_{\mu\nu}^{(us)}$ is given in Table 7.2. For the exchange of the baryon octet, the resulting force in $J = 3/2$ is measured by the coefficients $F_i(\alpha)$, defined by $h_{(3/2)i} = (2f^2/3\omega)F_i\ (\alpha)$. (For the $T = J = 3/2$ state in πN scattering $F = 2$.) The F_i are computed to be:

$$\begin{aligned}
F^{(1)} &= 4[\tfrac{5}{3}\alpha^2 - 3(1-\alpha)^2] \\
F^{27} &= \tfrac{4}{3}[3(1-\alpha)^2 + \alpha^2] \\
F^{10*} &= \tfrac{8}{3}[\alpha^2 - 3\alpha(1-\alpha)] \\
F^{10} &= \tfrac{8}{3}\alpha(3 - 2\alpha) \\
F^{8_2} &= 6(1-\alpha)^2 - \tfrac{10}{3}\alpha^2 \\
F^{8_1} &= -[6(1-\alpha)^2 + 2\alpha^2] \\
F^{8_1 \to 8_2} &= 0
\end{aligned} \tag{7.80}$$

These contributions are plotted in Fig. 7.4 as a function of the mixing parameter α. It will be observed that for $\alpha > \frac{1}{2}$, a $P_{3/2}$ decuplet is quite likely.

The value of α can be obtained from the self-consistency requirement that the decuplet exchange force gives rise to the baryon octet. From the crossing matrix one sees that decuplet exchange gives the matrix for the octet subspace:

$$D = \begin{pmatrix} \frac{1}{2} & \frac{1}{4}\sqrt{5} \\ \frac{1}{4}\sqrt{5} & 0 \end{pmatrix} \tag{7.81}$$

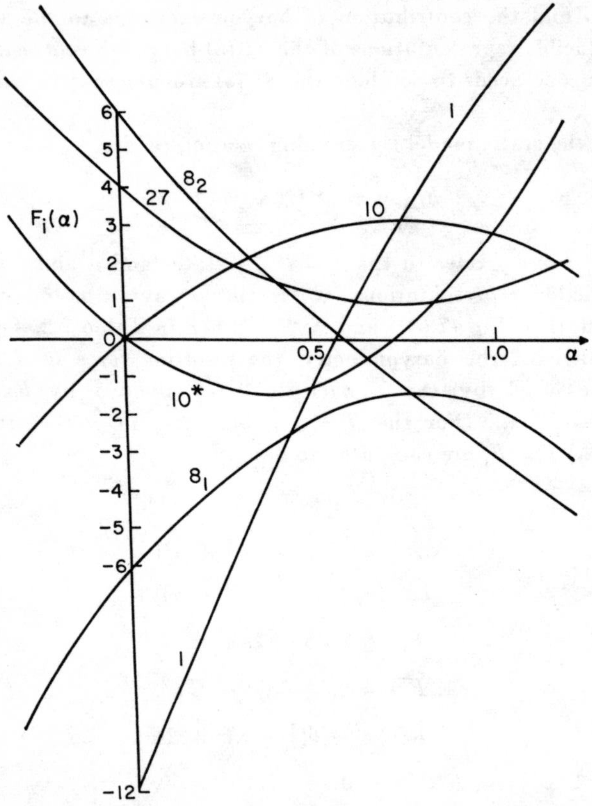

Fig. 7.4. The strength of the (octet) baryon exchange amplitude is given as a function of the mixing parameter α for the irreducible representations occurring in **8** × **8**. For comparison, note that F_i would be 2 for nucleon exchange in $T = 3/2$, πN scattering.

dropping the easily calculable kinematical factors. (For the spatial part the problem is the same as for the N–N^* bootstrap.) We can diagonalize D by MDM^{-1} where

$$M = \frac{1}{[2\sqrt{6}(1 + \sqrt{6})]^{1/2}} \begin{pmatrix} 1 + \sqrt{6} & \sqrt{5} \\ -\sqrt{5} & 1 + \sqrt{6} \end{pmatrix} \tag{7.82}$$

The eigenvalues of D are $\frac{1}{4}(1 \pm \sqrt{6})$ of which only the positive one gives attraction in the $P_{3/2}$ state. Thus (7.82) corresponds to an eigenamplitude $N[1 + \sqrt{6})\psi_{8_1} + \sqrt{5}\psi_{8_2}$, i.e., a definite mixing parameter [cf. Eq. (7.78)]

$$\alpha = \alpha_0 \equiv \frac{3}{2 + \sqrt{6}} = 0.674 \tag{7.83}$$

a value very near that which gives a maximal πN constituent in the $T = 1/2$, $Y = 1$ states (see Fig. 3.10) and also agrees well with the "experimental" values found by Glashow and Rosenfeld (29). Moreover, this value requires the $P_{3/2}$ decuplet, as is seen in Fig. 7.4. One still has to verify that the *residues* obtained in the bootstrap are in rough agreement. This is roughly true in the model used. (To improve the agreement one has to include the effect of **10** exchange on **10** and octet exchange on the octet amplitudes, in analogy to the πN problem.)

Thus to a first approximation it appears possible to regard the baryons and their $P_{3/2}$ excited states as a dynamical consequence of $SU(3)$ combined with conventional dispersion-theoretic notions. Golowich (30) has made a detailed study of forces for many states in meson–baryon scattering. The reader is referred to this work, and also reference 22, for a fuller picture of the dynamics of the meson–baryon interaction.

This example gives only a glimpse of the many interesting problems in the region where symmetry and dynamics overlap. Many believe that some day it will be possible to deduce the existing symmetries from dynamical considerations. Capps (31) and Cutkosky (32) have presented interesting models in which this is the case. At present, however, broken $SU(3)$ is much more precise than our imperfect understanding of dynamics.

References

1. J. M. Jauch and F. Rohrlich, *Theory of Photons and Electrons*, Addison-Wesley, Reading, Mass., 1955, Chap. 8.
2. M. Gell-Mann and M. L. Goldberger, *Proceedings of the Rochester Conference on High Energy Physics (1956)*.

3. G. F. Chew, *S-Matrix Theory of Strong Interactions*, W. A. Benjamin, New York, 1960.
4. P. Carruthers and J. P. Krisch, *Ann. Phys.* (*N.Y.*), **33**, 1 (1965).
5. S. Mandelstam, *Phys. Rev.*, **112**, 1344 (1958).
6. T. L. Trueman, and G. C. Wick, *Ann. Phys.* (*N.Y.*), **26**, 322 (1964).
7. E. U. Condon and G. H. Shortley, *The Theory of Atomic Spectra*, Cambridge Univ. Press, London, 1957, Chap. 3.
8. M. E. Rose, *Elementary Theory of Angular Momentum*, John Wiley, New York, 1957.
9. A. M. Baldin, V. I. Goldanskii, and I. L. Rosental, *Kinematics of Nuclear Reactions*, Oxford Univ. Press, London, 1961, p. 112.
10. H. Lehmann, K. Symanzik, and W. Zimmerman, *Nuovo Cimento*, **1**, 205 (1955); **6**, 319 (1957).
11. G. Barton, *Introduction to Advanced Field Theory*, Interscience, New York, 1963, Chap. 4.
12. A. R. Edmonds, *Angular Momentum in Quantum Mechanics*, Princeton Univ. Press, 1960.
13. F. J. Dyson, *Phys. Rev.*, **100**, 344 (1955).
14. S. Mandelstam, J. E. Paton, R. F. Peierls, and A. Q. Sarker, *Ann. Phys.* (*N.Y.*), **18**, 198 (1962).
15. A. O. Barut and B. C. Unal, *Nuovo Cimento*, **28**, 112 (1963).
16. A. Kotanski and K. Zalewski, *Acta Phys. Pol.*, **26**, 117 (1964).
17. M. M. Nieto, *Phys. Rev.*, **140**, B434 (1965).
18. M. Krammer, *Acta Phys. Austriaca, Suppl. 1*, 183 (1964).
19. R. E. Cutkosky, *Ann. Phys.* (*N.Y.*), **23**, 415 (1963).
20. D. Neville, *Phys. Rev.*, **132**, 844 (1963).
21. J. J. de Swart, *Nuovo Cimento*, **31**, 420 (1964).
22. P. Carruthers, *Lectures in Theoretical Physics*, Vol. VIIb, Univ. of Colorado Press, Boulder, Colo., 1965, p. 82.
23. G. F. Chew and F. E. Low, *Phys. Rev.*, **101**, 1571 (1956).
24. G. F. Chew, *Phys. Rev. Letters*, **9**, 233 (1962).
25. F. Zachariasen, *Phys. Rev. Letters*, **7**, 112 (1961).
26. E. Abers and C. Zemach, *Phys. Rev.*, **131**, 2305 (1963).
27. J. S. Ball and D. Y. Wong, *Phys. Rev.*, **133**, B179 (1964).
28. A. W. Martin and K. C. Wali, *Phys. Rev.*, **130**, 2455 (1963); *Nuovo Cimento*, **31**, 1324 (1964).
29. S. L. Glashow and A. H. Rosenfeld, *Phys. Rev. Letters*, **10**, 192 (1963).
30. E. Golowich, *Phys. Rev.*, **139**, B1297 (1965).
31. R. H. Capps, *Phys. Rev. Letters*, **10**, 312 (1963).
32. R. E. Cutkosky, *Phys. Rev.*, **131**, 1888 (1963).

Appendix I

Isoscalar Factors

The $SU(3)$ Clebsch-Gordan coefficients are given by the product of isoscalar factors and $SU(2)$ Clebsch-Gordan coefficients as discussed in Section 4.2. Tables A-I–A-V are taken from the review of de Swart cited in the preface. Tables A-I–A-V correspond to the decompositions $8 \times 8 = 27 + 10 + 10^* + 8_1 + 8_2 + 1$, $8 \times 10 = 35 + 27 + 10 + 8$, $8 \times 27 = 64 + 35 + 35^* + 27_1 + 27_2 + 10 + 10^* + 8$, $10 \times 10 = 35 + 28 + 27 + 10^*$, and $10 \times 10^* = 64 + 27 + 8 + 1$, respectively.

TABLE A-I

$Y = 2 \quad I = 1$

I_1,	Y_1;	I_2,	Y_2	27	μ_γ
$\frac{1}{2}$,	1;	$\frac{1}{2}$,	1	1	

$Y = 2 \quad I = 0$

I_1,	Y_1;	I_2,	Y_2	10*	μ_γ
$\frac{1}{2}$,	1;	$\frac{1}{2}$,	1	−1	

$Y = 1 \quad I = \frac{3}{2}$

I_1,	Y_1;	I_2,	Y_2	27	10	μ_γ
$\frac{1}{2}$,	1;	1,	0	$\sqrt{2}/2$	$-\sqrt{2}/2$	
1,	0;	$\frac{1}{2}$,	1	$\sqrt{2}/2$	$\sqrt{2}/2$	

$Y = 0 \quad I = 0$

I_1,	Y_1;	I_2,	Y_2	27	8_1	1	8_2	μ_γ
$\frac{1}{2}$,	1;	$\frac{1}{2}$,	−1	$\sqrt{15}/10$	$\sqrt{10}/10$	1/2	$\sqrt{2}/2$	
$\frac{1}{2}$,	−1;	$\frac{1}{2}$,	1	$-\sqrt{15}/10$	$-\sqrt{10}/10$	−1/2	$\sqrt{2}/2$	
1,	0;	1,	0	$-\sqrt{10}/20$	$-\sqrt{15}/5$	$\sqrt{6}/4$	0	
0,	0;	0,	0	$3\sqrt{30}/20$	$-\sqrt{5}/5$	$-\sqrt{2}/4$	0	

$Y = 1 \quad I = \frac{1}{2}$

I_1,	Y_1;	I_2,	Y_2	27	8_1	8_2	10*	μ_γ
$\frac{1}{2}$,	1;	1,	0	$\sqrt{5}/10$	$3\sqrt{5}/10$	1/2	−1/2	
1,	0;	$\frac{1}{2}$,	1	$-\sqrt{5}/10$	$-3\sqrt{5}/10$	1/2	−1/2	
$\frac{1}{2}$,	1;	0,	0	$3\sqrt{5}/10$	$-\sqrt{5}/10$	1/2	1/2	
0,	0;	$\frac{1}{2}$,	1	$3\sqrt{5}/10$	$-\sqrt{5}/10$	−1/2	−1/2	

$Y = -1 \quad I = \frac{3}{2}$

I_1,	Y_1;	I_2,	Y_2	27	10*	μ_γ
$\frac{1}{2}$,	−1;	1,	0	$\sqrt{2}/2$	$-\sqrt{2}/2$	
1,	0;	$\frac{1}{2}$,	−1	$\sqrt{2}/2$	$\sqrt{2}/2$	

$Y = 0 \quad I = 2$

I_1,	Y_1;	I_2,	Y_2	27
1,	0;	1,	0	1

μ_γ

$Y = -1 \quad I = \frac{1}{2}$

I_1,	Y_1;	I_2,	Y_2	27	8_1	8_2	10
$\frac{1}{2}$,	−1;	1,	0	$-\sqrt{5}/10$	$-3\sqrt{5}/10$	1/2	1/2
1,	0;	$\frac{1}{2}$,	−1	$\sqrt{5}/10$	$3\sqrt{5}/10$	1/2	1/2
$\frac{1}{2}$,	−1;	0,	0	$3\sqrt{5}/10$	$-\sqrt{5}/10$	−1/2	1/2
0,	0;	$\frac{1}{2}$,	−1	$3\sqrt{5}/10$	$-\sqrt{5}/10$	1/2	−1/2

μ_γ

$Y = 0 \quad I = 1$

I_1,	Y_1;	I_2,	Y_2	27	8_1	8_2	10	10*
$\frac{1}{2}$,	1;	$\frac{1}{2}$,	−1	$\sqrt{5}/5$	$-\sqrt{30}/10$	$\sqrt{6}/6$	$-\sqrt{6}/6$	$\sqrt{6}/6$
$\frac{1}{2}$,	−1;	$\frac{1}{2}$	1	$\sqrt{5}/5$	$-\sqrt{30}/10$	$-\sqrt{6}/6$	$\sqrt{6}/6$	$-\sqrt{6}/6$
1,	0;	1,	0	0	0	$\sqrt{6}/3$	$\sqrt{6}/6$	$-\sqrt{6}/6$
1,	0;	0,	0	$\sqrt{30}/10$	$\sqrt{5}/5$	0	1/2	1/2
0,	0;	1,	0	$\sqrt{30}/10$	$\sqrt{5}/5$	0	−1/2	−1/2

μ_γ

$Y = -2 \quad I = 1$

I_1,	Y_1;	I_2,	Y_2	27
$\frac{1}{2}$,	−1;	$\frac{1}{2}$,	−1	1

μ_γ

$Y = -2 \quad I = 0$

I_1,	Y_1;	I_2,	Y_2	10
$\frac{1}{2}$,	−1;	$\frac{1}{2}$,	−1	1

μ_γ

TABLE A-II

$Y = 2 \quad I = 2$

I_1,	Y_1;	I_2,	Y_2	35	μ_γ
$\frac{1}{2}$,	1;	$\frac{3}{2}$,	1	1	

$Y = 2 \quad I = 1$

I_1,	Y_1;	I_2,	Y_2	27	μ_γ
$\frac{1}{2}$,	1;	$\frac{3}{2}$,	1	-1	

$Y = 1 \quad I = \frac{5}{2}$

I_1,	Y_1;	I_2,	Y_2	35	μ_γ
1,	0;	$\frac{3}{2}$,	1	1	

$Y = 1 \quad I = \frac{3}{2}$

I_1,	Y_1;	I_2,	Y_2	35	27	10	μ_γ
1,	0;	$\frac{3}{2}$,	1	$-1/4$	$-\sqrt{5}/4$	$\sqrt{10}/4$	
0,	0;	$\frac{3}{2}$,	1	$\sqrt{5}/4$	$-3/4$	$-\sqrt{2}/4$	
$\frac{1}{2}$,	1;	1,	0	$\sqrt{10}/4$	$\sqrt{2}/4$	$1/2$	

$Y = 1 \quad I = \frac{1}{2}$

I_1,	Y_1;	I_2,	Y_2	27	8	μ_γ
1,	0;	$\frac{3}{2}$,	1	$\sqrt{5}/5$	$-2\sqrt{5}/5$	
$\frac{1}{2}$,	1;	1,	0	$-2\sqrt{5}/5$	$-\sqrt{5}/5$	

$Y = 0 \quad I = 2$

I_1,	Y_1;	I_2,	Y_2	35	27	μ_γ
1,	0;	1,	1	$\sqrt{3}/2$	$1/2$	
$\frac{1}{2}$,	-1;	$\frac{3}{2}$,	0	$1/2$	$-\sqrt{3}/2$	

$Y = 0 \quad I = 1$

I_1,	Y_1;	I_2,	Y_2	35	27	10	8	μ_γ
1,	0;	1,	0	$-\sqrt{3}/6$	$-3\sqrt{5}/10$	$\sqrt{3}/3$	$\sqrt{30}/15$	
0,	0;	1,	0	$\sqrt{2}/2$	$-\sqrt{30}/10$	0	$-\sqrt{5}/5$	
$\frac{1}{2}$,	1;	$\frac{1}{2}$,	-1	$\sqrt{3}/3$	$\sqrt{5}/5$	$\sqrt{3}/3$	$\sqrt{30}/15$	
$\frac{1}{2}$,	-1;	$\frac{3}{2}$,	1	$-\sqrt{3}/6$	$\sqrt{5}/10$	$\sqrt{3}/3$	$-2\sqrt{30}/15$	

$Y = 0 \quad I = 0$

I_1,	Y_1;	I_2,	Y_2	27	8	μ_γ
1,	0;	1,	0	$\sqrt{10}/5$	$-\sqrt{15}/5$	
$\frac{1}{2}$,	1;	$\frac{1}{2}$,	-1	$-\sqrt{15}/5$	$-\sqrt{10}/5$	

$Y = -1 \quad I = \frac{3}{2}$

I_1,	Y_1;	I_2,	Y_2	35	27	μ_γ
1,	0;	$\frac{1}{2}$,	-1	$\sqrt{2}/2$	$\sqrt{2}/2$	
$\frac{1}{2}$,	-1;	1,	0	$\sqrt{2}/2$	$-\sqrt{2}/2$	

$Y = -1 \quad I = \frac{1}{2}$

I_1,	Y_1;	I_2,	Y_2	35	27	10	8	μ_γ
1,	0;	$\frac{1}{2}$,	-1	$-1/4$	$-7\sqrt{5}/20$	$\sqrt{2}/4$	$\sqrt{5}/5$	
0,	0;	$\frac{1}{2}$,	-1	$3/4$	$-3\sqrt{5}/20$	$\sqrt{2}/4$	$-\sqrt{5}/5$	
$\frac{1}{2}$,	1;	0,	-2	$\sqrt{2}/4$	$3\sqrt{10}/20$	$1/2$	$\sqrt{10}/5$	
$\frac{1}{2}$,	-1;	1,	0	$-1/2$	$\sqrt{5}/10$	$\sqrt{2}/2$	$-\sqrt{5}/5$	

$Y = -2 \quad I = 1$

I_1,	Y_1;	I_2,	Y_2	35	27	μ_γ
1,	0;	0,	-2	$1/2$	$\sqrt{3}/2$	
$\frac{1}{2}$,	-1;	$\frac{1}{2}$,	-1	$\sqrt{3}/2$	$-1/2$	

$Y = -2 \quad I = 0$

I_1,	Y_1;	I_2,	Y_2	35	10	μ_γ
0,	0;	0,	-2	$\sqrt{2}/2$	$\sqrt{2}/2$	
$\frac{1}{2}$,	-1;	$\frac{1}{2}$,	-1	$-\sqrt{2}/2$	$\sqrt{2}/2$	

$Y = -3 \quad I = \frac{1}{2}$

I_1,	Y_1;	I_2,	Y_2	35	μ_γ
$\frac{1}{2}$,	-1;	0,	-2	1	

TABLE A-III

$Y = 3 \quad I = \frac{3}{2}$

I_1,	Y_1;	I_2,	Y_2	64
$\frac{1}{2}$,	1;	1,	2	1

$Y = 3 \quad I = \frac{1}{2}$

I_1,	Y_1;	I_2,	Y_2	35*
$\frac{1}{2}$,	1;	1,	2	-1

$Y = 2 \quad I = 2$

I_1,	Y_1;	I_2,	Y_2	64	35
$\frac{1}{2}$,	1;	$\frac{3}{2}$,	1	$\sqrt{6}/3$	$-\sqrt{3}/3$
1,	0;	1,	2	$\sqrt{3}/3$	$\sqrt{6}/3$

$Y = 2 \quad I = 1$

I_1,	Y_1;	I_2,	Y_2	64	35*	27_1	27_2
$\frac{1}{2}$,	1;	$\frac{3}{2}$,	1	$\sqrt{14}/21$	$-2/3$	$\sqrt{70}/14$	$\sqrt{6}/6$
$\frac{1}{2}$,	1;	$\frac{1}{2}$,	1	$2\sqrt{70}/21$	$\sqrt{5}/6$	$-\sqrt{14}/28$	$\sqrt{30}/12$
1,	0;	1,	2	$-\sqrt{21}/21$	$-\sqrt{6}/6$	$-\sqrt{105}/14$	$1/2$
0,	0;	1,	2	$\sqrt{14}/7$	$-1/2$	$-\sqrt{70}/28$	$-\sqrt{6}/4$

$Y = 2 \quad I = 0$

I_1,	Y_1;	I_2,	Y_2	35*	10*
$\frac{1}{2}$,	1;	$\frac{1}{2}$,	1	$-\sqrt{30}/6$	$-\sqrt{6}/6$
1,	0;	1,	2	$\sqrt{6}/6$	$-\sqrt{30}/6$

$Y = 1 \quad I = \frac{5}{2}$

I_1,	Y_1;	I_2,	Y_2	64	35
$\frac{1}{2}$,	1;	2,	0	$\sqrt{3}/3$	$-\sqrt{6}/3$
1,	0;	$\frac{3}{2}$,	1	$\sqrt{6}/3$	$\sqrt{3}/3$

$Y = 1 \quad I = \frac{3}{2}$

I_1,	Y_1;	I_2,	Y_2	64	35	35*	27_1	27_2	10	μ_γ
$\frac{1}{2}$,	1;	2,	0	$\sqrt{7}/21$	$-1/12$	$-\sqrt{5}/6$	$5\sqrt{42}/56$	$\sqrt{10}/8$	$-5\sqrt{2}/12$	
$\frac{1}{2}$,	1;	1,	0	$5\sqrt{7}/21$	$-5/12$	$\sqrt{5}/6$	$-3\sqrt{42}/56$	$\sqrt{10}/8$	$-\sqrt{2}/12$	
1,	0;	$\frac{3}{2}$,	1	$-\sqrt{21}/63$	$7\sqrt{3}/36$	$-\sqrt{15}/9$	$-5\sqrt{14}/56$	$\sqrt{30}/8$	$5\sqrt{6}/36$	
1,	0;	$\frac{1}{2}$,	1	$5\sqrt{42}/63$	$5\sqrt{6}/18$	$\sqrt{30}/18$	$\sqrt{7}/7$	0	$\sqrt{3}/9$	
0,	0;	$\frac{3}{2}$,	1	$\sqrt{105}/21$	$-\sqrt{15}/12$	$-\sqrt{3}/3$	$\sqrt{70}/56$	$-\sqrt{6}/8$	$\sqrt{30}/12$	
$\frac{1}{2}$,	-1;	1,	2	$\sqrt{35}/21$	$\sqrt{5}/6$	$-1/3$	$-\sqrt{210}/28$	$-\sqrt{2}/4$	$-\sqrt{10}/6$	

$Y = 1 \quad I = \frac{1}{2}$

I_1,	Y_1;	I_2,	Y_2	64	35*	27_1	27_2	10*	8	μ_γ
$\frac{1}{2}$,	1;	1,	0	$\sqrt{35}/21$	$-\sqrt{10}/6$	$3\sqrt{105}/70$	1/2	$-1/3$	$2\sqrt{5}/15$	
$\frac{1}{2}$,	1;	0,	0	$2\sqrt{35}/21$	$\sqrt{10}/6$	$-\sqrt{105}/70$	1/2	1/3	$\sqrt{5}/15$	
1,	0;	$\frac{3}{2}$,	1	$-\sqrt{42}/63$	$\sqrt{3}/9$	$-\sqrt{14}/7$	0	$-\sqrt{30}/9$	$2\sqrt{6}/9$	
1,	0;	$\frac{1}{2}$,	1	$-\sqrt{210}/63$	$-5\sqrt{15}/36$	$-19\sqrt{70}/280$	$\sqrt{6}/8$	$7\sqrt{6}/36$	$\sqrt{30}/45$	
0,	0;	$\frac{1}{2}$,	1	$\sqrt{210}/21$	$-\sqrt{15}/12$	$-13\sqrt{70}/280$	$-\sqrt{6}/8$	$-\sqrt{6}/12$	$-\sqrt{30}/15$	
$\frac{1}{2}$,	-1;	1,	2	$-2\sqrt{7}/21$	$\sqrt{2}/12$	$-\sqrt{21}/28$	$\sqrt{5}/4$	$-\sqrt{5}/6$	$-2/3$	

(continued)

TABLE A-III (*continued*)

$Y = 0 \quad I = 2$

I_1,	Y_1;	I_2,	Y_2	64	35	35*	27_1	27_2	μ_γ
$\frac{1}{2}$,	1;	$\frac{3}{2}$,	-1	$2\sqrt{21}/21$	$-\sqrt{3}/3$	$\sqrt{3}/6$	$-\sqrt{210}/28$	$\sqrt{2}/4$	
$\frac{1}{2}$,	-1;	$\frac{3}{2}$,	1	$2\sqrt{21}/21$	$\sqrt{3}/6$	$-\sqrt{3}/3$	$-\sqrt{210}/28$	$-\sqrt{2}/4$	
1,	0;	1,	0	$\sqrt{210}/21$	$\sqrt{30}/12$	$\sqrt{30}/12$	$\sqrt{21}/14$	0	
1,	0;	2,	0	0	$\sqrt{2}/4$	$-\sqrt{2}/4$	0	$\sqrt{3}/2$	
0,	0;	2,	0	$\sqrt{7}/7$	$-1/2$	$-1/2$	$\sqrt{70}/14$	0	

$Y = 0 \quad I = 3$

I_1,	Y_1;	I_2,	Y_2	64	μ_γ
1,	0;	2,	0	1	

$Y = 0 \quad I = 1$

I_1,	Y_1;	I_2,	Y_2	64	35	35*	27_1	27_2	10	10*	8	μ_γ
$\frac{1}{2}$,	1;	$\frac{3}{2}$,	-1	$2\sqrt{35}/63$	$-1/9$	$-5/18$	$3\sqrt{14}/28$	$\sqrt{30}/12$	$-2\sqrt{5}/9$	$-\sqrt{5}/9$	$4/9$	
$\frac{1}{2}$,	-1;	$\frac{3}{2}$,	1	$-2\sqrt{35}/63$	$5/18$	$1/9$	$-3\sqrt{14}/28$	$\sqrt{30}/12$	$-\sqrt{5}/9$	$-2\sqrt{5}/9$	$-4/9$	
$\frac{1}{2}$,	1;	$\frac{1}{2}$,	-1	$10\sqrt{7}/63$	$-\sqrt{5}/9$	$2\sqrt{5}/9$	$-3\sqrt{70}/70$	$\sqrt{6}/6$	$-1/9$	$4/9$	$2\sqrt{5}/45$	
$\frac{1}{2}$,	-1;	$\frac{1}{2}$,	1	$10\sqrt{7}/63$	$2\sqrt{5}/9$	$-\sqrt{5}/9$	$-3\sqrt{70}/70$	$-\sqrt{6}/6$	$-4/9$	$1/9$	$2\sqrt{5}/45$	
0,	0;	1,	0	$5\sqrt{7}/21$	$-\sqrt{5}/6$	$-\sqrt{5}/6$	$-\sqrt{70}/70$	0	$1/3$	$-1/3$	$-2\sqrt{5}/15$	
1,	0;	0,	0	$10\sqrt{7}/63$	$2\sqrt{5}/9$	$2\sqrt{5}/9$	$4\sqrt{70}/70$	0	$2/9$	$-2/9$	$-\sqrt{5}/45$	
1,	0;	1,	0	0	$\sqrt{30}/12$	$-\sqrt{30}/12$	0	$1/2$	$\sqrt{6}/6$	$\sqrt{6}/6$	0	
1,	0;	2,	0	$-\sqrt{14}/63$	$\sqrt{10}/36$	$\sqrt{10}/36$	$-\sqrt{35}/14$	0	$5\sqrt{2}/18$	$-5\sqrt{2}/18$	$2\sqrt{10}/9$	

$Y = 0 \quad I = 0$

I_1, Y_1; I_2, Y_2	64	27_1	27_2	8	μ_γ
$\frac{1}{2}$, 1; $\frac{1}{2}$, −1	$2\sqrt{21}/21$	$\sqrt{210}/70$	$\sqrt{2}/2$	$2\sqrt{15}/15$	
$\frac{1}{2}$, −1; $\frac{1}{2}$, 1	$-2\sqrt{21}/21$	$-\sqrt{210}/70$	$\sqrt{2}/2$	$-2\sqrt{15}/15$	
1, 0; 1, 0	$-\sqrt{21}/21$	$-4\sqrt{210}/70$	0	$2\sqrt{15}/15$	
0, 0; 0, 0	$2\sqrt{7}/7$	$-4\sqrt{70}/70$	0	$-\sqrt{5}/5$	

$Y = -1 \quad I = \frac{5}{2}$

I_1, Y_1; I_2, Y_2	64	35*	μ_γ
$\frac{1}{2}$, −1; 2, 0	$\sqrt{3}/3$	$-\sqrt{6}/3$	
1, 0; $\frac{3}{2}$, −1	$\sqrt{6}/3$	$\sqrt{3}/3$	

(*continued*)

TABLE A-III *(continued)*

$Y = -1 \quad I = \frac{3}{2}$

I_1,	Y_1;	I_2,	Y_2	64	35*	35	27_1	27_2	10*	μ_γ
$\frac{1}{2}$,	-1;	2,	0	$-\sqrt{7}/21$	$1/12$	$\sqrt{5}/6$	$-5\sqrt{42}/56$	$\sqrt{10}/8$	$-5\sqrt{2}/12$	
$\frac{1}{2}$,	-1;	1,	0	$5\sqrt{7}/21$	$-5/12$	$\sqrt{5}/6$	$-3\sqrt{42}/56$	$-\sqrt{10}/8$	$\sqrt{2}/12$	
1,	0;	$\frac{3}{2}$,	-1	$\sqrt{21}/63$	$-7\sqrt{3}/36$	$\sqrt{15}/9$	$5\sqrt{14}/56$	$\sqrt{30}/8$	$5\sqrt{6}/36$	
1,	0;	$\frac{1}{2}$,	-1	$5\sqrt{42}/63$	$5\sqrt{6}/18$	$\sqrt{30}/18$	$\sqrt{7}/7$	0	$-\sqrt{3}/9$	
0,	0;	$\frac{3}{2}$,	-1	$\sqrt{105}/21$	$-\sqrt{15}/12$	$-\sqrt{3}/3$	$\sqrt{70}/56$	$\sqrt{6}/8$	$-\sqrt{30}/12$	
$\frac{1}{2}$,	1;	1,	-2	$\sqrt{35}/21$	$\sqrt{5}/6$	$-1/3$	$-\sqrt{210}/28$	$\sqrt{2}/4$	$\sqrt{10}/6$	

$Y = -1 \quad I = \frac{1}{2}$

I_1,	Y_1;	I_2,	Y_2	64	35	27_1	27_2	10	8	μ_γ
$\frac{1}{2}$,	-1;	1,	0	$-\sqrt{35}/21$	$\sqrt{10}/6$	$-3\sqrt{105}/70$	$1/2$	$-1/3$	$-2\sqrt{5}/15$	
$\frac{1}{2}$,	-1;	0,	0	$2\sqrt{35}/21$	$\sqrt{10}/6$	$-\sqrt{105}/70$	$-1/2$	$-1/3$	$\sqrt{5}/15$	
1,	0;	$\frac{3}{2}$,	-1	$-\sqrt{42}/63$	$\sqrt{3}/9$	$-\sqrt{14}/7$	0	$\sqrt{30}/9$	$2\sqrt{6}/9$	
1,	0;	$\frac{1}{2}$,	-1	$\sqrt{210}/63$	$5\sqrt{15}/36$	$19\sqrt{70}/280$	$\sqrt{6}/8$	$7\sqrt{6}/36$	$-\sqrt{30}/45$	
0,	0;	$\frac{1}{2}$,	-1	$\sqrt{210}/21$	$-\sqrt{15}/12$	$-13\sqrt{70}/280$	$\sqrt{6}/8$	$\sqrt{6}/12$	$-\sqrt{30}/15$	
$\frac{1}{2}$,	1;	1,	-2	$2\sqrt{7}/21$	$-\sqrt{2}/12$	$\sqrt{21}/28$	$\sqrt{5}/4$	$-\sqrt{5}/6$	$2/3$	

$Y = -2 \quad I = 2$

I_1,	Y_1;	I_2,	Y_2	64	35*	μ_γ
$\frac{1}{2}$,	-1;	$\frac{3}{2}$,	-1	$\sqrt{6}/3$	$-\sqrt{3}/3$	
1,	0;	1,	-2	$\sqrt{3}/3$	$\sqrt{6}/3$	

$Y = -2 \quad I = 0$

I_1,	Y_1;	I_2,	Y_2	35	10	μ_γ
$\frac{1}{2}$,	-1;	$\frac{1}{2}$,	-1	$\sqrt{30}/6$	$-\sqrt{6}/6$	
1,	0;	1,	-2	$\sqrt{6}/6$	$\sqrt{30}/6$	

$Y = -2 \quad I = 1$

I_1,	Y_1;	I_2,	Y_2	64	35	27_1	27_2	μ_γ
$\frac{1}{2}$,	-1;	$\frac{3}{2}$,	-1	$-\sqrt{14}/21$	$2/3$	$-\sqrt{70}/14$	$\sqrt{6}/6$	
$\frac{1}{2}$,	-1;	$\frac{1}{2}$,	-1	$2\sqrt{70}/21$	$\sqrt{5}/6$	$-\sqrt{14}/28$	$-\sqrt{30}/12$	
1,	0;	1,	-2	$\sqrt{21}/21$	$\sqrt{6}/6$	$\sqrt{105}/14$	$1/2$	
0,	0;	1,	-2	$\sqrt{14}/7$	$-1/2$	$-\sqrt{70}/28$	$\sqrt{6}/4$	

$Y = -3 \quad I = \frac{3}{2}$

I_1,	Y_1;	I_2,	Y_2	64	μ_γ
$\frac{1}{2}$,	-1;	1,	-2	1	

$Y = -3 \quad I = \frac{1}{2}$

I_1,	Y_1;	I_2,	Y_2	35	μ_γ
$\frac{1}{2}$,	-1;	1,	-2	1	

TABLE A-IV

$Y = 2 \quad I = 3$

I_1,	Y_1;	I_2,	Y_2	28	μ_γ
$\frac{3}{2}$,	1;	$\frac{3}{2}$,	1	1	

$Y = 2 \quad I = 2$

I_1,	Y_1;	I_2,	Y_2	35	μ_γ
$\frac{3}{2}$,	1;	$\frac{3}{2}$,	1	-1	

$Y = 2 \quad I = 1$

I_1,	Y_1;	I_2,	Y_2	27	μ_γ
$\frac{3}{2}$,	1;	$\frac{3}{2}$,	1	1	

$Y = 2 \quad I = 0$

I_1,	Y_1;	I_2,	Y_2	10*	μ_γ
$\frac{3}{2}$,	1;	$\frac{3}{2}$,	1	-1	

$Y = 0 \quad I = 1$

I_1,	Y_1;	I_2,	Y_2	35	27	10*	μ_γ
$\frac{3}{2}$,	1;	$\frac{1}{2}$,	-1	$-\sqrt{6}/6$	$-\sqrt{2}/2$	$-\sqrt{3}/3$	
$\frac{1}{2}$,	-1;	$\frac{3}{2}$,	1	$-\sqrt{6}/6$	$\sqrt{2}/2$	$-\sqrt{3}/3$	
1,	0;	1,	0	$-\sqrt{6}/3$	0	$\sqrt{3}/3$	

$Y = 0 \quad I = 0$

I_1,	Y_1;	I_2,	Y_2	27	μ_γ
1,	0;	1,	0	1	

$Y = -1 \quad I = \frac{3}{2}$

I_1,	Y_1;	I_2,	Y_2	28	35	27	10*	μ_γ
$\frac{3}{2}$,	1;	0,	-2	$\sqrt{5}/10$	1/2	$3\sqrt{5}/10$	1/2	
0,	-2;	$\frac{3}{2}$,	1	$\sqrt{5}/10$	$-1/2$	$3\sqrt{5}/10$	$-1/2$	
1,	0;	$\frac{1}{2}$,	-1	$3\sqrt{5}/10$	1/2	$-\sqrt{5}/10$	$-1/2$	
$\frac{1}{2}$,	-1;	1,	0	$3\sqrt{5}/10$	$-1/2$	$-\sqrt{5}/10$	1/2	

$Y = 1 \quad I = \frac{5}{2}$

I_1,	Y_1;	I_2,	Y_2	28	35	μ_γ
$\frac{3}{2}$,	1;	1,	0	$\sqrt{2}/2$	$\sqrt{2}/2$	
1,	0;	$\frac{3}{2}$,	1	$\sqrt{2}/2$	$-\sqrt{2}/2$	

$Y = 1 \quad I = \frac{3}{2}$

I_1,	Y_1;	I_2,	Y_2	35	27	μ_γ
$\frac{3}{2}$,	1;	1,	0	$-\sqrt{2}/2$	$-\sqrt{2}/2$	
1,	0;	$\frac{3}{2}$,	1	$-\sqrt{2}/2$	$\sqrt{2}/2$	

$Y = 1 \quad I = \frac{1}{2}$

I_1,	Y_1;	I_2,	Y_2	27	10*	μ_γ
$\frac{3}{2}$,	1;	1,	0	$\sqrt{2}/2$	$\sqrt{2}/2$	
1,	0;	$\frac{3}{2}$,	1	$\sqrt{2}/2$	$-\sqrt{2}/2$	

$Y = 0 \quad I = 2$

I_1,	Y_1;	I_2,	Y_2	28	35	27	μ_γ
$\frac{3}{2}$,	1;	$\frac{1}{2}$,	-1	$\sqrt{5}/5$	$\sqrt{2}/2$	$\sqrt{30}/10$	
$\frac{1}{2}$,	-1;	$\frac{3}{2}$,	1	$\sqrt{5}/5$	$-\sqrt{2}/2$	$\sqrt{30}/10$	
1,	0;	1,	0	$\sqrt{15}/5$	0	$-\sqrt{10}/5$	

$Y = -1 \quad I = \frac{1}{2}$

I_1,	Y_1;	I_2,	Y_2	35	27	μ_γ
1,	0;	$\frac{1}{2}$,	-1	$-\sqrt{2}/2$	$-\sqrt{2}/2$	
$\frac{1}{2}$,	-1;	1,	0	$-\sqrt{2}/2$	$\sqrt{2}/2$	

$Y = -2 \quad I = 1$

I_1,	Y_1;	I_2,	Y_2	28	35	27	μ_γ
1,	0;	0,	-2	$\sqrt{5}/5$	$\sqrt{2}/2$	$\sqrt{30}/10$	
0,	-2;	1,	0	$\sqrt{5}/5$	$-\sqrt{2}/2$	$\sqrt{30}/10$	
$\frac{1}{2}$,	-1;	$\frac{1}{2}$,	-1	$\sqrt{15}/5$	0	$-\sqrt{10}/5$	

$Y = -2 \quad I = 0$

I_1,	Y_1;	I_2,	Y_2	35	μ_γ
$\frac{1}{2}$,	-1;	$\frac{1}{2}$,	-1	-1	

$Y = -3 \quad I = \frac{1}{2}$

I_1,	Y_1;	I_2,	Y_2	28	35	μ_γ
$\frac{1}{2}$,	-1;	0,	-2	$\sqrt{2}/2$	$\sqrt{2}/2$	
0,	-2;	$\frac{1}{2}$,	-1	$\sqrt{2}/2$	$-\sqrt{2}/2$	

$Y = -4 \quad I = 0$

I_1,	Y_1;	I_2,	Y_2	28	μ_γ
0,	-2;	0,	-2	1	

TABLE A-V

$Y = 3 \quad I = \frac{3}{2}$

I_1,	Y_1;	I_2,	Y_2	64
$\frac{3}{2}$,	1;	0,	2	1
				μ_γ

$Y = 2 \quad I = 2$

I_1,	Y_1;	I_2,	Y_2	64
$\frac{3}{2}$,	1;	$\frac{1}{2}$,	1	1
				μ_γ

$Y = 2 \quad I = 1$

I_1,	Y_1;	I_2,	Y_2	64	27
$\frac{3}{2}$,	1;	$\frac{1}{2}$,	1	$\sqrt{21}/7$	$2\sqrt{7}/7$
1,	0;	0,	2	$2\sqrt{7}/7$	$-\sqrt{21}/7$
					μ_γ

$Y = 1 \quad I = \frac{5}{2}$

I_1,	Y_1;	I_2,	Y_2	64
$\frac{5}{2}$,	1;	1,	0	1
				μ_γ

$Y = 0 \quad I = 1$

I_1,	Y_1;	I_2,	Y_2	64	27	8
$\frac{3}{2}$,	1;	$\frac{3}{2}$,	-1	$\sqrt{21}/21$	$\sqrt{14}/7$	$\sqrt{6}/3$
1,	0;	1,	0	$\sqrt{210}/21$	$3\sqrt{35}/35$	$-2\sqrt{15}/15$
$\frac{1}{2}$,	-1;	$\frac{1}{2}$,	$+1$	$\sqrt{210}/21$	$-4\sqrt{35}/35$	$\sqrt{15}/15$
						μ_γ

$Y = 0 \quad I = 0$

I_1,	Y_1;	I_2,	Y_2	64	27	8	1
$\frac{3}{2}$,	1;	$\frac{3}{2}$,	-1	$\sqrt{35}/35$	$\sqrt{210}/35$	$\sqrt{10}/5$	$\sqrt{10}/5$
1,	0;	1,	0	$2\sqrt{105}/35$	$\sqrt{70}/14$	0	$-\sqrt{30}/10$
$\frac{1}{2}$,	-1;	$\frac{1}{2}$,	1	$3\sqrt{70}/35$	$-\sqrt{105}/35$	$-\sqrt{5}/5$	$\sqrt{5}/5$
0,	-2;	0,	2	$2\sqrt{35}/35$	$-3\sqrt{210}/70$	$\sqrt{10}/5$	$-\sqrt{10}/10$
							μ_γ

$Y = -1 \quad I = \frac{5}{2}$

I_1,	Y_1;	I_2,	Y_2	64
1,	0;	$\frac{3}{2}$,	-1	1
				μ_γ

$Y = -1 \quad I = \frac{3}{2}$

I_1,	Y_1;	I_2,	Y_2	64	27
1,	0;	$\frac{3}{2}$,	-1	$\sqrt{14}/7$	$\sqrt{35}/7$
$\frac{1}{2}$,	-1;	1,	0	$\sqrt{35}/7$	$-\sqrt{14}/7$
					μ_γ

$Y = 1 \quad I = \frac{3}{2}$

I_1,	Y_1;	I_2,	Y_2	64	27	μ_γ
$\frac{5}{2}$,	1;	1,	0	$\sqrt{14}/7$	$\sqrt{35}/7$	
1,	0;	$\frac{1}{2}$,	1	$\sqrt{35}/7$	$-\sqrt{14}/7$	

$Y = 1 \quad I = \frac{1}{2}$

I_1,	Y_1;	I_2,	Y_2	64	27	8	μ_γ
$\frac{3}{2}$,	1;	1,	0	$\sqrt{7}/7$	$4\sqrt{35}/35$	$\sqrt{10}/5$	
1,	0;	$\frac{1}{2}$,	1	$2\sqrt{7}/7$	$\sqrt{35}/35$	$-\sqrt{10}/5$	
$\frac{1}{2}$,	−1;	0,	2	$\sqrt{14}/7$	$-3\sqrt{70}/35$	$\sqrt{5}/5$	

$Y = 0 \quad I = 3$

I_1,	Y_1;	I_2,	Y_2	64	μ_γ
$\frac{3}{2}$,	1;	$\frac{3}{2}$,	−1	1	

$Y = 0 \quad I = 2$

I_1,	Y_1;	I_2,	Y_2	64	27	μ_γ
$\frac{3}{2}$,	1;	$\frac{3}{2}$,	−1	$\sqrt{7}/7$	$\sqrt{42}/7$	
1,	0;	1,	0	$\sqrt{42}/7$	$-\sqrt{7}/7$	

$Y = -1 \quad I = \frac{1}{2}$

I_1,	Y_1;	I_2,	Y_2	64	27	8	μ_γ
1,	0;	$\frac{3}{2}$,	−1	$\sqrt{7}/7$	$4\sqrt{35}/35$	$\sqrt{10}/5$	
$\frac{1}{2}$,	−1;	1,	0	$2\sqrt{7}/7$	$\sqrt{35}/35$	$-\sqrt{10}/5$	
0,	−2;	$\frac{1}{2}$,	1	$\sqrt{14}/7$	$-3\sqrt{70}/35$	$\sqrt{5}/5$	

$Y = -2 \quad I = 2$

I_1,	Y_1;	I_2,	Y_2	64	μ_γ
$\frac{1}{2}$,	−1;	$\frac{3}{2}$,	−1	1	

$Y = -2 \quad I = 1$

I_1,	Y_1;	I_2,	Y_2	64	27	μ_γ
$\frac{1}{2}$,	−1;	$\frac{3}{2}$,	−1	$\sqrt{21}/7$	$2\sqrt{7}/7$	
0,	−2;	1,	0	$2\sqrt{7}/7$	$-\sqrt{21}/7$	

$Y = -3 \quad I = \frac{3}{2}$

I_1,	Y_1;	I_2,	Y_2	64	μ_γ
0,	−2;	$\frac{3}{2}$,	−1	1	

Vector and Axial Vector Currents; Algebra of Currents

In Chapter 1 a general prescription was given for the construction of the isospin operator for Bose fields. The isospin was given as the space integral of the time component of the isovector current $\mathbf{j}_\mu$:

$$\tfrac{1}{2} i\phi^\dagger \overleftrightarrow{\partial}_\mu \mathbf{t}\phi \quad \text{or} \quad i\psi^\dagger \overleftrightarrow{\partial}_\mu \mathbf{t}\psi \tag{AII-1}$$

for self-conjugate and pair-conjugate fields, respectively. The analogous construction for spin 1/2 particles is clearly

$$\mathbf{T} = \int d^3x \psi^\dagger \mathbf{t}\psi \tag{AII-2}$$

where the $2t + 1$ components of $\psi^\dagger$ transform as in Eq. (1.58). Eq. (AII-2) can also be written in the form

$$\mathbf{T} = \int d^3x \mathcal{V}_0(x), \quad \mathcal{V}_\mu = \bar{\psi}\gamma_\mu \mathbf{t}\psi \tag{AII-3}$$

(Here $\bar{\psi} = \psi^\dagger\gamma_0$ and the four Dirac matrices γ_μ are chosen to obey $\gamma_\mu{}^\dagger = \gamma_0\gamma_\mu\gamma_0$ and $\{\gamma_\mu,\gamma_\nu\} = 2g_{\mu\nu}$. The metric tensor $g_{\mu\nu}$ is diagonal with $g_{00} = -g_{ii} = 1$, $i = 1, 2, 3$.) The isospin current of the Dirac field ψ is then given by the second expression in Eq. (AII-3). These results have been used in constructing Eq. (5.33).

The isospin current is of importance not only in electromagnetic and strong interactions but also in the description of strangeness-conserving leptonic weak interactions. It has been established that the latter are of the current-current type, where the strong current is $\mathcal{V}_\mu + \mathcal{A}_\mu$ where $\mathcal{V}_\mu$ is the combination

$\mathcal{V}_{1\mu} + i\mathcal{V}_{2\mu}$ of the isospin current $\mathcal{V}_\mu$ and $\mathcal{A}_\mu$ the $\mathcal{A}_{1\mu} + i\mathcal{A}_{2\mu}$ component of the isovector axial vector current $\mathcal{A}_\mu$. Gell-Mann has suggested that the vector and axial vector currents are of prime importance for the description of the strong interactions themselves (1).

In order to bring out the interesting mathematical relations suggested by such an approach we shall restrict our attention to a model in which only one basic spinor field is needed for the construction of the vector and axial vector currents. At first we consider isospin as the relevant internal symmetry. Denoting the isospin doublet (comprised of p and n, if desired) by ψ, we construct

$$\mathcal{V}_{\mu m} = \bar{\psi}\gamma_\mu \frac{\tau_m}{2}\psi$$

$$\mathcal{A}_{\mu m} = \bar{\psi}\gamma_\mu\gamma_5 \frac{\tau_m}{2}\psi \tag{AII-4}$$

where $\gamma_5 = i\gamma_0\gamma_1\gamma_2\gamma_3$, $\gamma_5{}^2 = 1$, and $\gamma_5{}^\dagger = \gamma_5$. In Eq. (AII-4) we have extended τ_m so that $\tau_0 = I$; τ_1, τ_2, and τ_3 as usual comprise the Pauli spin vector. It is convenient to break up the 32 operators in Eq. (AII-4) into space and time components

$$\mathcal{V}_{0m} = \psi^\dagger \frac{\tau_m}{2}\psi$$

$$\mathcal{A}_{am} = \psi^\dagger\gamma_0\gamma_a\gamma_5 \frac{\tau_m}{2}\psi = \psi^\dagger\sigma_a \frac{\tau_m}{2}\psi$$

$$\mathcal{V}_{am} = \psi^\dagger\gamma_0\gamma_a \frac{\tau_m}{2}\psi = \psi^\dagger\sigma_a\gamma_5 \frac{\tau_m}{2}\psi \tag{AII-5}$$

$$\mathcal{A}_{0m} = \psi^\dagger\gamma_5 \frac{\tau_m}{2}\psi$$

Here m runs from 0 to 3 and a from 1 to 3. We have used the relation $\sigma_a = \gamma_0\gamma_a\gamma_5$ to simplify these expressions. σ_a is the usual 4×4 spin matrix, defined by $\sigma_a = \sigma_{bc}$ (a, b, and c in cyclic order; a, b, and c take on the values 1 to 3). The σ_{bc} in turn are the space components of the matrix $\sigma_{\mu\nu} = i/2[\gamma_\mu,\gamma_\nu]$. Note that $2\mathcal{V}_{00}$ is the baryon number density while $\mathcal{V}_0$ is the isospin density.

First consider the current densities $\mathcal{V}_{0m}$ and $\mathcal{A}_{0m}$. The space integrals of these 16 quantities

$$\begin{aligned} V_{0m} &= \int d^3x \mathcal{V}_{0m}(x) \\ A_{0m} &= \int d^3x \mathcal{A}_{0m}(x) \end{aligned} \qquad \text{(AII-6)}$$

generate on equal-time commutation, the algebra of the form $U(2) \times U(2)$. The following general formula is useful in this and more complicated problems. Consider the linear combination of components of $\psi^\dagger$ and ψ by two commuting matrices M and N: $\psi^\dagger M_i N_j \psi$. Using the canonical commutation rules

$$\begin{aligned} \{\psi_\lambda(x),\psi_\mu{}^\dagger(x')\}_{t=t'} &= \delta_{\lambda\mu}\delta(\mathbf{x} - \mathbf{x}') \\ \{\psi_\lambda(x),\psi_\mu(x')\}_{t=t'} &= 0 \end{aligned} \qquad \text{(AII-7)}$$

one easily establishes the identity

$$\begin{aligned} &[\psi^\dagger(x)M_iN_k\psi(x),\psi^\dagger(x')M_jN_l\psi(x')]_{t=t'} \\ &\quad = \delta(\mathbf{x} - \mathbf{x}')\psi^\dagger(x)\{\tfrac{1}{2}\{M_i,M_j\}[N_k,N_l] + \tfrac{1}{2}\{N_k,N_l\}[M_i,M_j]\}\psi(x) \end{aligned} \qquad \text{(AII-8)}$$

(The reader is warned (2) that the uncritical use of (AII-7) can lead to incorrect results arising from the singular nature of the field operators.) Thus one only needs to know the multiplication law for the M_i and N_k, to obtain the commutator of the densities $\psi^\dagger M_i N_k \psi$.

For the quantities V_{0m} and A_{0m} of Eq. (AII-6) the explicit forms of (AII-5) yield (with $M = I$ or γ_5 and $N_k = \tau_k/2$)

$$\begin{aligned} [V_{0m},V_{0n}] &= i\varepsilon_{mnr}V_{0r} \\ [V_{0m},A_{0n}] &= i\varepsilon_{mnr}A_{0r} \\ [A_{0m},A_{0n}] &= i\varepsilon_{mnr}V_{0r} \end{aligned} \qquad \text{(AII-9)}$$

where ε_{mnr} is the usual antisymmetric tensor for the 1, 2, and 3 values of the indices but vanishes if any of the m, n, or r takes on the value 0. The eight Hermitian operators generate the algebra of the group $U(2) \times U(2)$ as can be seen by making a change of basis

$$J_{\pm m} = \tfrac{1}{2}[V_{0m} \pm A_{0m}]. \tag{AII-10}$$

The $J_{\pm m}$ comprise two independent angular momenta for $m = 1$, 2, and 3. For all m we have

$$\begin{aligned} [J_{\pm m}, J_{\pm n}] &= i\varepsilon_{mnr} J_{\pm r} \\ [J_{\pm m}, J_{\mp n}] &= 0 \end{aligned} \tag{AII-11}$$

The four hermitian operators J_{+m} correspond to the generators of the (reducible) unitary group $U^{(+)}(2)$ while the J_{-m} correspond to an independent group $U^{(-)}(2)$. Because of the second equation of (AII-11), the group structure is simply the direct product $U^{(+)}(2) \times U^{(-)}(2)$.

Since V_{00} and A_{00} commute with the V_{am}, A_{am} ($a = 1, 2, 3$), we can consider the latter six operators separately. The combinations (AII-10) then generate two independent $SU(2)$ algebras. For $m, n, r = 1, 2, 3$ (AII-9) is well known as the algebra of the four-dimensional real orthogonal group $O(4)$. Eq. (AII-11) exhibits the isomorphism of $O(4)$ and $SU(2) \times SU(2)$.

Note that under space inversion ($\psi(\mathbf{x}) \to \gamma_0\psi(-\mathbf{x})$) V_{0m} transforms into V_{0m} while A_{0m} changes sign. Hence the parity operation P interchanges $\mathbf{J}_+$ and $\mathbf{J}_-$.

$$P\mathbf{J}_{\pm}P^{-1} = \mathbf{J}_{\mp} \tag{AII-12}$$

The currents corresponding to $J_{\pm m}$ have the form

$$\bar{\psi}\gamma_\mu\left(\frac{1 \pm \gamma_5}{2}\right)\left(\frac{\tau_m}{2}\right)\psi$$

The $1 \pm \gamma_5$ can be regarded as acting on both spinors; defining the left- and right-handed spinors in the usual way by $\psi_L = \frac{1}{2}(1 + \gamma_5)\psi$ and $\psi_R = \frac{1}{2}(1 - \gamma_5)\psi$ we see that $J_{+\mu}$ involves only ψ_L, while $J_{-\mu}$ is composed of ψ_R. This fact accounts for the adjective "chiral" often applied to $U^{(+)}(2) \times U^{-}(2)$ or $SU^{(+)}(2) \times SU^{(-)}(2)$.

We next stress the crucial point that the group associated with the algebra $U^{(+)}(2) \times U^{(-)}(2)$ *cannot* be a symmetry group of the Hamiltonian. The known nonconservation of the axial vector current implies that

$$i\,\frac{d\mathbf{A}(t)}{dt} = [\mathbf{A}(t),H] \neq 0 \tag{AII-13}$$

Even the mass term $(m\bar{\psi}\psi)$ of a typical Lagrangian does not commute with **A**. ($\bar{\psi}\psi = \bar{\psi}_L\psi_R + \bar{\psi}_R\psi_L$ transforms as the representation $(j_+,j_-) = (1/2,1/2)$ of $SU^{(+)}(2) \times SU^{(-)}(2)$, $j_\pm$ being the magnitude of the "angular momenta" $J_\pm$.)

For this and other reasons there seems little hope that the algebra of $U^{(+)}(2) \times U^{(-)}(2)$ can be a useful approximate *symmetry* algebra (i.e., an algebra whose operators commute with the Hamiltonian) as was the case with $SU(3)$. Nevertheless, one can speculate that the algebra (AII-9) is true and investigate the consequences of imposing these operator conditions on the usual structure of field theory. The time of writing is not suitable for an evaluation of the success of such efforts.

A glance at the operators comprising the vector and axial vector currents (Eq. AII-5) shows that other algebras may be formed. The space integrals of these densities are

$$\begin{aligned} V_{0m} &= \int d^3x\psi^\dagger \frac{\tau_m}{2}\psi \\ A_{am} &= \int d^3x\psi^\dagger\sigma_a \frac{\tau_m}{2}\psi \\ V_{am} &= \int d^3x\psi^\dagger\sigma_a\gamma_5 \frac{\tau_m}{2}\psi \\ A_{0m} &= \int d^3x\psi^\dagger\gamma_5 \frac{\tau_m}{2}\psi \end{aligned} \tag{AII-14}$$

It should be noticed that V_{0m} and A_{am} are even under space inversion while V_{am} and A_{0m} are odd. Thus the commutator of two odd operators is even and no closed algebra can be formed of odd operators. However the 16 even parity operators have the same commutation rules as the matrices $\tau_m/2$, $\sigma_a\tau_m/2$. The commutation rules are given by

$$[V_{0m}, V_{0n}] = i\varepsilon_{mnr}V_{0r}$$

$$[V_{0m}, A_{an}] = i\varepsilon_{mnr}A_{ar} \tag{AII-15}$$

$$[A_{am}, A_{bn}] = i\delta_{ab}\varepsilon_{mnr}V_{0r} + i\delta_{mn}\varepsilon_{abc}A_{c0}$$

The first relation is old, while the second merely says that A_{am} is an isoscalar ($n = 0$) or an isovector ($n = 1, 2, 3$). Hence the possibly interesting dynamical information is contained in the remaining commutator. The sixteen independent Hermitian generators V_{0m}, A_{am} (or $\tau_m/2, \sigma_a\tau_m/2$) generate the algebra of the four-dimensional unitary group $U(4)$.

Can the group $U(4)$ be a symmetry group? First, note the meaning of the transformations. In addition to the usual isospin transformations (V_{0m}) the operators A_{am} of the algebra correspond to changes of the spin variables. Clearly A_{am} can commute with H only if the latter is independent of the spin (exclusive of the orbital angular momentum) as well as the isospin. Such a spin-isospin independent force was considered for nuclear physics, with fair success as long ago as 1937 by Wigner (3). The idea has been applied to particle physics recently by Sakita (4), and Gursey and Radicati (5). The second point concerns the essentially noncovariant nature of the separation of spin and orbital momentum. Indeed, nearly all successes of this theory have been confined to the low-energy domain. It may be useful to discuss the $U(4)$ mixed symmetry from the point of view of dynamical models based on dispersion theory. In such models (for instance the reciprocal bootstrap model of Section 7.3) one certainly expects a definite correlation of angular momentum, parity and isospin. In fact there is obviously a strong spin-orbit force operative in the four p states (P_{11}, P_{13}, P_{31}, P_{33}) of the Chew-Low theory. Thus the $U(4)$ symmetry cannot be expected to hold for a Lagrangian, or for the S matrix. Nevertheless, in the Chew N, N^* bootstrap only the P_{11} and P_{33} states have such attractive forces as to give binding. The difference in energy, of order $1/M$ relative to the nucleon mass, can then be regarded as due to a small-spin isospin-dependent force within the states belonging to the 20-dimensional representation to which the $P_{11}(N)$ and $P_{33}(N^*)$ particles would be assigned in the $U(4)$ scheme. The forces in the remaining states P_{13} and P_{31} are extremely spin and isospin dependent but are, after all, quite unimportant relative to the N and N^* effects. It therefore appears that the $U(4)$ (or $U(6)$) symmetry is of dynamical origin and has only a limited validity.

If we recall that the projection operators a, and $\bar{a}$ have the properties

$$a = \tfrac{1}{2}(1 + \gamma_5) \qquad \bar{a} = \tfrac{1}{2}(1 - \gamma_5)$$
$$a^2 = a, \quad \bar{a}^2 = \bar{a}, \quad a\bar{a} = 0 \tag{AII-16}$$

then it becomes clear that two other $U(4)$ algebras can be constructed from the set of Eq. (AII-14). The two sets of 16 generators, labeled by $(+)$ and $(-)$, are

$$J_{\pm m} = \int d^3x \tfrac{1}{2}(\mathcal{V}_{0m} \pm \mathcal{A}_{0m}) = \int d^3x \psi^\dagger \frac{1 \pm \gamma_5}{2} \frac{\tau_m}{2} \psi$$
$$K_{\pm am} = \int d^3x \tfrac{1}{2}(\mathcal{A}_{am} \pm \mathcal{V}_{am}) = \int d^3x \psi^\dagger \sigma_a \frac{(1 \pm \gamma_5)}{2} \frac{\tau_m}{2} \psi \tag{AII-17}$$

Any operator labeled with plus commutes with any operator labeled with minus. The sets (J_{+m}, K_{+am}) and (J_{-m}, K_{-am}) have the same commutation relations as (V_{0m}, A_{am}) in Eq. (AII-15) and hence correspond to two independent $U(4)$ groups labeled $U^{(+)}(4)$ and $U^{(-)}(4)$. We therefore see that the space integrals of the 32 operators making up the vector and axial vector currents (AII-5) generate the algebra of $U^{(+)}(4) \times U^{(-)}(4)$ on equal-time commutation (6).

The group $U^{(+)}(4) \times U^{(-)}(4)$ is not expected to be an approximate symmetry group describing the hadrons. However certain of its subgroups may be good symmetry groups. For example the $U(4)$ defined by Eq. (AII-15) may be an approximate static symmetry group. The V_{0m} and A_{am} are the positive parity components of $U^{(+)}(4) \times U^{(-)}(4)$. Of course the isospin-baryon number group $U(2)_T$ is contained in any of the groups under consideration. Notice the following independent subgroup decompositions

$$\begin{aligned} &U^{(+)}(4) \times U^{(-)}(4) \supset U(4) \supset U(2)_S \times U(2)_T \\ &U^{(+)}(4) \times U^{(-)}(4) \supset U^{(+)}(2) \times U^{(-)}(2) \supset U(2)_T \end{aligned} \qquad \text{(AII-18)}$$

Here S stands for the group containing spin transformations, as discussed following Eq. (AII-15).

The preceding analysis, based as it was on the vector and axial vector currents, may seem insufficiently general. After all, the starting point was rooted in the weak interactions. Therefore, we generalize by considering all 16 possible linear combinations of $\bar{\psi}_a\psi_b$ by means of the Dirac matrices: $\Gamma_i = 1, i\gamma_5, \gamma_\mu, \gamma_\mu\gamma_5, \sigma_{\mu\nu}$ (S,P,V,A,T). By means of the 16 Γ_i and the 4 τ_m we can construct the 64 densities $D(\Gamma_i\tau_m)$:

$$D(\Gamma_i\tau_m) = \bar{\psi}\Gamma_i\tau_m\psi/2 \qquad \text{(AII-19)}$$

We now proceed to examine the algebra obeyed by the space integrals

$$A(\Gamma_i\tau_m) = \int d^3x D(\Gamma_i\tau_m) \qquad \text{(AII-20)}$$

First note that the 16 linearly-independent Hermitian matrices $\gamma_0\Gamma_i$ generate the algebra of $U(4)$. (The quadratic form $\psi^\dagger\psi$ is left invariant by the arbitrary infinitesimal unitary transformation $\psi \to (1 + i\varepsilon_j\gamma_0\Gamma_j)\psi$ where the ε_i are 16 real infinitesimal parameters.) It is then clear that the 64 Hermitian operators $A(\Gamma_i\tau_m)$ generate the algebra of the group $U(8)$.

In order to investigate the subalgebras contained in this algebra we write out the 64 densities, along with appropriate specializations to space and time components.

$$S_m = \psi^\dagger \gamma_0 \frac{\tau_m}{2} \psi$$

$$P_m = \psi^\dagger i\gamma_0\gamma_5 \frac{\tau_m}{2} \psi$$

$$V_{\mu m} = \psi^\dagger \gamma_0 \gamma_\mu \frac{\tau_m}{2} \psi \begin{cases} \psi^\dagger \frac{\tau_m}{2} \psi, & \mu = 0 \\ \psi^\dagger \sigma_a \gamma_5 \frac{\tau_m}{2} \psi, & \mu = a \end{cases}$$

$$A_{\mu m} = \psi^\dagger \gamma_0 \gamma_\mu \gamma_5 \frac{\tau_m}{2} \psi \begin{cases} \psi^\dagger \gamma_5 \frac{\tau_m}{2} \psi, & \mu = 0 \\ \psi^\dagger \sigma_a \frac{\tau_m}{2} \psi, & \mu = a \end{cases} \tag{AII-21}$$

$$J_{\mu\nu m} = \psi^\dagger \gamma_0 \sigma_{\mu\nu} \frac{\tau_m}{2} \psi \begin{cases} \psi^\dagger \gamma_b \frac{\tau_m}{2} \psi, & (\mu,\nu) = (0,b) \\ \psi^\dagger \gamma_0 \sigma_{ab} \frac{\tau_m}{2} \psi, & (\mu,\nu) = (a,b) \end{cases}$$

In Eq. (AII-21), the Roman letters a and b take on the values 1, 2, and 3.

The addition of the scalar and tensor terms permits the construction of two new $U(4)$ algebras similar to $U(4)$ considered previously, with γ_0 replacing γ_5. The matrix content of the linear combinations is

$$\frac{1 \pm \gamma_0}{2} \frac{\tau_m}{2}, \qquad \frac{1 \pm \gamma_0}{2} \sigma_a \frac{\tau_m}{2} \tag{AII-22}$$

with $a = 1, 2, 3$. Note that $(1 \pm \gamma_0)/2$ are energy (Casimir) projection operators in the rest frame, and so one might follow Marshak and Okubo (7) in calling these subgroups "Casimir subgroups" $U_c^{\pm}(4)$ in contrast to the "chiral" groups $U^{(\pm)}(4)$ based on the helicity projection operators $(1 \pm \gamma_5)/2$.

Thus the group $U(8)$ contains, in addition to the chiral subgroup $U^{(+)}(4) \times U^{(-)}(4)$, the Casimir subgroup $U_c^{(+)}(4) \times U_c^{(-)}(4)$. Note that the latter group also contains $U(4)$ as a subgroup. We have previously noted the essentially low-energy character of $U(4)$. Therefore it is of some interest (8) that the Casimir subgroup contains another $U(4)$ subgroup based on the relativistic spin operator S_a with components 1, $\gamma_0\sigma_x$, $\gamma_0\sigma_y$, and σ_z. The space components of S_a clearly obey the same algebra as the Pauli spin matrices. The $U(4)$ algebra based on the 16 matrices $S_a\tau_m/2$ (rather, the $U(6)$ counterpart) was proposed by Barnes, Carruthers, and von Hippel (9) as a phenomenological symmetry of the vertex function. A peculiar feature of this group is its selection of a special direction (z), the direction of motion of a particle. It appears then that this symmetry cannot be fulfilled in the traditional sense but only for a selected class of matrix elements. In fact the generators do not commute with the kinetic energy, although the mass term is invariant. Indeed subsequent applications (10) of this idea to scattering reactions have not (11) reproduced the mysterious success of the collinear group [as named by Dashen and Gell-Mann (8)] for the vertex function (9, 12).

In practice it is quite useful to know how the 64 densities $D(\Gamma_i\tau_m)$ transform under the operation of G conjugation. This operation was introduced in Section 1.4. It is $G = \mathcal{C} \exp(i\pi T_2)$ where $\mathcal{C}$ is defined for Dirac fields by

$$\mathcal{C}\psi(x)\mathcal{C}^{-1} = C\bar{\psi}^T(x) \qquad \text{(AII-23)}$$

T denoting the transpose and the matrix C defined by $C\gamma_\mu{}^T C^{-1} = -\gamma_\mu$. Under C, the isoscalar covariants transform as

$$\mathcal{C}\!:\!\bar{\psi}\Gamma_i\psi\!:\!\mathcal{C}^{-1} = \omega_i\!:\!\bar{\psi}\Gamma_i\psi\!: \qquad \text{(AII-24)}$$

where $\omega_i = +1$ for $\Gamma = S$, A, and P and $\omega_i = -1$ for $\Gamma = V$, and T. Next consider the $(2t + 1)$-component field transforming in the standard way [Eq. (1.58)] under isospin rotations $O(\boldsymbol{\alpha}) = \exp(i\boldsymbol{\alpha}\cdot\mathbf{T})$

$$O(\boldsymbol{\alpha})\psi_\mu O(\boldsymbol{\alpha}) = \psi_\nu D_{\nu\mu}{}^*(\boldsymbol{\alpha}) \qquad \text{(AII-25)}$$

for $O = \exp(i\pi t_2)$ we have, using $t_2{}^T = -t_2$,

$$\exp(i\pi T_2)\psi_\mu \exp(-i\pi T_2) = [\exp(i\pi t_2)]_{\mu\nu}\psi_\nu \qquad \text{(AII-26)}$$

It is then elementary to show that the isospin densities transform as

$$G: \bar{\psi}\Gamma_i \mathbf{t}\psi : G^{-1} = -\omega_i : \bar{\psi}\Gamma_i \mathbf{t}\psi : \qquad \text{(AII-27)}$$

For example, the isovector vector current is even under G, while the isovector axial vector current is odd. This transformation corresponds to the invariance of the $SU(4)$ algebra of (AII-15) under the substitution $\mathbf{A}_a \to -\mathbf{A}_a$, $\mathbf{V}_0 \to +\mathbf{V}_0$, $A_{a0} \to A_{a0}$.

It will be noted that under charge conjugation the densities corresponding to the different components of the relativistic spin operator transform differently, since S_z comes from the axial vector density and S_x, S_y from the tensor density:

$$\begin{aligned} S_z &= \int d^3x \psi^\dagger \sigma_z \psi \underset{\mathscr{C}}{\to} S_z \\ (S_x, S_y) &= \int d^3x \psi^\dagger \gamma_0 (\sigma_x, \sigma_y) \psi \underset{\mathscr{C}}{\to} -(S_x, S_y) \end{aligned} \qquad \text{(AII-28)}$$

Finally, we note the changes of notation necessary to extend the previous results to the case in which the internal symmetry group is $SU(3)$ instead of $SU(2)$. In place of the isospinor ψ we introduce the quark field q transforming according to the fundamental representation **3**.

In addition to the eight 3×3 matrices λ_i of Chapter 2 it is convenient to introduce the unit matrix. Defining $\lambda_0 = \sqrt{2/3}\, I$ we see that the commutation rules may be expressed as

$$\begin{aligned} [\lambda_i, \lambda_j] &= 2i f_{ijk} \lambda_k \\ \{\lambda_i, \lambda_j\} &= 2 d_{ijk} \lambda_k \end{aligned} \qquad \text{(AII-29)}$$

where i, j, and k run from 0 to 8. f_{ijk} is defined to be zero if any index takes on the value zero. The coefficient d_{ijk} is defined as before except that it is equal to $(2/3)^{1/2}$ when one index is zero and the other two are equal.

In place of the $16 \times 4 = 64$ densities of Eq. (AII-21) we now have $16 \times 9 = 144$ Hermitian generators

$$A(\Gamma_i \lambda_m) = \int d^3x \bar{\psi} \Gamma_i \frac{\lambda_m}{2} \psi \qquad \text{(AII-30)}$$

These $(12)^2$ operators generate (8) the algebra of the unitary group in twelve dimensions $U(12)$. Notable subgroups of $U(12)$ include the chiral and Casimir subgroups $U^{(+)}(6) \times U^{(-)}(6)$ based on the structures $(1 \pm \gamma_5)\lambda_m/4$, $\sigma_a(1 \pm \gamma_5)\lambda_m/4$, and $(1 \pm \gamma_0)\lambda_m/4$‘ $\sigma_a(1 \pm \gamma_0)\lambda_m/4$, respectively. The chiral subgroup contains the "static" $U(6)$ group of Sakita, Gursey, and Radicati, while the Casimir subgroup contains, in addition, the collinear group of ref. 9, constructed from the relativistic spin operator as discussed following Eq. (AII-22). Further developments and a description of applications made to date will be found in a paper by Ne'eman (13).

References for Appendix II

1. M. Gell-Mann, *Phys. Rev.*, **125**, 1067 (1962).
2. J. Schwinger, *Phys. Rev. Letters*, **3**, 296 (1959).
3. E. P. Wigner, *Phys. Rev.*, **51**, 106 (1957).
4. B. Sakita, *Phys. Rev.*, **136**, B1756 (1964).
5. F. Gursey, and L. A. Radicati, *Phys. Rev. Letters*, **13**, 173 (1964).
6. R. P. Feynman, M. Gell-Mann, and G. Zweig, *Phys. Rev. Letters*, **13**, 678 (1964).
7. R. E. Marshak, and S. Okubo, *Phys. Rev. Letters*, **13**, 818 (1964).
8. R. Dashen, and M. Gell-Mann, *Phys. Lett.*, **17**, 145 (1965); **17**, 148 (1965).
9. K. J. Barnes, P. Carruthers, and F. von Hippel, *Phys. Rev. Letters*, **14**, 82 (1965).
10. H. J. Lipkin, and S. Meshkov, *Phys. Rev. Letters*, **14**, 670 (1965).
11. J. D. Jackson, *Phys. Rev. Letters*, **15**, 990 (1965).
12. K. J. Barnes, *Phys. Rev. Letters*, **14**, 798 (1965).
13. Y. Ne'eman, Lectures given at the Pacific Summer School in Physics, Honolulu, 1965, to be published.

Author Index

Subject Index